AQA GCSE SCIENCE
HIGHER

REVISION AND PRACTICE BOOK

Editor: Steve Witney

Ian Brandon, Barbara Drozdowska, Joyce Gustard,
Terry Mansfield, Christine Woodward

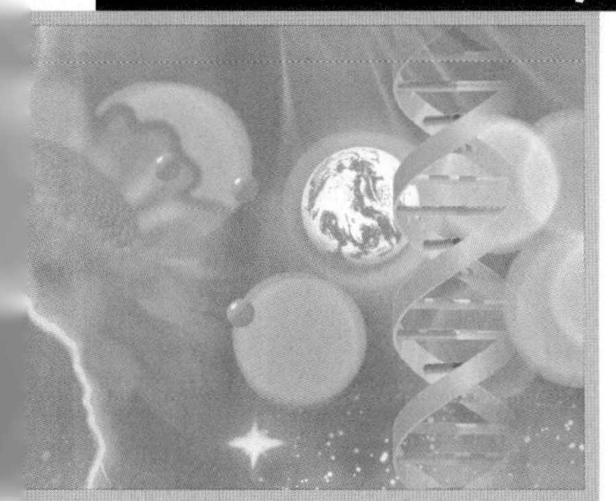

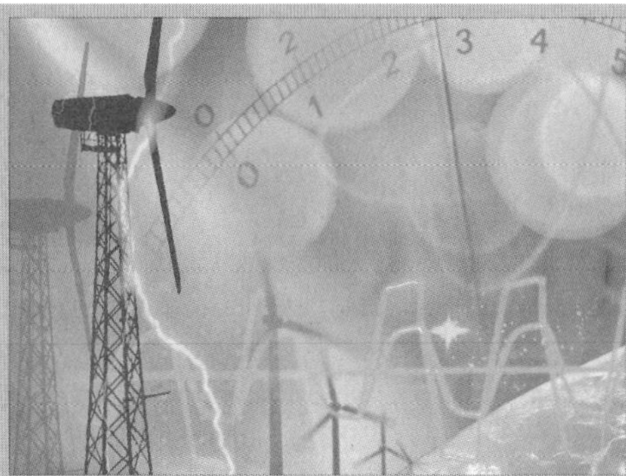

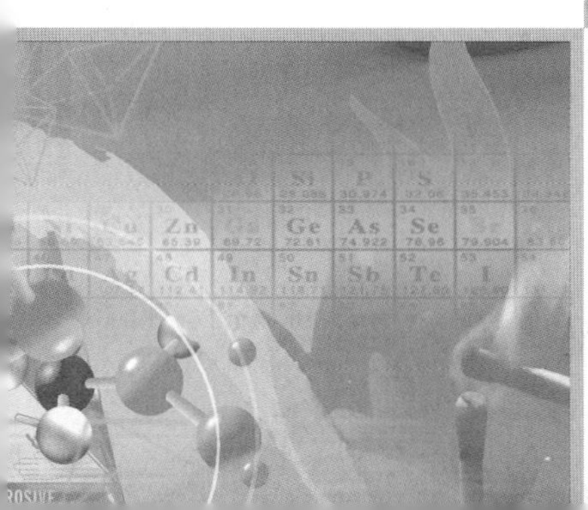

Hodder & Stoughton

A MEMBER OF THE HODDER HEADLINE GROUP

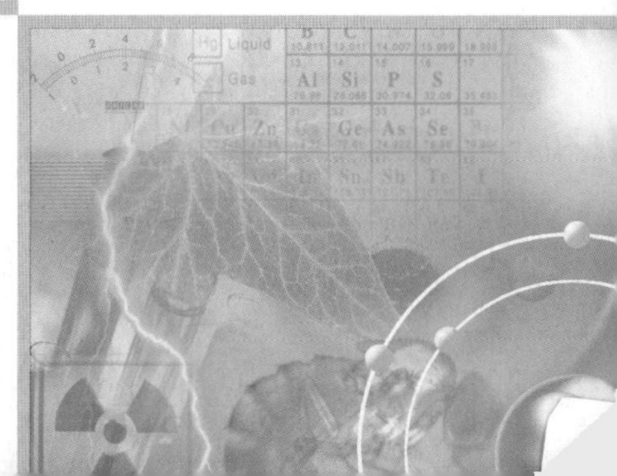

Acknowledgements
The publishers would like to thank the following company for permission to reproduce examination questions in this book.

AQA (44–45, 96–97, 154–155)

Orders: please contact Bookpoint Ltd, 130 Milton Park, Abingdon, Oxon OX14 4SB. Telephone: (44) 01235 827720. Fax: (44) 01235 400454. Lines are open from 9.00–6.00, Monday to Saturday, with a 24 hour message answering service. You can also order through our website www.hodderheadline.co.uk

British Library Cataloguing in Publication Data
A catalogue record for this title is available from the British Library

ISBN 0 340 81304 0

First published 2004
Impression number 10 9 8 7 6 5 4 3 2 1
Year 2009 2008 2007 2006 2005 2004

Typeset by Tech-Set Ltd. Printed in Spain for Hodder & Stoughton Educational, a division of Hodder Headline, 338 Euston Road, London NW1 3BH.

Contents

Specification matching summary

The contents of this book are designed to cover all aspects of the knowledge and understanding needed if you are taking either the AQA Modular or the AQA Co-ordinated GCSE Double Award Science examination.

The contents are divided into chapters that match the organisation of the Modular course. However, each block of four modules covers one section of the Co-ordinated course and the core content of one of the separate science GCSE courses in: Biology, Chemistry, Physics, and Biology (Human).

Modules	Co-ordinated Science	Separate Science
1, 2, 3, 4	Life Processes and Living Things	Biology/Biology (Human)
5, 6*, 7, 8	Materials and their Properties	Chemistry
9, 10, 11, 12	Physical Processes	Physics

*Part of Module 6 – 'The Structure of the Earth' is also examined within the Co-ordinated Science *Physical Processes* examination paper and within the separate Physics examination (both Co-ordinated and Modular).

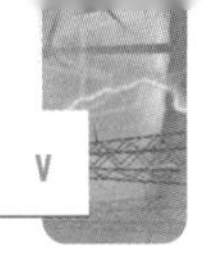

How to use this book

This book can be used throughout your science course in addition to forming the basis of your science revision programme before your examinations. It contains all the information you need to know in brief easy-to-follow notes and diagrams. Key terms are highlighted in orange.

The book includes a number of useful Examiner's tips to help you understand and remember the work you have covered for your GCSE examination. Read these carefully to see how the advice relates to the topic you are revising.

Throughout each module are short Check Your Understanding questions. These are not actual examination questions, but give you a quick check on the progress you are making. Answers are given at the back of the book.

At the end of each module is a complete Topic Test. Before completing a topic test you may need to go back and read through the module again, this will help you to remember the facts and ideas. The answers provided at the back of the book have been broken down to show you how marks may be awarded in the final examination. Completing the tests will help you to highlight both the strong and weak areas in your knowledge and understanding. If you score very low marks for a topic test you will at least have identified an area on which you need to spend more time.

At the end of the biology, chemistry and physics sections are examination questions taken from recent AQA examinations, together with model answers. The answers have been annotated with useful examiner's comments, hints and explanations. Read through the questions and see if you would have given the same answers. Check how and why the marks have been awarded. Read and take note of the hints and apply these when you do practice questions and of course the real thing!

A number of key terms, together with their meanings, are given in the combined Glossary/Index on pages 171 to 184. Use the glossary as a checklist – do you know the meaning of each of the terms? If not, then learn them. As a test, ask a friend to pick a few words for you to give the meanings.

Equations and units.

There are a number of equations, particularly in the physics modules, that must be learnt by heart. These have been written inside a box with an orange border. Learn the words, not just the symbols, and also learn the UNITS that go with each QUANTITY.

If you are following the Modular science course, Modules 1, 2, 5, 6, 9 and 10 will be examined by End of Module Tests. The tests will be taken at appropriate times during the course, probably in Year 10. But don't ignore these modules when you are revising for your final examinations at the end of Year 11. The parts of the modules highlighted in the text by an orange background tint down the left-hand side, like this paragraph, may also be examined in the terminal papers.

Text that has a solid orange line like this down the left-hand side is the extra content you need to know for Higher Tier papers. Where a section of text is both Higher Tier material and will be examined in both the End of Module Tests and in the final examination, it has an orange tinted background *and* an orange line down the left-hand side (see the bottom of page 2, for example).

If you were intending to take the examination at Higher Tier but have now changed to a Foundation Tier entry, you can still use this book for revision. Just miss out the parts with orange lines alongside them.

Help with your science revision

Organising yourself

Give yourself plenty of time to revise the subject thoroughly. Have a plan, don't leave it until the last moment. Remember that if you are taking the modular course you will probably have some of your GCSE exams in Year 10. These need to be revised for too.

Work out how many days you have until your exams and how many hours you can realistically spend on revision. Use this information to plan an efficient revision timetable. Remember, add in some leisure activities, you can't be revising all of the time.

Break your revision up into slots of short 30 minute sessions with a break after each session. For most people little and often is better than trying to do everything in one go. After your break start the next revision session by quickly reviewing what you revised in the previous session. This helps to fix it in your mind. Make sure you give yourself a little reward for completing a session and achieving a target.

Find somewhere quiet and comfortable to work, if possible with a desk or table. Make sure you are away from distractions like the TV, or younger brothers and sisters. Have pens, pencils, highlighter pens, notepads, your textbook, notes, past papers and this revision book to hand and ready to use. You might not need them all at once, but it saves time if they are all readily available.

As you revise, the list of topics you feel you understand well will grow and your list of weaker topics will get smaller (hopefully!). Leave some extra time closer to the exams to go through and sort out your weaker areas. If you are really struggling with a concept or topic ask your science teacher for help.

Pulling it all together

Don't just revise a topic only once – it won't stick. Go back to the topic as frequently as you can. Don't just read through this book, do something active. Highlight the key points with colours and symbols. Rewrite sections from the book as a series of bullet points. Try the questions, and ask friends or family to test you. If possible record key points, equations and definitions on a tape, then play the tape back frequently.

'Go for 3'

This is a simple technique where you write down key words and then make a list of at least three important things about them. Examination questions rarely expect you to give more than three pieces of information For example:

atom
1 The smallest part of an element.
2 Nucleus contains protons and neutrons.
3 Electrons orbit the nucleus.

proton
1 Found in the nucleus of an atom.
2 Has a single positive charge.
3 Has a relative mass of 1.

A letter sequence/mnemonic

Make up a letter sequence or series of words to help remember an important fact, for example, AAA = All Arteries carry blood Away from the heart.

A mind map/spider diagram

You can use a mind map to summarise a topic and show the links between the ideas that you need to learn. You could use a spider diagram to ask yourself those important questions that you know you will need to be able to answer. For example:

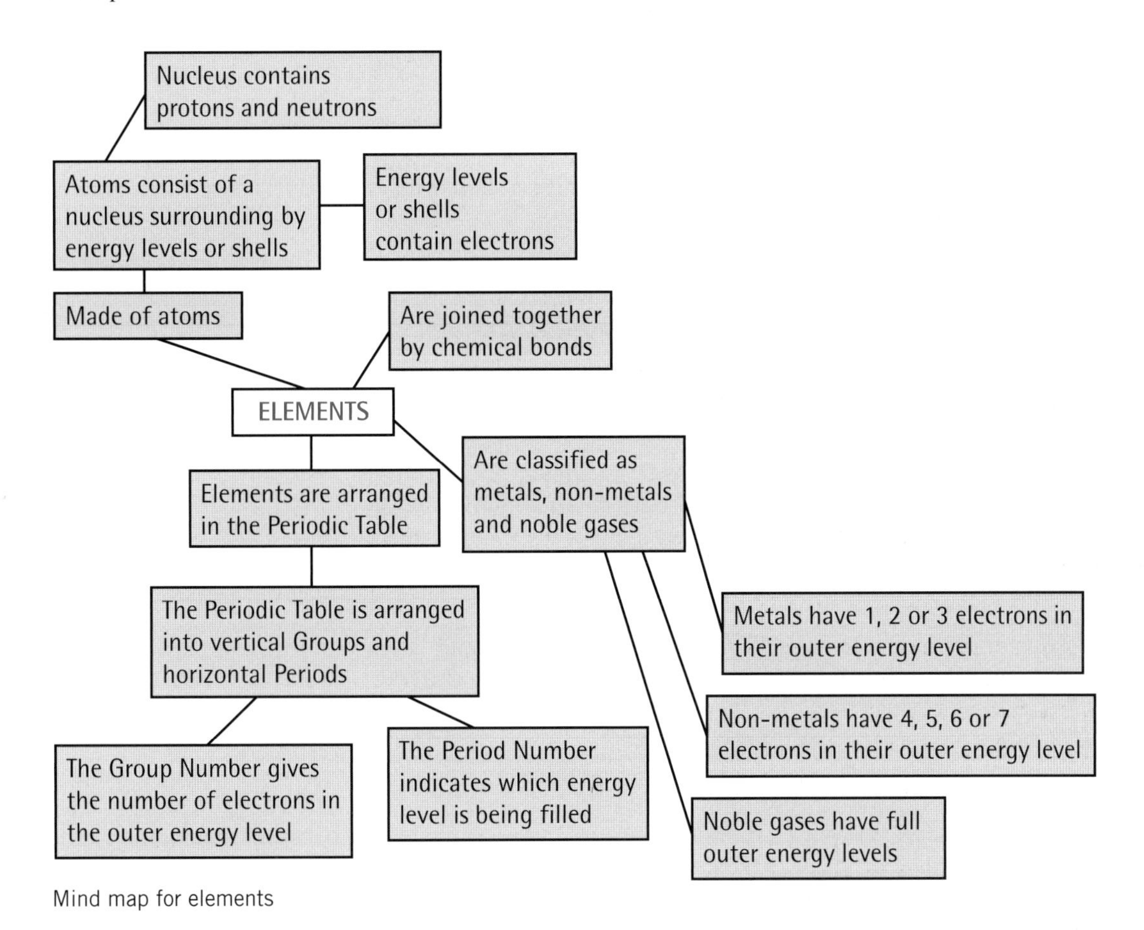

Mind map for elements

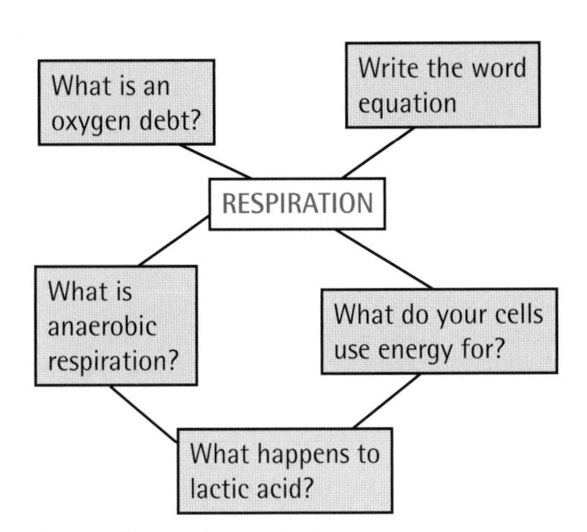

Spider diagram for respiration

Key fact cards

Choose part of a topic. On one side of a postcard write down four or five key facts about that topic. Keep the cards in a pile. For example:

> Parallel circuits
>
> Potential difference across each component is the same.
>
> The bigger the resistance of a component the smaller the current flowing through it.
>
> The total current flowing = sum of the currents through each component.
>
> $I_{total} = I_1 + I_2 + ...$

A key fact card for parallel circuits

When you have a few minutes to spare learn one or two of the cards. Ask someone to pull a card from the pile and test you. If you can answer their questions put the card at the bottom of the pile. If you can't put the card at the top and learn it next time you have a few spare minutes.

Annotated diagrams

Draw simple diagrams, pictures, graphs or tables and add your notes, labels or instructions. For example:

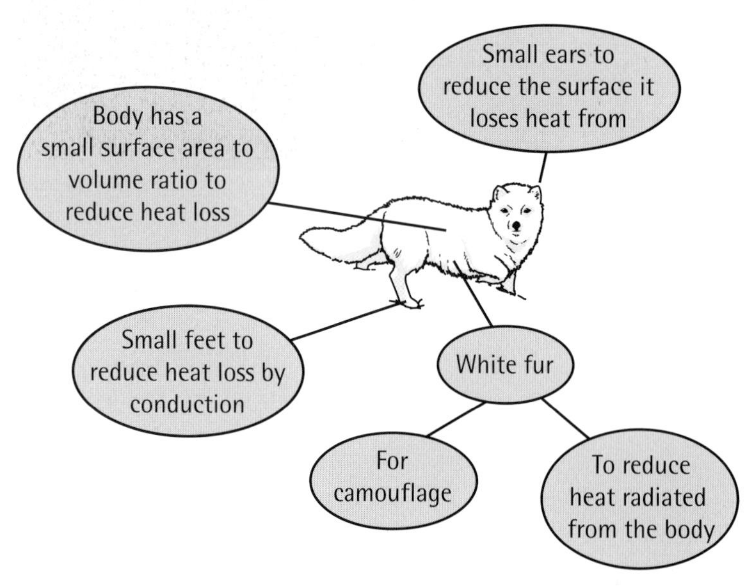

An annotated diagram about arctic foxes

MODULE 1

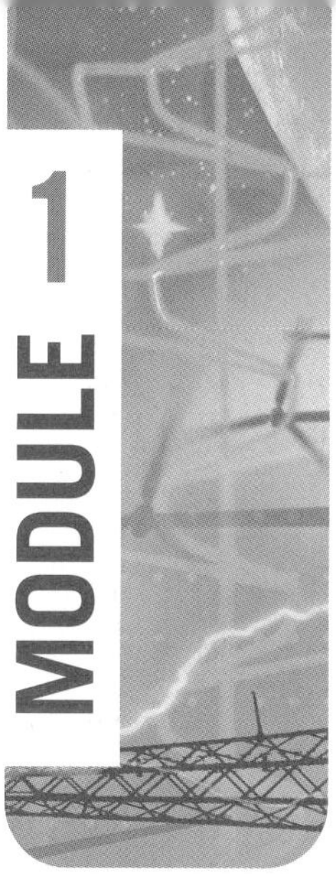

HUMANS AS ORGANISMS

Cells

Organelles called mitochondria are in the cytoplasm. Energy from respiration is released from the mitochondria. Cells which use lots of energy, like muscle cells, have lots of mitochondria.
cell membrane – controls the passage of substances into and out of the cell.
nucleus – controls the cell's activities.
cytoplasm – where most chemical reactions occur.
These reactions are controlled by enzymes.

You must be able to LABEL THESE PARTS on a diagram and STATE THEIR FUNCTIONS.

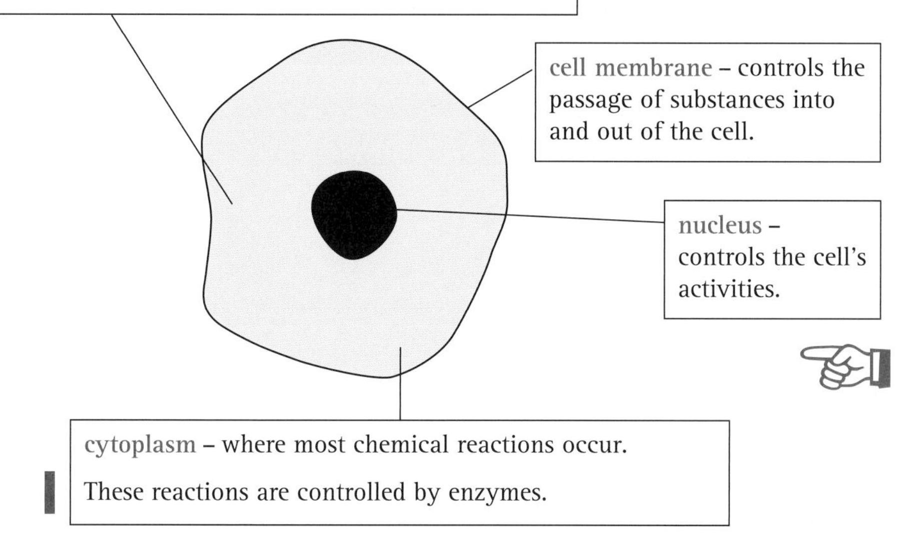

FIGURE 1.1 A typical animal cell

Some cells look different from this one but still contain the same parts. These cells have adapted to fulfil a particular role in the body.

Sperm cells have a tail to enable swimming to the egg.

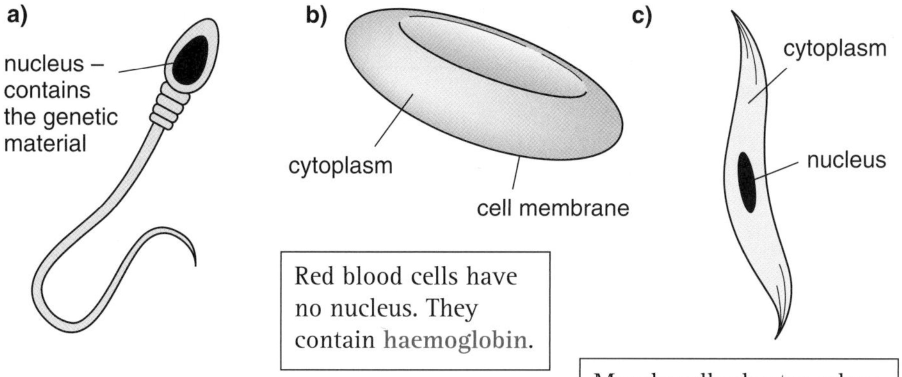

a)
nucleus – contains the genetic material
b)
cytoplasm
cell membrane
Red blood cells have no nucleus. They contain haemoglobin.
c)
cytoplasm
nucleus

Muscle cells shorten when the muscle contracts.

FIGURE 1.2 a) A sperm cell, b) a red blood cell and c) a muscle cell

How do substances get into and out of cells?

Diffusion is the movement of molecules of a gas or any substance in solution from a region where they are in **HIGHER** concentration to a region where they are in **LOWER** concentration.

Diffusion will be faster if:
- the differences in concentration are large
- the surface area of the membrane is large.

In the alveoli in the lungs the concentration of oxygen is always large because we are breathing in more oxygen all the time. So oxygen always diffuses into the blood (see Figure 1.3 below and Figure 1.7 on page 5).

The many alveoli increase the surface area of the lungs and so maximise the speed of diffusion of oxygen and carbon dioxide between the blood and the air in the lungs.

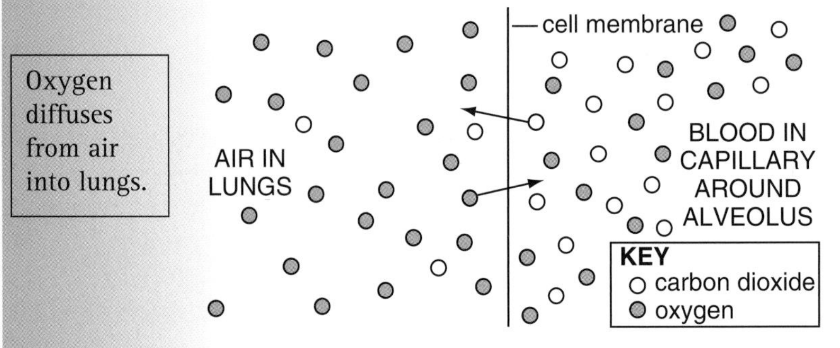

FIGURE 1.3 Diffusion in the lungs

Dissolved soluble foods and ions can diffuse through cell membranes. This happens in the small intestine where the surface area is increased by villi.

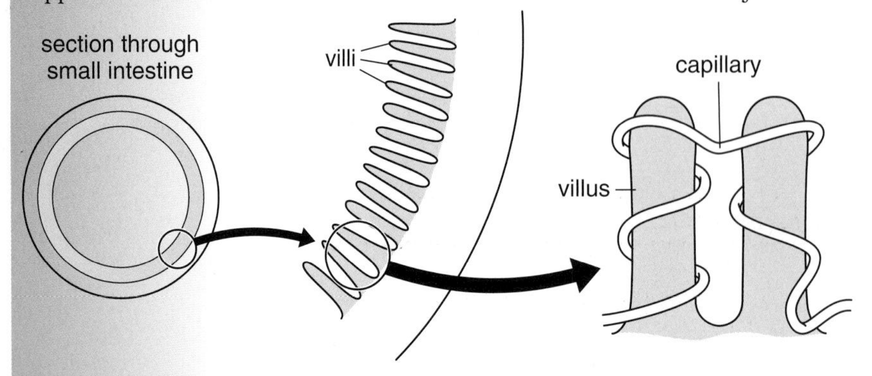

FIGURE 1.4 Section through the small intestine

Soluble foods and ions can diffuse quickly into blood as every villus is near to a blood capillary.

All exchange surfaces in organisms must have:
- a large surface area
- thin membranes
- a good vascular supply (blood vessels or plant veins).

Think of a leaf, this has a very thin section so that gases can easily enter and leave the leaf. It has a good supply of veins to carry the gases and dissolved substances (e.g. sugars) to other cells.

Think of a fish gill, this has a large surface area provided by the many gill filaments. It has a good capillary blood supply and each gill filament is very thin.

The digestive system

Enzymes speed up the breakdown of large molecules into smaller molecules, which can then diffuse into the blood. Different enzymes break down different types of food.

Insoluble food	Broken down by enzyme	Soluble food
starch	amylase	sugars
proteins	protease	amino acids
fats	lipase	fatty acids and glycerol

Amylase is made in the salivary glands, pancreas and small intestine.

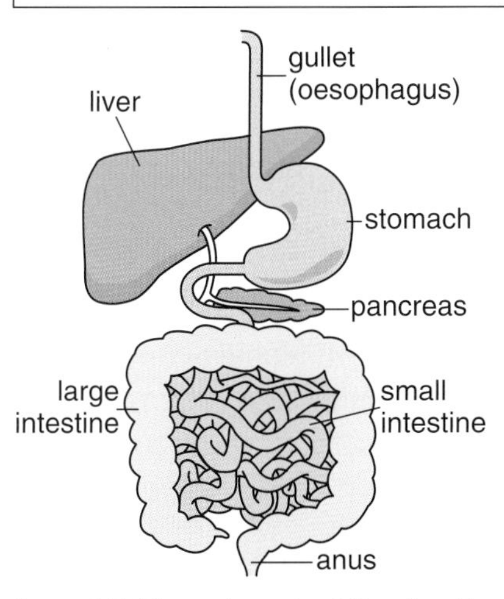

Protease is made in the stomach, pancreas and small intestine.

Lipase is made in the pancreas and small intestine.

FIGURE 1.5 The main parts of the digestive system

Part of digestive system	What happens here?
mouth	Teeth chew and break up the food. Amylase from the salivary glands begins the digestion of starch.
stomach	Produces hydrochloric acid to kill bacteria and make effective conditions for enzymes to work. Protease enzymes begin digestion of protein.
small intestine	Digestion continues. Soluble food is absorbed into the bloodstream.
large intestine	Water is absorbed into the bloodstream.
anus	Faeces, made up of indigestible food, leaves at the anus.

The liver makes bile which is stored in the gall bladder. Bile does three things:

1 It neutralises the acid that was added in the stomach.
2 It makes the right alkaline conditions for the enzymes in the small intestine to work.
3 It breaks fat down into small droplets which have a large surface area.

Cover this page and try to redraw the flowchart. Start with the parts of the body, then add the information.

Summary of digestion

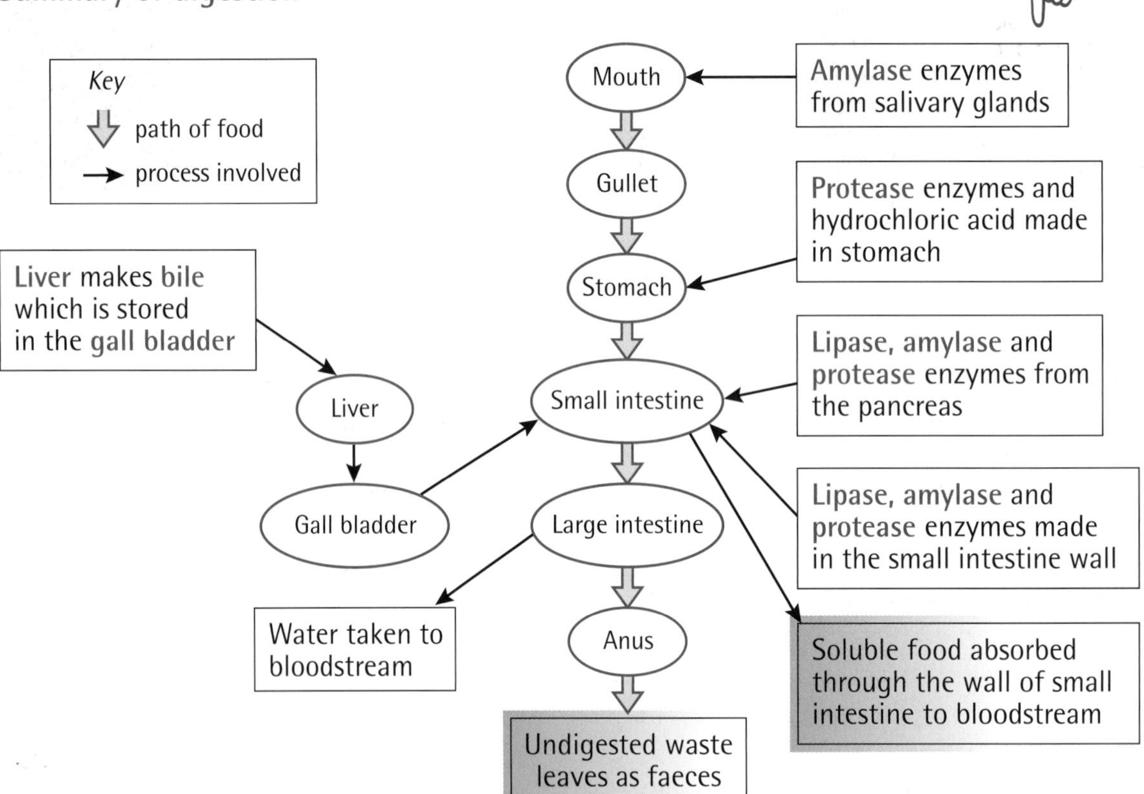

CHECK YOUR UNDERSTANDING

❶ In the lungs, there is always more oxygen in the air than in the blood. Why?

❷ a) What is starch broken down into? b) Which enzyme does this?

❸ a) What is fat broken down into? b) Which enzyme does this?

❹ Name two substances made in the stomach.

❺ Where is soluble food absorbed into the bloodstream?

The breathing system

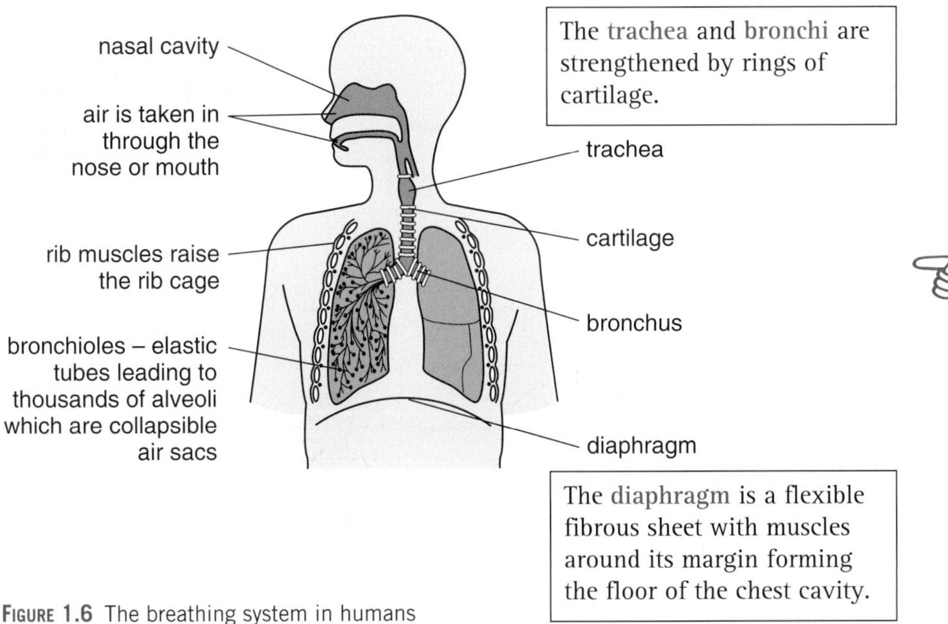

The diaphragm is a flexible fibrous sheet with muscles around its margin forming the floor of the chest cavity.

FIGURE 1.6 The breathing system in humans

Make sure that you are familiar with the diagram of the breathing system.

The breathing organs are the lungs. Here oxygen is taken into the bloodstream and carbon dioxide passes out to the air in the alveoli. The lungs are in the thorax protected by the ribcage and are separated from the abdomen by the diaphragm.

Ventilation – the movement of air into and out of the lungs.

To move air in (inhale):
- The rib cage moves out.
- The diaphragm flattens.

To move air out (exhale):
- The rib cage moves down.
- The diaphragm becomes raised.

When we inhale, the muscles between the ribs contract and pull the ribs upwards and outwards. At the same time the muscles of the diaphragm contract causing it to flatten. The volume of the thorax is therefore increased and this decreases the pressure inside the thorax. Air then enters the lungs from the outside.

In the alveoli oxygen diffuses into the bloodstream and carbon dioxide diffuses from the bloodstream into the air, which is then exhaled.

The alveoli provide a large surface area, a moist surface and a good capillary supply so that gases diffuse quickly. Alveolar membranes are very thin.

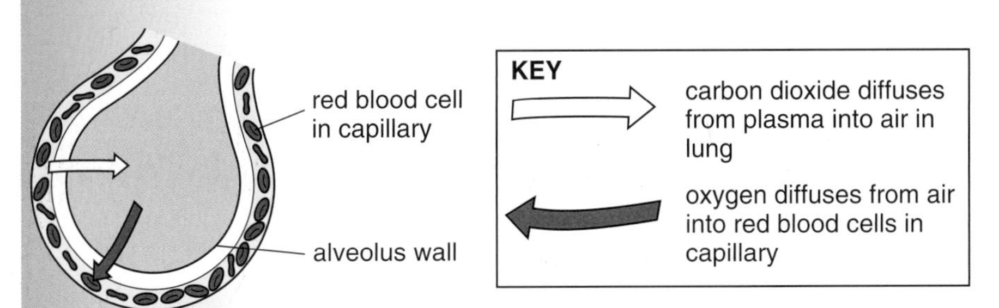

FIGURE 1.7 An alveolus and its capillary blood supply

Respiration

Respiration happens in all cells. It is a chemical reaction to release energy from food. The equation below summarises aerobic respiration. Aerobic means with oxygen.

glucose + oxygen ⟶ carbon dioxide + water + energy

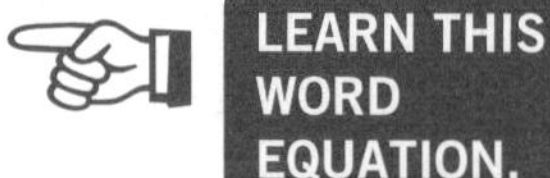

Aerobic respiration happens when oxygen is plentiful and is happening to you now as you read this book.

Aerobic respiration inside your cells happens in organelles called mitochondria.

If you run quickly across a field oxygen cannot get to your cells fast enough so they start to respire in a different way to give you less energy, but still enough to let you run. This type of respiration is called anaerobic respiration. Anaerobic means without oxygen. Your muscles can become fatigued, they ache, and stop working efficiently.

Lactic acid is a waste product of anaerobic respiration produced by the incomplete breakdown of glucose.

glucose ⟶ lactic acid + energy

This can make your muscles ache so it needs to be removed immediately after running. To do this the body takes in extra oxygen (by panting) and the lactic acid is then broken down into carbon dioxide and water.

The oxygen that you need after running is called oxygen debt, because you 'owe' it to your muscles. It has to be repaid after you stop running.

What is the energy used for?

keeps your body at the right temperature when it is cold outside

builds up large molecules from small ones, e.g. proteins from amino acids

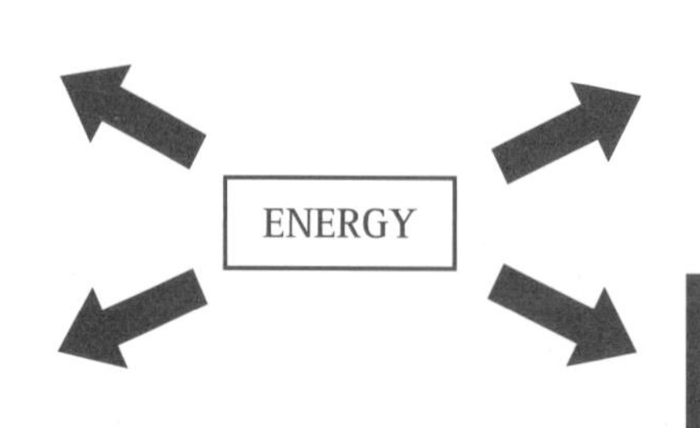

is needed for muscle contraction when you move

is needed for the active transport of materials across boundaries

CHECK YOUR UNDERSTANDING

1. Write the equation for aerobic respiration.
2. Where does aerobic respiration occur?
3. Name four things that cells use energy for.

The circulatory system

- Useful substances, such as food and oxygen, must be transported from where they enter the body to all cells.
- Waste products, like carbon dioxide, must be transported from the cells to where they leave the body.
- The blood (mainly the plasma) transports these substances in the circulatory system.
- The heart is the pump that keeps the system moving.

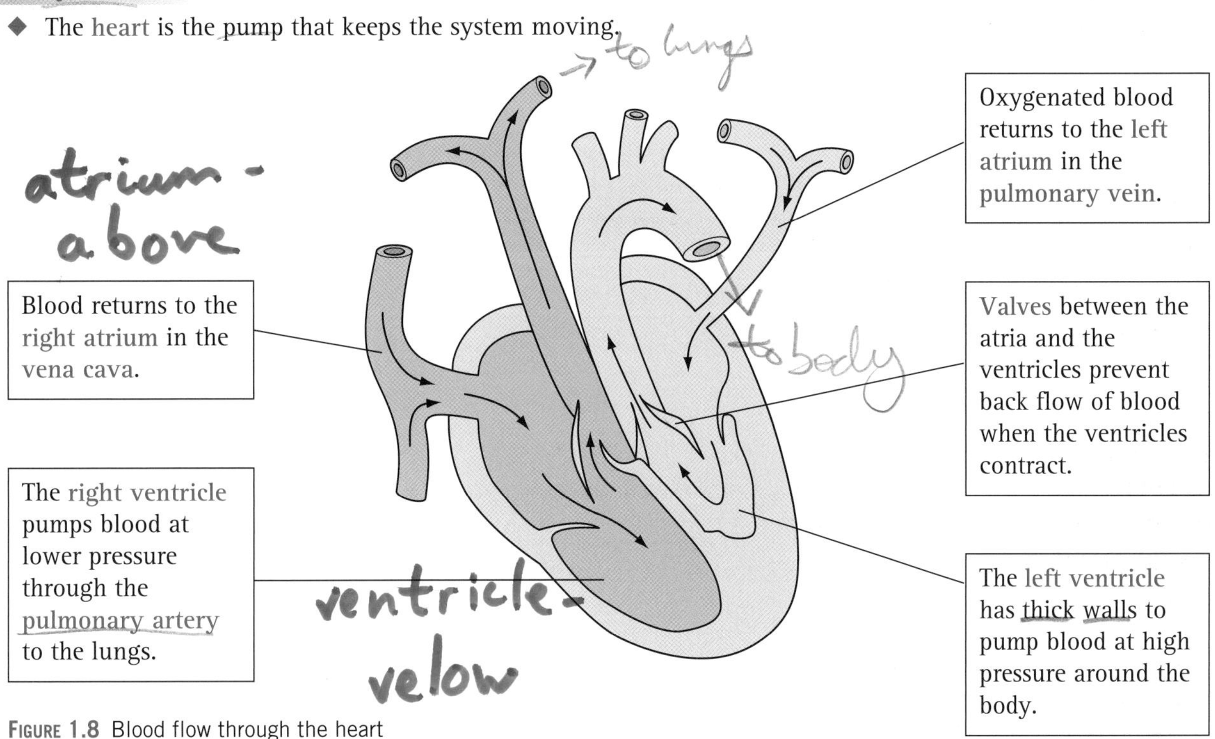

FIGURE 1.8 Blood flow through the heart

Things to remember about the heart:

- Both sides contract at once.
- The atria (plural of atrium) contract and push blood into the ventricles (gravity helps with this and so the atria have thinner muscle walls than the ventricles).
- The valves between the atria and ventricles close.
- The ventricles contract and push blood in two directions – to the lungs from the right side and to the body from the left side.
- The ventricles then relax and valves in the aorta and the pulmonary artery close.

Blood vessels

Blood leaves the heart in arteries. These have thick walls with muscle and elastic tissue in them. They stretch to receive blood then the walls contract to move the blood on. This is felt as a pulse. Arteries need thick walls as the blood they carry is pumped under high pressure.

Veins carry blood back to the heart. They have thinner walls because the blood is no longer at such high pressure. Many large veins, like those in the legs, have valves to help prevent the backflow of blood as it travels 'uphill' to the heart.

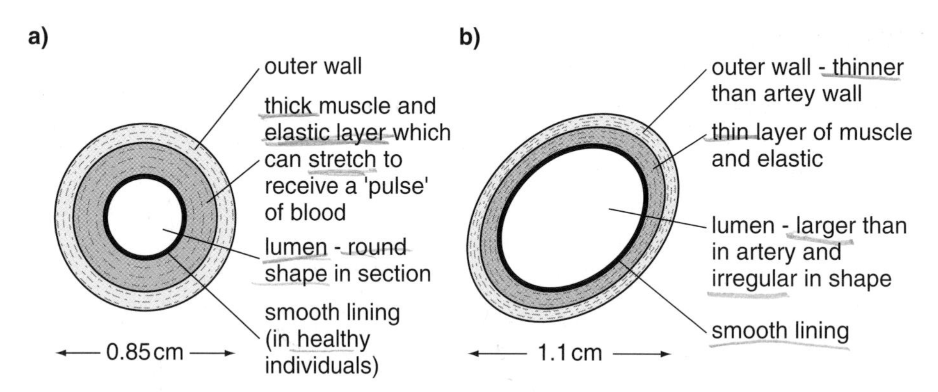

FIGURE 1.9 Transverse section through a) an artery, b) a vein

Capillaries join arteries to veins. In the muscles and organs, substances pass through the capillary walls into and out of cells. The walls must be very thin (only one cell thick) to allow this to happen.

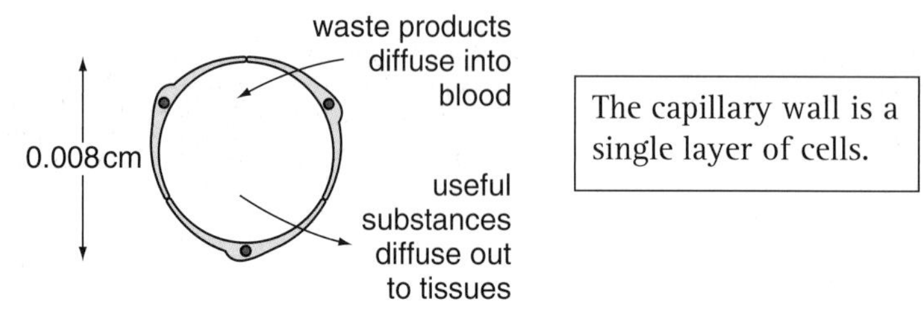

The capillary wall is a single layer of cells.

FIGURE 1.10 Transverse section through a capillary

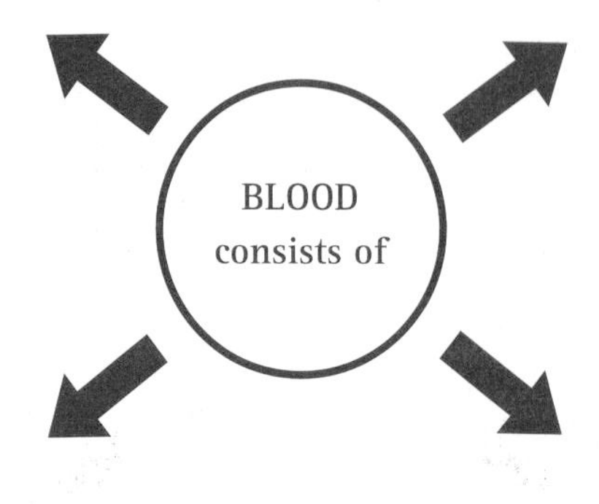

White blood cells – these help the body to fight disease-causing micro-organisms. They have a nucleus.

Plasma – this is the main transport system of the body. It carries:

- carbon dioxide from the organs and muscles to the lungs
- soluble food from the small intestine to the cells
- urea from the liver to the kidney.

Red blood cells – these have no nucleus. Instead they are packed with a red pigment called haemogloblin. In the capillaries surrounding the alveoli in the lungs this haemoglobin combines with oxygen to form oxyhaemoglobin. When the blood reaches the organs and muscles the oxyhaemoglobin breaks down into haemoglobin and oxygen again.

Platelets – these are small pieces of cells without a nucleus. They are involved in blood clotting at the site of a wound.

Micro-organisms and disease

Diseases can be caused by micro-organisms called bacteria or viruses entering our body.

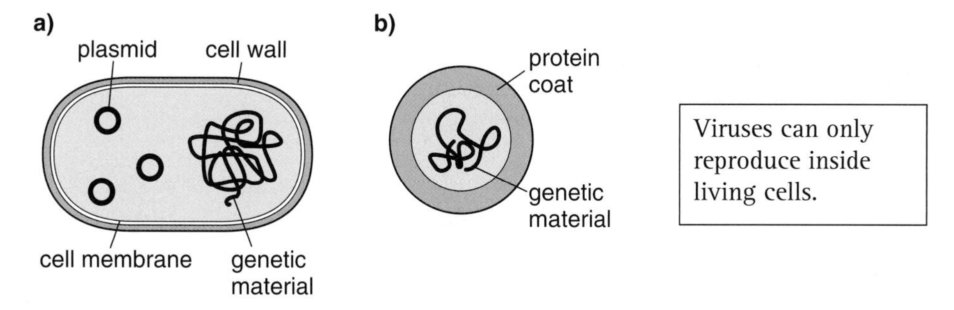

FIGURE 1.11 Section through a) a bacterial cell, b) a virus

Viruses can only reproduce inside living cells.

To lessen the likelihood of becoming infected with micro-organisms, we should live in hygienic conditions. Some of the things we should do are:

- Wash our bodies and clothes regularly.
- Cook food properly as this kills many bacteria.
- Keep flies from food; they carry bacteria on their bodies.
- Store food in a cool place; bacteria need warmth to grow.
- Stay away from people with infectious diseases; viruses can be passed by coughs and sneezes.

The stomach produces hydrochloric acid which can kill some micro-organisms.

The skin forms a water-tight barrier.

Blood produces clots which seal wounds.

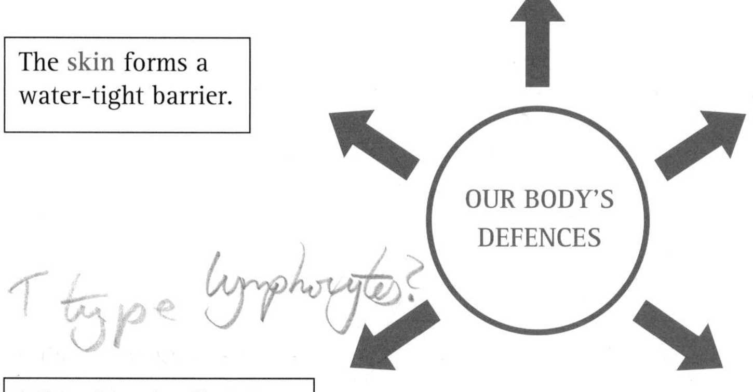

White blood cells kill micro-organisms by engulfing them or producing antibodies to destroy them.

The air passages produce sticky mucus to trap pollen, dust and micro-organisms. This is then swallowed and passes through the digestive system.

White blood cells fight micro-organisms in a number of ways:

- By engulfing and ingesting them.
- By making antibodies which destroy particular bacteria or viruses. One antibody is needed for each different micro-organism.
- By producing anti-toxins to combat the poisons released by micro-organisms.

The cytoplasm of the white blood cell moves round and engulfs the bacterium.

Enzymes are discharged in the vacuole of the white blood cell, which will break down the bacterium.

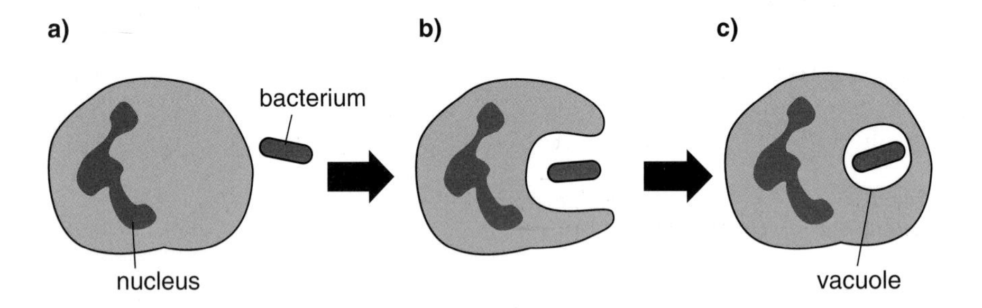

FIGURE 1.12 A white blood cell engulfing and destroying a bacterium

Vaccination

Babies, young children and people travelling to certain places overseas are given vaccinations by a doctor or nurse. In this process a weakened form of the micro-organism is put into the bloodstream. The white blood cells then make antibodies against the micro-organism. Once the body has made an antibody, it can make it again very quickly. This means that if the real micro-organism enters the body later, the antibodies are ready and waiting to destroy it. The person is now immune to that disease. Sometimes a 'booster' injection is given a few years later to 'top up' the immunity.

CHECK YOUR UNDERSTANDING

1. Which part of the blood helps to form clots? platelets
2. List three precautions that we can take to help us avoid getting micro-organisms into our body.

- keep food away from flies
- wash hands
- cook food properly
- ~~cover cuts with plaster~~

Topic Test

Use the information on cells to answer these questions.

1 How are a) sperm cells, b) red blood cells and c) muscle cells adapted for their function? (3 marks)

2 Write down the function of these cell parts:
   a) nucleus
   b) cytoplasm
   c) cell membrane. (3 marks)

3 Name two ways to increase the rate of diffusion. (2 marks)

4 List three features that all exchange surfaces must have. (3 marks)

5 Copy and complete this table to show the digestion of insoluble food to soluble particles.

Insoluble food	Enzyme	Soluble food
starch		sugars
	protease	
		fatty acids and glycerol

(5 marks)

6 Write down three functions of bile. (3 marks)

7 Explain how the ribs and diaphragm allow air to enter the lungs. (5 marks)

8 Write down the sequence of events that happens when the heart contracts. (5 marks)

9 Explain what happens to cause an oxygen debt. (3 marks)

10 Explain how a vaccination helps to keep us healthy. (5 marks)

Total: 37 marks

MAINTENANCE OF LIFE

Maintenance in plants

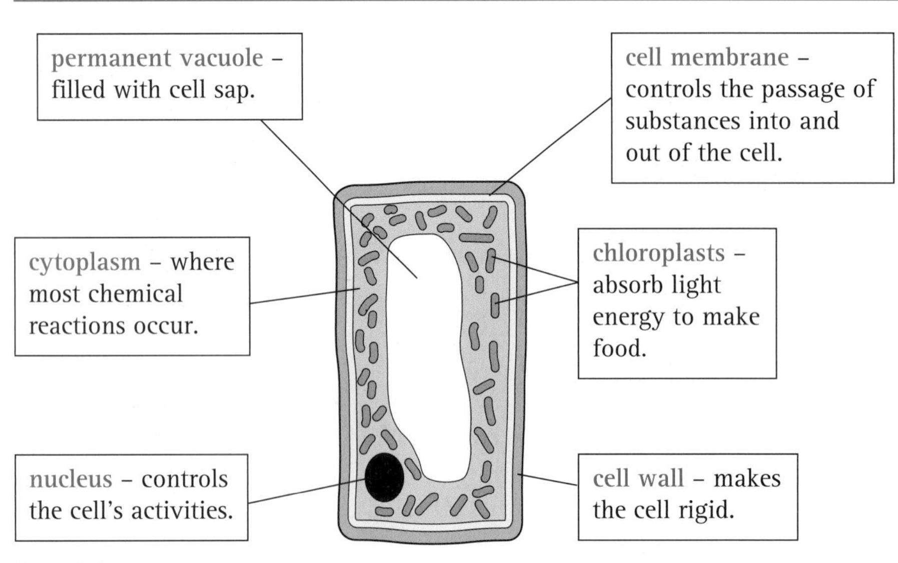

FIGURE 2.1 A typical plant cell

Different types of plant cell have different shapes which relate to their function.

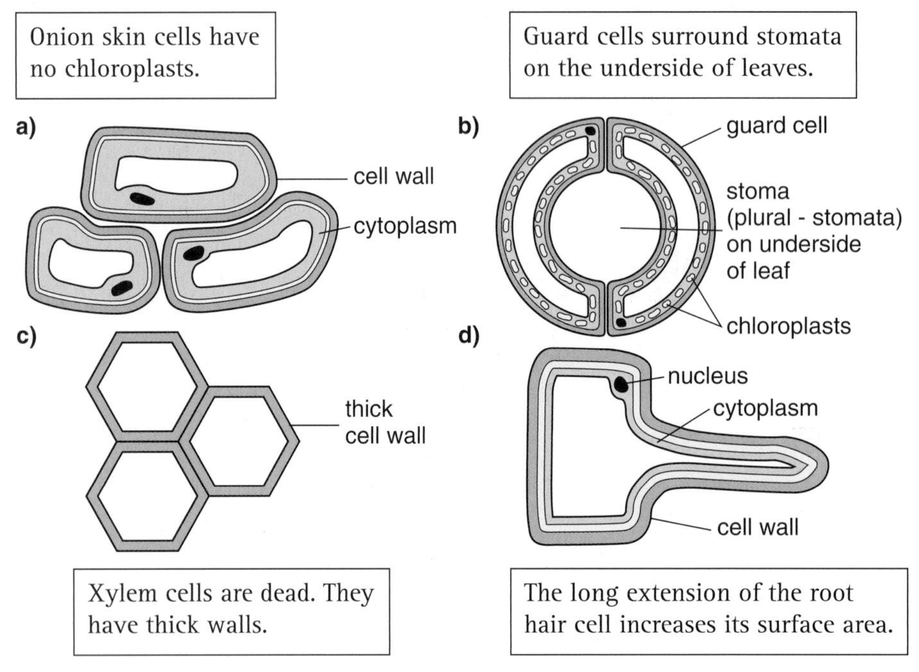

FIGURE 2.2 Variety in plant cells: a) onion skin cells, b) guard cells, c) xylem cells and d) a root hair cell

Photosynthesis

Photosynthesis is summarised by the equation:

carbon dioxide + water (+ light energy) ⟶ glucose + oxygen

LEARN THIS WORD EQUATION.

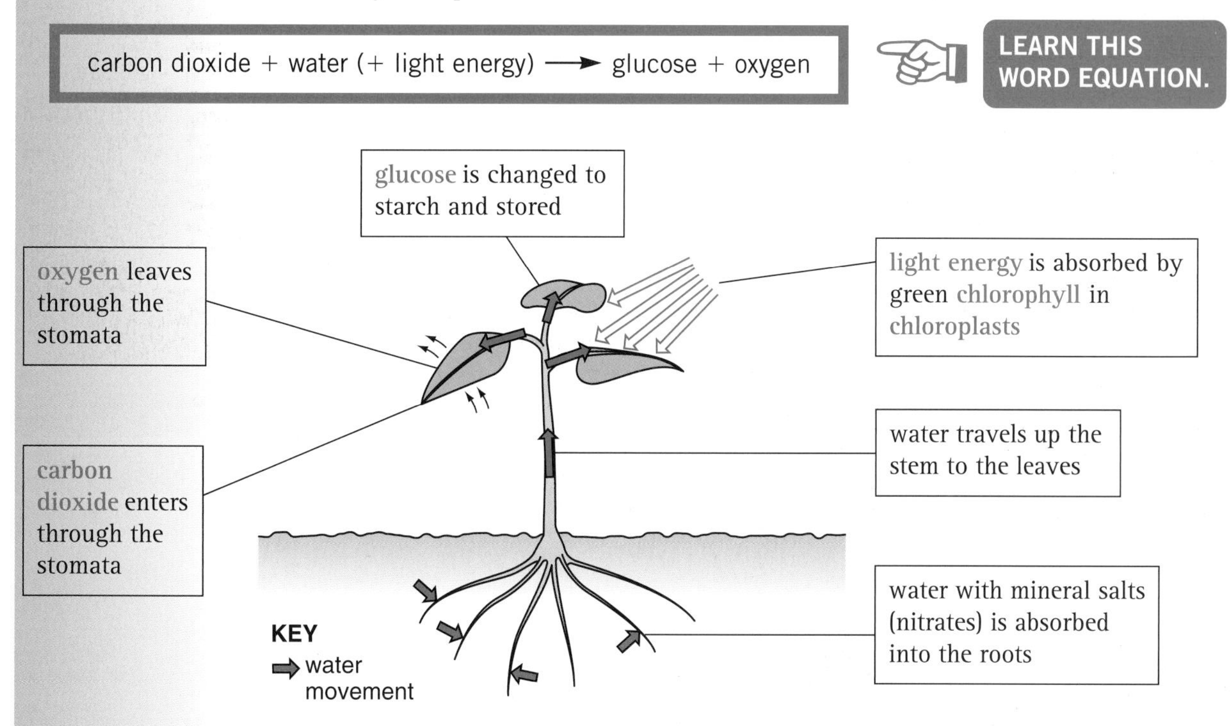

FIGURE 2.3 How a plant obtains the materials it needs for photosynthesis

When plants respire they release energy.

This energy is used to build small sugar molecules into larger molecules.

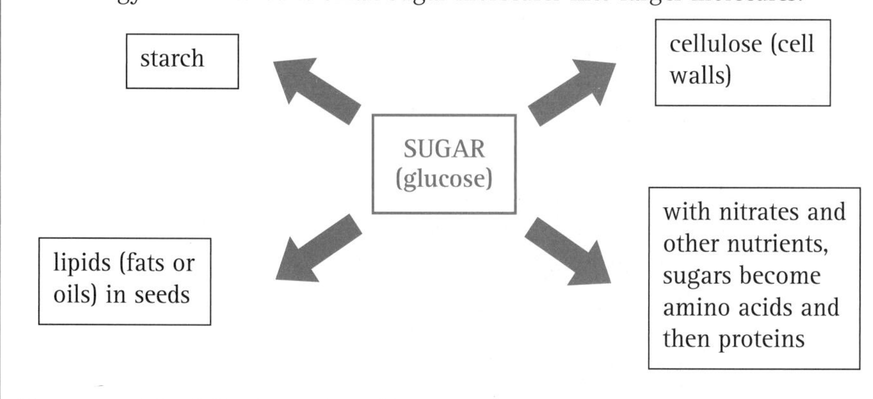

Plants need the following mineral ions:

- nitrate – to make proteins
- phosphate – for photosynthesis and respiration
- potassium – helps the enzymes used in photosynthesis and respiration.

If mineral ions are lacking the plant shows these symptoms:

- nitrate lacking –poor growth and older yellow leaves
- phosphate lacking – poor root growth and purple younger leaves
- potassium lacking – yellow leaves with dead spots on them.

The rate of photosynthesis is reduced by:

- lower temperature
- less carbon dioxide
- less light.

These are called limiting factors because they can limit photosynthesis.

Transport in plants

REMEMBER – **Diffusion** is the movement of molecules from a region of higher concentration to one of lower concentration (see page 2).

Plants lose water vapour from their leaf surfaces by transpiration. The rate of transpiration depends on the weather. It is faster in dry, hot, windy conditions. The water evaporates through the stomata. These are usually on the underside of the leaf and are controlled by guard cells. These cells can change shape to alter the size of the stomata. If a plant loses water faster than the roots replace it, the guard cells close the stomata to reduce water loss. Losing too much water makes the plant wilt. When cells wilt they become floppy or flaccid. In young seedlings this means they bend over. When cells are full of water they become firm or turgid.

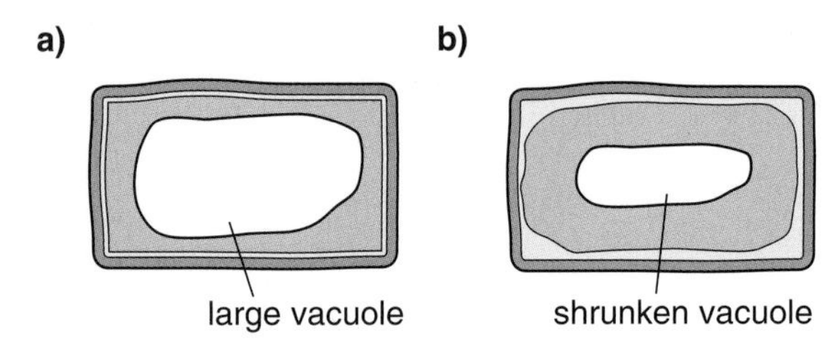

a) In the turgid cell, the cell membrane is pressing against the cell walls.

b) In the flaccid cell, the cell membrane pulls away from the cell wall at the corners, reducing the pressure on it.

Figure 2.4 What happens in a) a turgid plant cell and b) a flaccid plant cell

CHECK YOUR UNDERSTANDING

1. What sort of weather conditions are needed for a plant to transpire rapidly?
2. Plants have a waxy **cuticle** on their leaves to stop too much water loss through them. Why do plants that live in deserts have a **thicker** cuticle?

Flowering plants have special tissues for carrying water and nutrients.

- Xylem tissue carries water up the plant from the roots to the leaves via the stem. (See page 12 for a diagram of some xylem cells.)
- Phloem tissue carries sugars and other nutrients from the leaves to the rest of the plant. For example, in a potato plant, the sugar is carried down to the underground stems we know as potatoes, where it is stored as starch. In contrast to xylem tissue, phloem tissue carries material both up and down.

The movement of water is by a special kind of diffusion called osmosis.

Osmosis is the diffusion of water from a dilute to a more concentrated solution through a selectively permeable membrane. The membrane allows water molecules to pass through but not solute molecules.

Figure 2.5 shows how water enters the plant from the soil. The root hair cells increase the surface area of the roots so that they can take in the water more quickly.

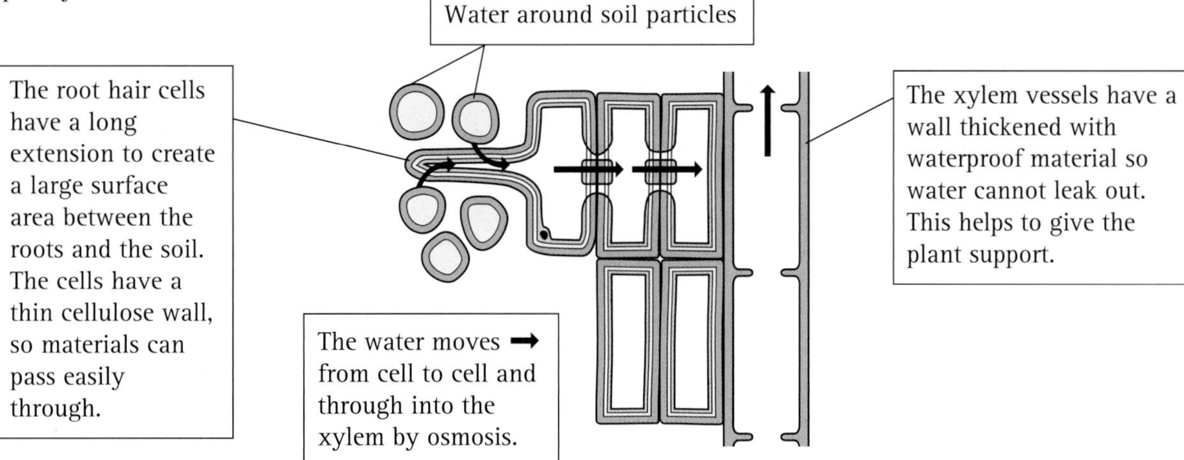

FIGURE 2.5 The role of the root hair cell in the uptake of water and the movement of water through the root to the xylem

Plants can absorb substances when there is a lower concentration of these substances outside the cell than inside. For example, if there is less phosphate in the soil water than in the cells, the phosphate can still be absorbed by the plant roots. This process requires energy supplied from respiration. It is called active transport and can only happen in living, respiring cells.

When cells absorb water by osmosis, pressure builds within the cell. Luckily plant cell walls are made from cellulose and so can withstand this pressure. This pressure keeps the cells rigid and gives them support and is especially important in young seedlings. These cells are turgid and are said to have turgor.

Exchange surfaces in plants

- Thin leaves so that gases don't have far to diffuse.
- The leaves are broad and there are lots of them so they can catch lots of sunlight energy.
- The leaves have a large surface area.
- The leaves are held out on the stems so that they face the Sun.
- The roots are long and go deep into the soil.
- The roots have root hairs which greatly increase their surface area.
- The ends of the root hairs are very fine so that solutes and water don't have far to travel.

How plants respond to their surroundings

Plants are sensitive to:

- the direction of gravity
- water
- light intensity.

As a result roots grow downwards to where the water is and their shoots grow upwards towards the light.

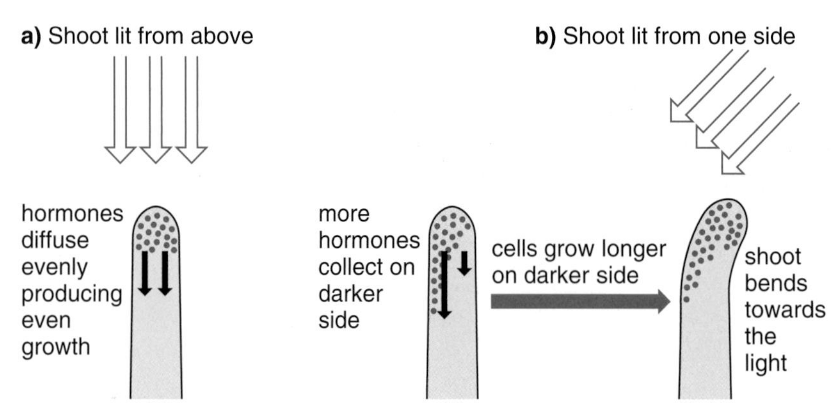

FIGURE 2.6 Plant responses to light

Plant shoots grow towards the light due to the uneven distribution of hormones which collect on the side away from the light and make the plant cells there grow faster.

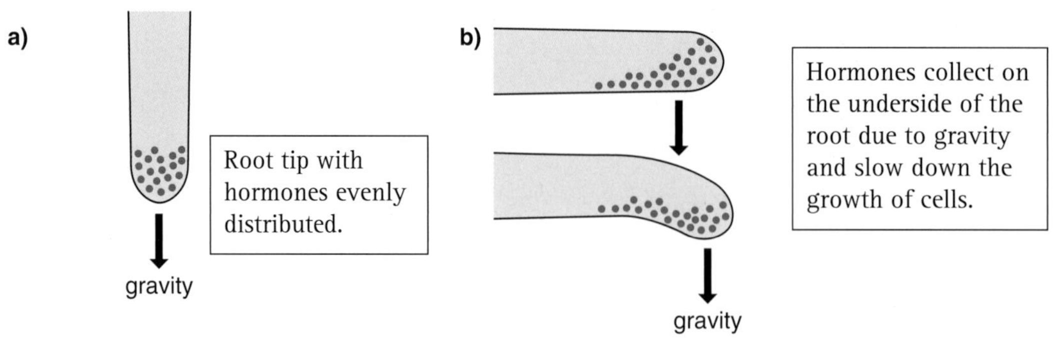

FIGURE 2.7 Plant responses to gravity

In roots, the hormones collect at the bottom and so the root grows downwards. If the root is placed on its side the hormones collect at the base, again gravity makes the root grow downwards.

Plant growers can use plant hormones to:

- Stimulate the growth of roots from cuttings to get lots of identical plants.
- Kill weeds by making them grow fast, get weak and die.
- Control the ripening of fruit on the plant. This allows it to ripen more slowly so that it can be transported from one country to another and still arrive in good condition.

Maintenance in humans

How humans respond to their surroundings

The nervous system allows us to react to our environment and co-ordinate our behaviour. Cells called receptors detect stimuli. The table shows where the receptors are and what they do.

Receptor	Function
in the eye	sensitive to light
in the ears	sensitive to sound
in the ears	allow us to keep our balance
on the tongue	sensitive to chemicals; enable us to taste
in the skin	sensitive to touch, pressure and temperature changes
in the nose	sensitive to chemicals; enable us to smell

The eye

The receptor which you need to know in some detail is the eye.

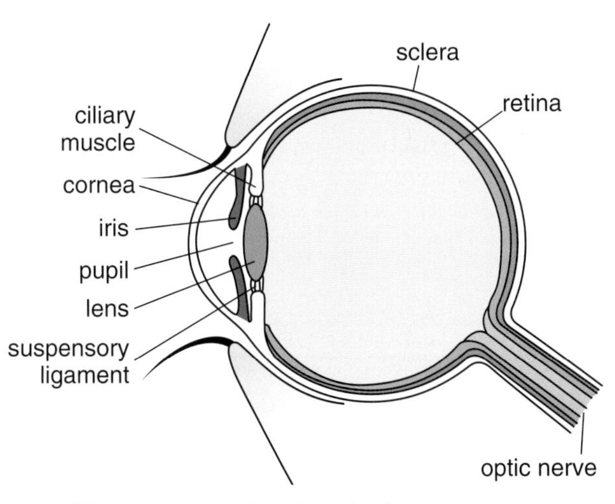

FIGURE 2.8 A vertical section through a human eye

You should be able to label these parts and know their functions.

Parts of the eye:

- The sclera – A tough outer layer, which is transparent at the front where it is called the cornea. The cornea bends the light when it enters the eye.
- The iris – This is muscular and controls the amount of light entering the eye by controlling the size of the pupil.
- The lens – This is held in position by suspensory ligaments and ciliary muscles. The lens focuses the light on to the retina.

  The shape of the lens can be altered by the ciliary muscles contracting to focus light from near objects (like this book) or relaxing to focus light from distant objects (like the horizon).

- The retina – This contains light-sensitive receptor cells. These send impulses to the brain along sensory neurones in the optic nerve.

Reflex actions

Information from the receptors passes along neurones in nerves to the brain. The brain then co-ordinates the response. Sometimes these responses are rapid and automatic and are called reflex actions. We don't think about them, and they are often protective.

Examples of reflex actions are:

- Blinking when an object comes towards the eye – to protect the eye from damage.
- The widening of the iris to narrow the pupil when a bright light is shone in the eye – to protect the retina from too much light.
- Removing the hand from a hot object – to protect the skin from burning.

A footballer saving a goal is not a reflex action as he has to think about it and decide what to do!

In a simple reflex action, electrical impulses transmit information from the receptor cells along a sensory neurone to the central nervous system (the brain and the spinal cord). They then pass from the spinal cord along a motor neurone to an effector like a muscle or gland. The muscle or gland then brings about the response.

There are often three neurones involved – sensory, relay and motor.

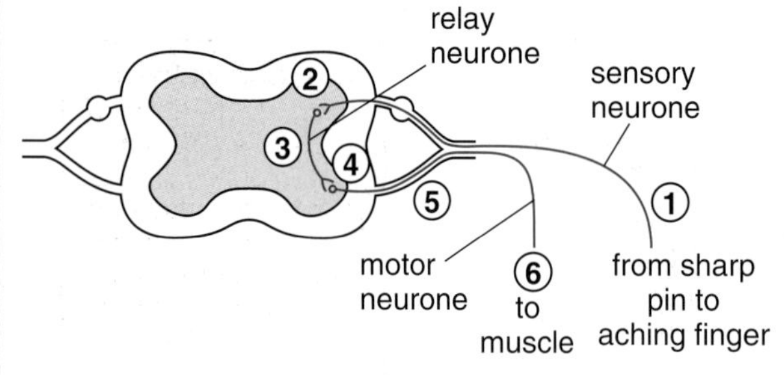

FIGURE 2.9 Section through spinal cord to show reflex arc

The sequence of events in a reflex arc is:

1. Impulses from the receptor pass along the sensory neurone to the central nervous system.
2. At a synapse between the sensory neurone and the relay neurone a chemical is released.
3. This chemical causes the impulses to be sent along the relay neurone.
4. At the next synapse, between the relay neurone and the motor neurone, more of the chemical is released so that the impulse travels to the motor neurone.
5. The motor neurone carries the impulse to the effector (muscle).
6. The muscle contracts and brings about the response (moving the hand away). If the effector is a gland it secretes a chemical.

In any reflex action you should be able to identify the stimulus, the receptor, the co-ordinator, the effector and the response.

CHECK YOUR UNDERSTANDING

❶ Name the receptors sensitive to light, sound and taste.

❷ What happens to the ciliary muscles when the eye lens focuses on far objects?

❸ Name the stimulus, receptor, co-ordinator, effector and response for the reflex action in Figure 2.9.

How the body maintains its internal conditions

Automatic systems in the body ensure that:

- body temperature is correct.
- the right amount of water and sugar is in the bloodstream.

Removing waste products

- Carbon dioxide is produced by all cells when they respire. It is taken to the lungs in the bloodstream and then breathed out.
- Urea is produced by the liver when extra amino acids, not needed by the body, are broken down. The urea is taken to the kidney by the bloodstream and dissolved in water to form urine. It is stored temporarily in the bladder.

a)

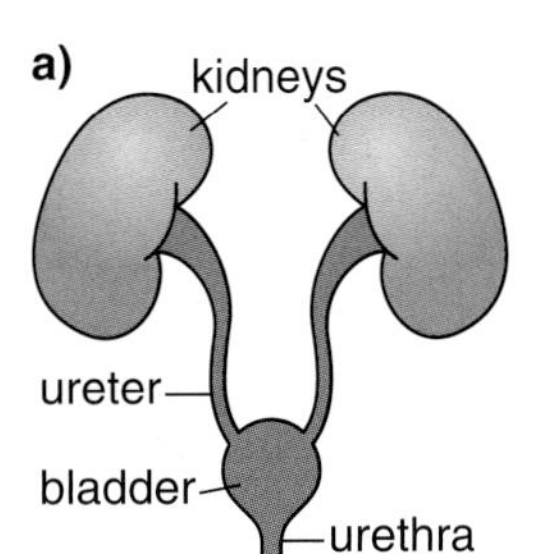

b)

urea made in the liver by the breakdown of excess amino acids

↓ put in bloodstream

urea is removed by the kidneys, which form urine

↓

urine is stored in the bladder

↓ urine is released through the urethra

FIGURE 2.10 a) The excretory system in humans. b) The process of removal of urea

Controlled internal conditions include:

- The water content of the body. Water leaves the body via the lungs when we breathe out, via the skin when we sweat, and via the kidneys when we pass urine.
- The ion content of the body (sometimes called mineral salts). Ions are lost through the skin when we sweat and through the kidneys in urine.
- The temperature must be controlled so that enzymes can work at their best. Sweating helps to cool the body by evaporation. When it is hot we drink more to balance out the water lost in sweat.

The sugar content of the blood is controlled by hormones. These are proteins made in glands and carried in the bloodstream to their target organs.

Hormone	Gland producing hormone	Target organ
insulin	pancreas	liver
glucagon	pancreas	liver

If blood sugar is too high, insulin causes the liver to store some as glycogen. If blood sugar is too low, glucagon causes the liver to change some glycogen back to sugar.

A diabetic person does not make enough insulin and has to either inject insulin or control the sugar content of the food eaten.

CHECK YOUR UNDERSTANDING

1. Name two waste products that must be removed from the blood.
2. Name the hormone which lowers the blood sugar level.

The kidneys

The blood in our body passes continuously through the kidneys.

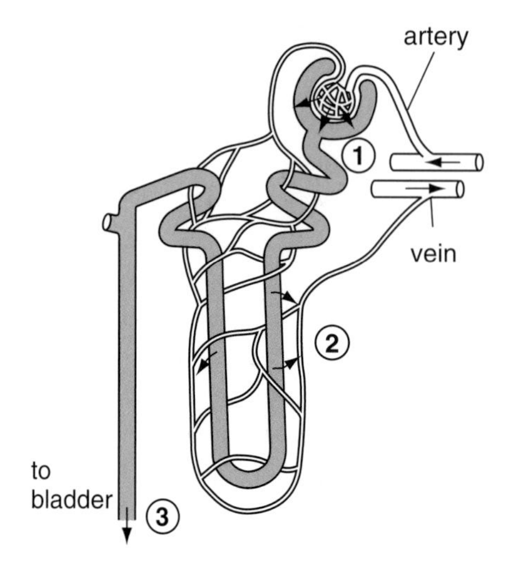

1 Blood is filtered by the kidneys. The artery carries blood under high pressure into tiny kidney tubules. The high pressure causes all small molecules to leave the blood and enter the tubule.

2 Further down the tubule useful ions, glucose and amino acids as well as some water are reabsorbed into the blood. The glucose and dissolved ions may be actively absorbed against a concentration gradient. Energy is required for this.

3 At the end of the tubule the urea, excess ions and excess water is released as urine. This is stored in the bladder.

FIGURE 2.11 A kidney tubule

Controlling the water content of the blood

If the water content of blood is too low, the pituitary gland releases more ADH (a hormone) into the blood. This causes the kidney to absorb more water into the blood, producing more concentrated urine. If the water content of the blood is too high, less ADH is released and so more dilute urine is produced.

Controlling body temperature

The thermoregulatory centre in the brain is sensitive to blood temperature. It also receives impulses from sensors in the skin.

If the body temperature (the core temperature) is too high:

- Arterioles supplying the skin capillaries dilate, so that more blood flows to the surface and loses heat by radiation from the skin's surface.
- Sweat glands release more sweat to the surface of the skin, this evaporates and so cools the skin.

If the core temperature is too low:

- Arterioles supplying the skin capillaries constrict, so that less blood flows to the surface and less heat is lost.
- Less sweat is produced.
- Muscles may shiver, respiration is needed in the muscles to produce these tiny contractions, this respiration releases some energy as heat.

Controlling blood glucose concentration

Blood glucose concentration is monitored and controlled by the pancreas. If the blood glucose concentration is too high the pancreas secretes insulin into the blood. The insulin travels to the liver and causes it to change glucose into glycogen (which is insoluble). This glycogen is then stored.

If the blood glucose concentration is too low the pancreas secretes another hormone called glucagon which causes the liver to convert some of the stored glycogen into soluble glucose.

CHECK YOUR UNDERSTANDING

1. Name three substances that are reabsorbed in the kidney tubule.
2. Name the hormone which controls the water content of the blood.

The effect of drugs

A drug is a chemical that changes the way our bodies work, or changes the way we think or react. Even drugs that are used legally may harm us, so we need to know the dangers involved.

If we use drugs a lot, they change the chemical processes in our bodies so that we become dependent on them. This means we feel very ill if we don't have the drug.

Sometimes we can become addicted to the drugs. This means that our bodies will show physical symptoms (withdrawal symptoms) if the drug is taken away. These symptoms can include vomiting, headaches, sweating and stomach pains.

Solvents

Young people sometimes experiment with solvents such as glue or lighter fuel.

Solvents can cause many problems:

- They cause the person to behave in strange ways.
- They may cause permanent damage to the lungs, the liver and the brain.
- If sniffed from a polythene bag, the person may suffocate because the bag stops them breathing.

Alcohol

Another widely used, but legal drug is alcohol. Alcohol is found in drinks such as beer, wines, spirits and 'alcopops'.

If alcohol is taken in large quantities it can:

- Affect the nervous system by slowing down reactions. This is especially dangerous if the person then drives a car. Even walking down the road can be dangerous.
- Lead to lack of self control; people are more likely to fight when they have had too much alcohol to drink.
- Lead to unconsciousness or even a coma.
- Damage the liver and the brain.

Tobacco

Tobacco is a drug which contains an addictive substance called nicotine. After just a few cigarettes the person needs to have more.

The effects of smoking:

- Tobacco smoke contains substances like tar which cause lung cancer and bronchitis.
- Can cause diseases such as emphysema where the alveoli are broken, reducing the surface area of the lungs.
- Can cause disease of the heart as blood vessels are more likely to fur up if a person smokes.
- Tobacco smoke contains the poisonous gas carbon monoxide. This combines irreversibly with haemoglobin more readily than oxygen does and so fills all the carrying sites. In pregnant women this can mean that the fetus is deprived of oxygen and can often be small at birth or even die in the womb.
- Causes extra mucus secretions in the lungs.

Smoking and cancer

A link between smoking and ill-health was first noticed by the ship's doctor who travelled with Columbus to South America. But no scientific studies were carried out until the late 1940s. Then, further studies all showed the same link. Since then all investigations have shown that smoking greatly increases the risk of lung cancer.

CHECK YOUR UNDERSTANDING

1. What is a drug?
2. Give two examples of drugs.
3. What damage can alcohol do to someone who drinks too much over a long period of time?
4. Name three diseases caused by smoking.

Topic Test

1 Write down the function of a) the cell membrane, b) the cell wall, and c) the chloroplasts. (3 marks)

2 How does the shape of the root hair cell relate to its function? (1 mark)

3 What is the glucose that plants produce turned into? (4 marks)

4 Write the word equation for photosynthesis. (1 mark)

5 What do plants use a) nitrate, b) phosphate and c) potassium for? (3 marks)

6 Write the definition of diffusion. (2 marks)

7 a) When do plants use active transport?
b) Why can it only occur in living cells? (2 marks)

8 Give three ways that commercial growers of plants use hormones. (3 marks)

9 Copy the table and fill in the gaps.

Receptors	What it detects
	touch and pressure changes
tongue	

(2 marks)

10 a) What does the eye lens do?
b) What does the iris do? (2 marks)

11 What changes the shape of the eye lens? (2 marks)

12 Name three internal conditions that must be controlled by the body. (3 marks)

13 What does insulin do? (1 mark)

14 What does being dependent on a drug mean? (1 mark)

Total: 30 marks

ENVIRONMENT

Why do plants and animals live where they do?

Plants and animals are said to be adapted when they are able to survive in their normal environment. The conditions they need to grow and reproduce are available. Some animals have had to adapt to extremely harsh environments. Some examples are given in the table below:

ARCTIC ENVIRONMENT		DESERT ENVIRONMENT	
Arctic conditions	**Adaptations**	**Desert conditions**	**Adaptations**
Very cold	Thick fur to trap a thick layer of air. Air is a poor conductor of heat. Thick layer of fat (or blubber in whales). Fat is a good insulator.	Very hot	Thin fur on top of the body. Little body fat so heat is easily lost from skin capillaries.
Very cold	Compact body shape with small ears to reduce surface area for heat loss. Small feet to reduce heat loss by conduction.	Very hot	Body shape gives maximum surface area for heat loss. For example, Fennec foxes have large ears to radiate heat and long, thin legs.
White background in winter	White fur in winter for camouflage and to reduce radiation heat loss.	Sandy background	Fur of sandy brown colour for camouflage.

Adaptations of plants to arid conditions

Arid or very dry conditions are found in deserts where it may not rain for several years and there are sand dunes which are rapid draining.

Cacti are well adapted to desert conditions.

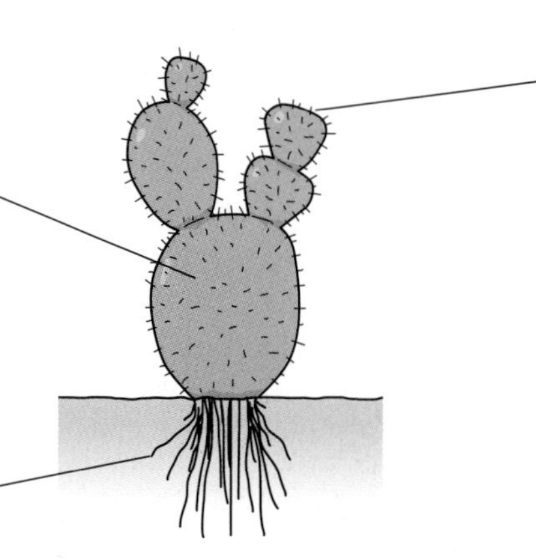

FIGURE 3.1 Adaptations of a cactus

Plant and animal populations

Competition for light – trees may shade smaller plants so that they do not get enough light for photosynthesis.

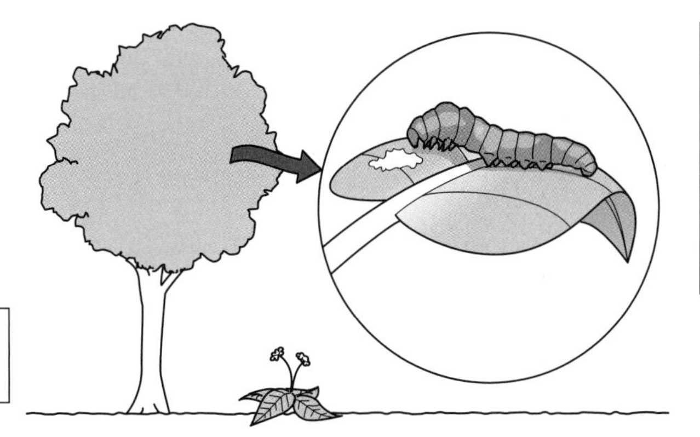

Grazing e.g. by caterpillars. This may reduce the number of leaves so less photosynthesis takes place and so less growth.

Competition for space to grow.

Competition for mineral ions such as nitrates which are needed for making proteins.

Competition for water from the soil – water is needed for turgor support.

FIGURE 3.2 Factors affecting plant population

Count the number of times the idea of competition has been used on this page. The plants and animals really do affect each other and can change the environment.

Predator – an animal that kills and eats other animals.
Prey – animals that are eaten by another animal.

The population of plants in a community will be affected by:

- The amount of food available and the number of animals competing for the same food source. For example, if there are too many grazing animals, the grass will be eaten and trampled to ground level and will not grow so the population of herbivores (sheep or rabbits) will be reduced.
- The proportions of predators and prey. If there is more food for the prey, they will rear more young, providing more food for the predators so they will also breed more. When the number of predators (e.g. foxes) increases, they eat more prey (e.g. rabbits), so the number of prey will soon be reduced.
- Disease. Illnesses spread easily if the population gets too large and closely packed.

CHECK YOUR UNDERSTANDING

1. Explain how polar bears are adapted for surviving in very cold conditions.
2. What do animals compete for in their environment?
3. Why are there few plants on a woodland floor?
4. The disease myxomatosis killed many rabbits in the UK. Suggest how this affected a) plant growth and b) the fox population.
5. If many of the leaves on an apple tree were eaten by caterpillars in the spring, why would the apple crop be very much reduced that autumn?

❻ What structural features would you expect in the kidney of a desert rodent?

❼ Disease spreads easily if a population is closely packed. What else spreads from animal to animal?

❽ What would you expect to happen to the number of young raised as a) food shortage and b) severe cold weather, hit a population of animals?

❾ How does camouflage aid survival?

Energy and biomass in a food chain

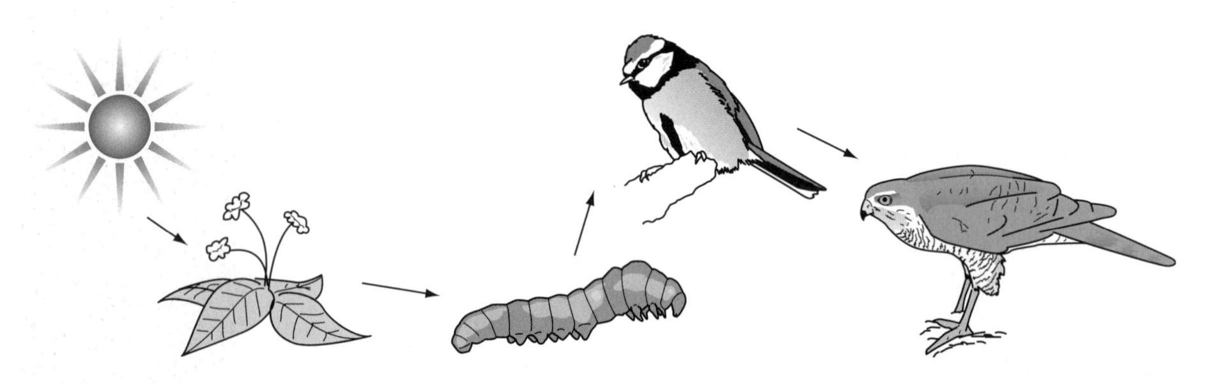

Green leaves capture a small percentage of light energy.

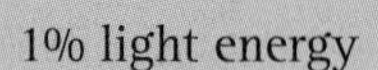

1% light energy

Plants use some energy for making sugars, cellulose and proteins – i.e. making plant biomass.

10% energy in plant biomass

Some of the energy in the plants eaten by a herbivore is used for animal growth i.e. stored as more protein in the muscles.

20% energy in animal biomass

Some of the energy of the herbivore eaten by the carnivore (blue tit) is made into muscle protein as the carnivore grows.

20% energy in animal biomass

Carnivores may be eaten by bigger carnivores. More of the energy is converted into biomass.

Make sure you use the words sunlight energy or light energy NOT Sun. It is the ENERGY which is important.

Some energy is used for plant respiration and is therefore lost from the food chain.

At each link in the food chain, some of the energy is used by animals for respiration – that is making chemical energy for use in the cells, use by muscles and for keeping the body warm. Some energy is lost in urine and faeces. Energy is lost from the food chain and so there is less to be passed on at each link.

FIGURE 3.3 What happens to energy and biomass in a food chain

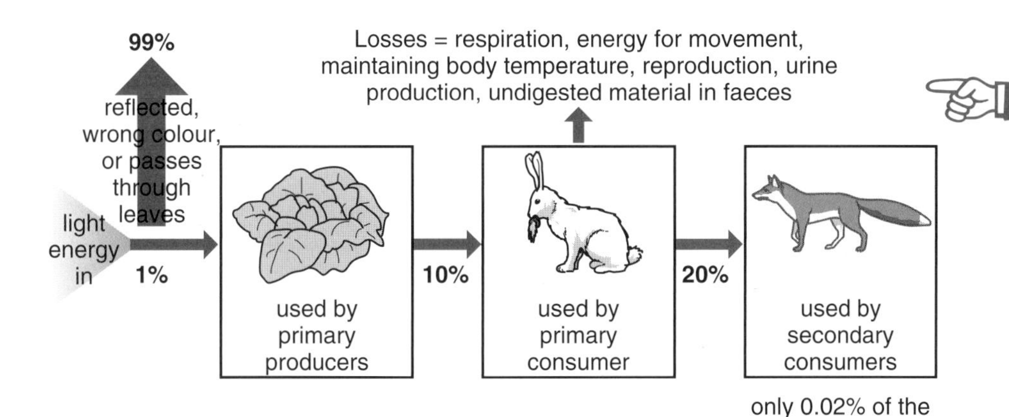

Figure 3.4 A simple three-link food chain showing where the energy is lost in the chain

If you are given numbers, work out what they tell you – they won't be difficult. In Figure 3.4, take the energy from the Sun as equivalent to £100. Work out the amount the lettuce traps: 1% of £100 = £1. The rabbit gets 10% of £1 which is 10p. So how much does the fox get? This shows that you can't have a food chain with too many links as there will be very little energy for the last carnivore.

THINK – From your knowledge of the organisms in this food chain, what changes in size would you see as you pass along the chain and what changes in population numbers in a given area?

Applying this idea to a food web, we see that at each feeding level the animals are larger but there are fewer of them. The biomass (mass of living material) at each level gets less – this can be drawn as a pyramid of biomass.

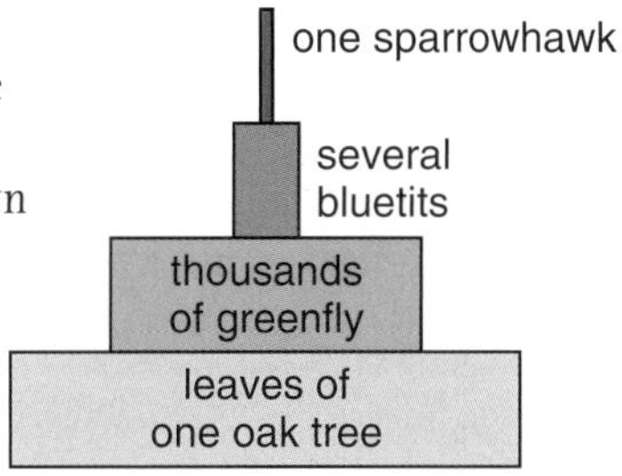

one sparrowhawk
several bluetits
thousands of greenfly
leaves of one oak tree

Figure 3.5 A pyramid of biomass for an oak tree

Make sure that your rectangles get smaller as the biomass reduces.

Food production

In terms of farming, there are a number of important energy losses:

- Maintaining the high body temperature of mammals and birds, for example chickens.
- Movement – especially for free range animals approaching maturity.
- Undigested material in faeces.

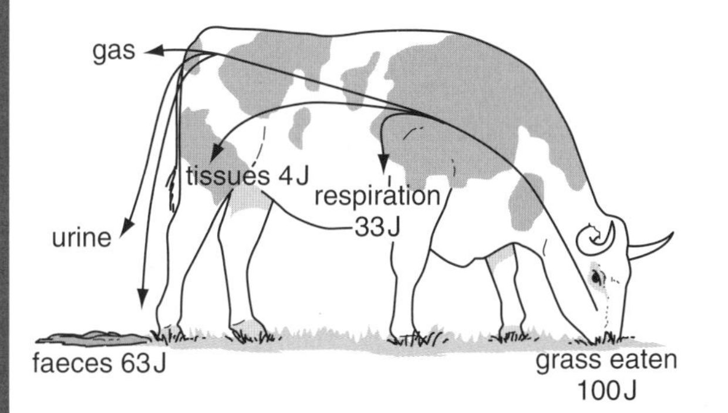

Energy in = 100 J
Energy converted into cow biomass = 4 J
Energy lost at this link of the chain = 96 J

Figure 3.6 Energy conversion in a beef cow

Minimising energy losses and maximising production in food production:

- Reduce the number of links in the chain.
- Restrict the movement of animals.
- Reduce heat loss from the animal's body – warm, windproof accommodation.
- Computerise food supply for efficient muscle growth and to reduce waste.
- Kill the animals for food as soon as they have finished the fast growth phase.
- Restrict reproduction.

Farming needs to be a compromise between productivity, care for the animals and care for the environment. The shopper wants cheap produce, but the animals in 'factory farming' may pay the cost:

- Battery hens produce more eggs very cheaply but this is a cruel existence for the hens. Barn living gives them more freedom but less than if they were free range outside.
- Piglets experience great stress in intensive rearing, but grow more quickly than free range pigs.
- Cows can be given hormones to increase their milk yield but this damages their health.
- The faeces produced in intensive rearing needs to be disposed of via a sewage treatment plant to prevent water pollution, and this adds to production costs.

To ensure the best quality of fruit available, it is picked and packed before it is ripe. It is ripened using a hormone treatment (ethylene gas) during transport. This reduces bruising and increases shelf-life, but much of the fruit is still unripe when sold.

CHECK YOUR UNDERSTANDING

1. Give one reason why green plants trap so little of the sunlight energy which falls on them.
2. For food production, why would a three-link chain be more efficient than a five-link chain?
3. What does a pyramid of biomass show?
4. Why do free range piglets gain weight more slowly than those intensively reared in pens?
5. What are the environmental problems associated with 'factory farming'?
6. Why do organic and free range products cost more to produce?

Nutrient cycles

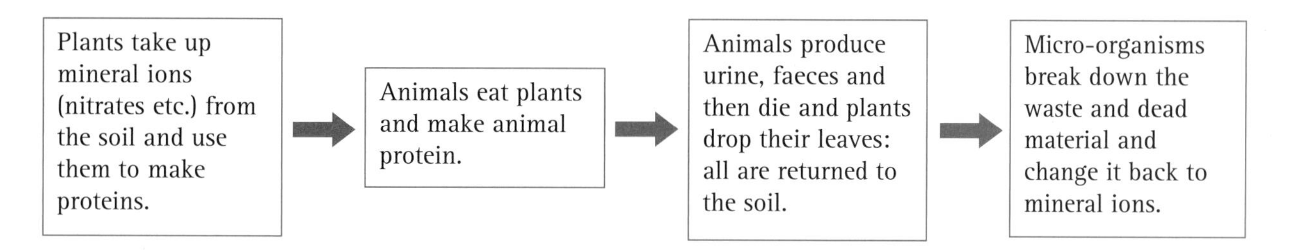

Microbes or micro-organisms are bacteria and fungi which release enzymes to digest waste and dead material. They can't use it all for growth so substances returned to the soil are taken up by plant roots and the cycle starts again. Micro-organisms are most active in warm, damp conditions with lots of oxygen. Man uses decomposition by micro-organisms in sewage works and for composting. Much household waste can now be composted.

Learn the cycle and the conditions in which micro-organisms break down dead material fastest.
See also page 13 – mineral ions and plants.

Carbon

- The element carbon is very important – it is found in a large number of biological compounds such as sugars, starch, fats, proteins and cellulose. These compounds make up plant and animal biomass.
- Carbon is in the gas carbon dioxide produced by respiration.
- Carbon is constantly being cycled in the environment.

The carbon cycle

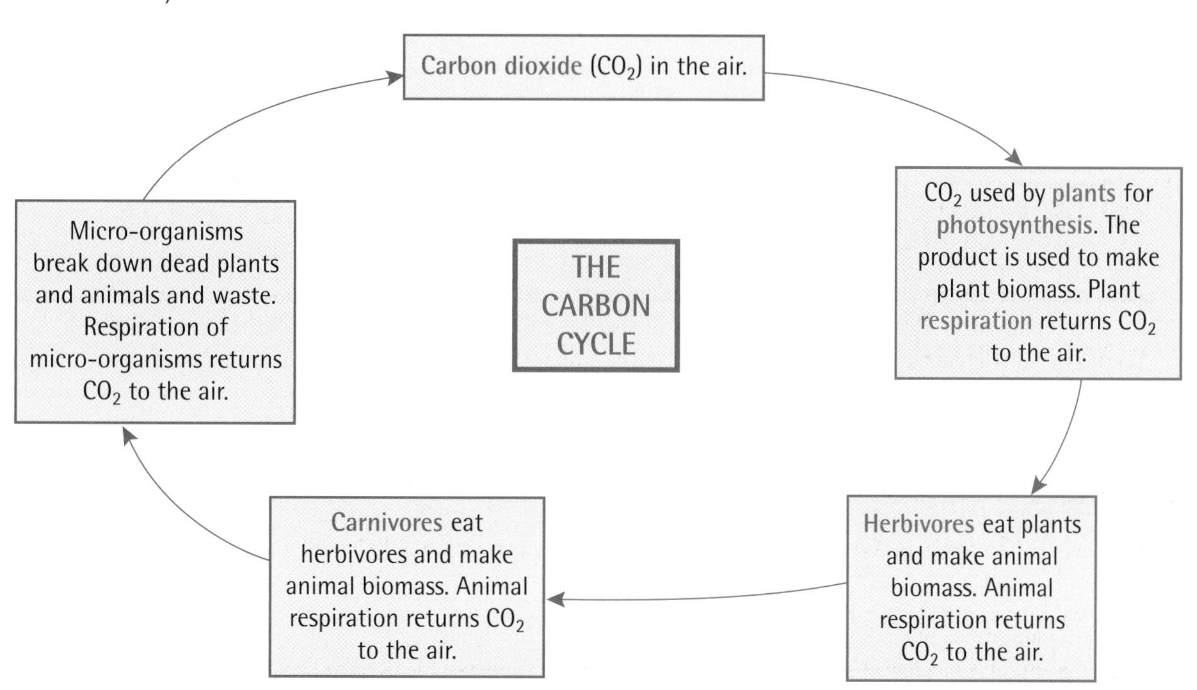

How do humans affect the carbon dioxide balance?

Humans have increased the carbon dioxide levels by:

1. Deforestation – cutting down and burning trees to use the land for cattle ranching.
2. Farming – this increases the number of bacteria and fungi in the soil and thus the amount of respiration.
3. Transport – burning fossil fuels: petrol and diesel.
4. Generating electricity – burning coal, oil and gas in power stations.

Deforestation also means that less carbon dioxide is removed from the air – fewer trees so less photosynthesis. This means that less carbon dioxide is locked up in the cellulose of wood.

The nitrogen cycle

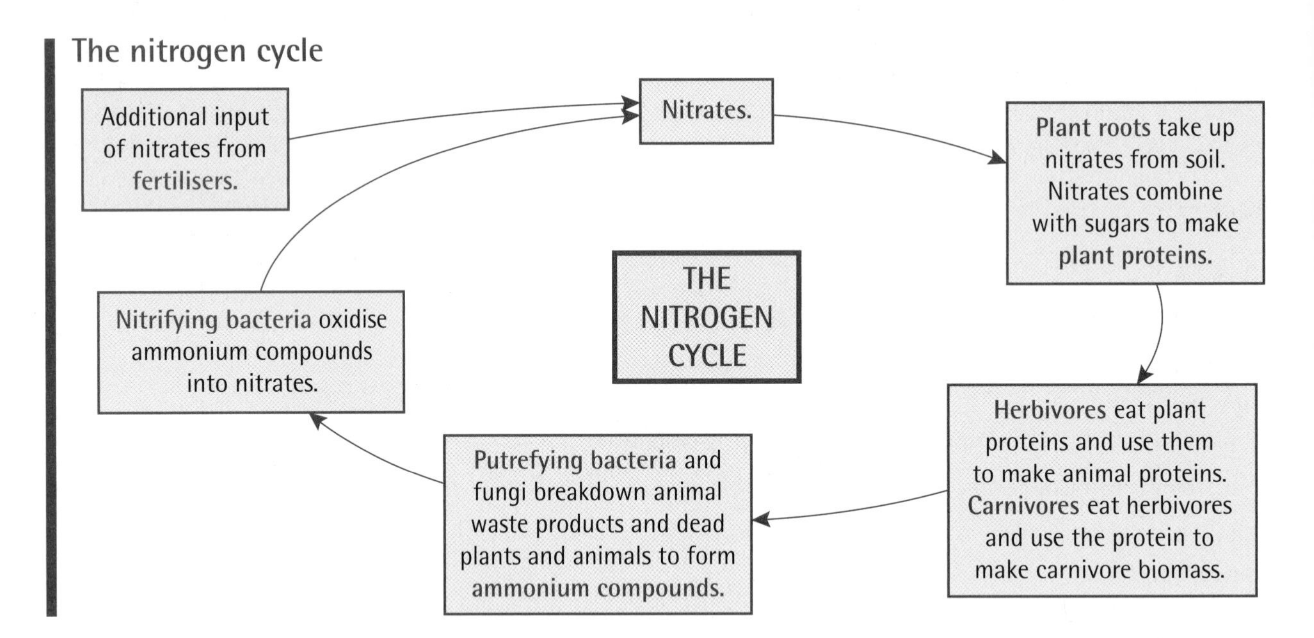

CHECK YOUR UNDERSTANDING

1. In a stable community the 'take up' and 'return' are balanced, but what happens if man removes or harvests plants from the environment?
2. What are the ideal conditions for composting?
3. What is the only process that removes carbon dioxide from the air?
4. Complete the sequence of compounds a nitrogen molecule passes through.

   nitrates → plant proteins → __________ → __________ → nitrates
5. Fill in the gaps in the following sentence.

   Micro-organisms need cellulase to break down __________, and __________ to break down proteins.

The effect of humans on the environment

Rapid growth in the human population has increased demand for:

1. Land for building.
2. Building materials – leading to increased quarrying.
3. Energy – so more power stations are needed with the result that non-renewable fuel resources (coal, oil and natural gas) are rapidly being used up.
4. Food – resulting in more intensive farming and thus more pesticides and fertilisers being used.
5. Transport of materials from producers to towns.

More people produce:

1. More sewage which needs treatment to prevent sea or river pollution.
2. More refuse – we are rapidly running out of landfill sites so waste must be recycled, composted or incinerated.
3. Air pollution from industries and transport.
4. Water pollution if toxic chemicals from industry or excess fertilisers or pesticides from intensive farming wash into rivers.

Acid rain

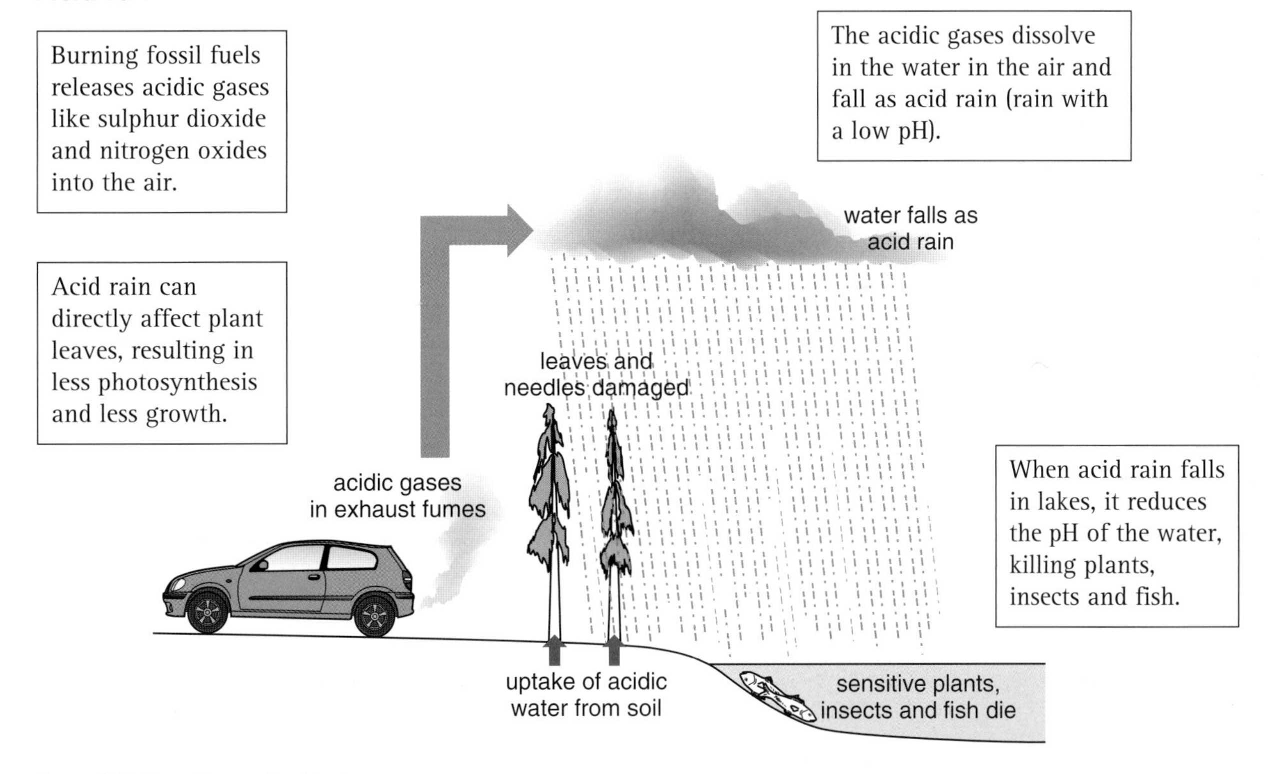

FIGURE 3.7 The effects of acid rain

Ways to reduce the acid rain problem

- Use of low sulphur fuels.
- Use of bulk transport for goods – railways.
- Less use of private cars – better public transport.
- Use of alternative renewable energy sources like wind power, solar power or hydroelectric power.

Global warming

The greenhouse effect is caused because the layer of carbon dioxide and methane in the atmosphere absorbs heat radiated from the Earth and re-radiates it back to Earth. The amount of carbon dioxide and methane in the atmosphere is increasing. The result is global warming, which sounds nice, but the change in temperature will change climates resulting in both more storms and more droughts, and the melting of the polar ice caps and of glaciers will cause flooding in low coastal areas such as Bangladesh, Holland and eastern England.

Sources of the increased levels of carbon dioxide and methane include:

- Increased numbers of cows – more carbon dioxide from respiration and methane from the fermentation of grass.
- Increased areas of paddy fields – bacteria in flooded fields release methane.
- More combustion of fossil fuels – more carbon dioxide produced.

Ways to reduce the problem of global warming

- Develop alternative energy resources so we burn less fossil fuels.
- Increase use of public transport for people and bulk rail transport for goods.
- Eat more vegetable protein and less beef.
- Increase energy efficiency in homes.

Eutrophication

Harvesting crops stops the recycling of nutrients, so farmers have to use fertilisers to add nutrients to the soil so that the next year's crops will grow well. Heavy rainfall before the crop has taken up the fertilisers results in the nutrients washing into streams where they cause plants there to grow too well, and eutrophication of the water occurs.

Eutrophication – sequence of events:

1. Fertiliser in the water causes algae, floating weeds and submerged plants to grow rapidly.
2. Competition for light causes submerged plants to die.
3. Aerobic bacteria increase in numbers as they decompose the dead plants.
4. Aerobic respiration of bacteria reduces the dissolved oxygen level in the water.
5. Sensitive invertebrates and fish die as a result of the low oxygen level in the water.

The addition of plant nutrients from sewage or bacterial nutrients from food factory waste also causes eutrophication.

CHECK YOUR UNDERSTANDING

1. Name the substances in sewage which could cause rapid plant growth.
2. The run-off from a pig-pen flows into a pond. What effects will be seen?
3. Give two reasons why it is not advisable to add fertilisers to fields in the autumn.

Topic Test

1 Look at the diagram of energy conversion in a beef cow, Figure 3.6 on page 27.

a) What percentage of the energy intake is lost from the food chain?

b) How is this energy lost?

c) Does any energy pass to an alternative food chain?

d) How could beef productivity be increased? (4 marks)

2 The grass proteins in the faeces of the cow are broken down by bacteria and fungi. Copy and complete the flowchart below adding the names of the chemical compounds or the bacteria at A, B and C.

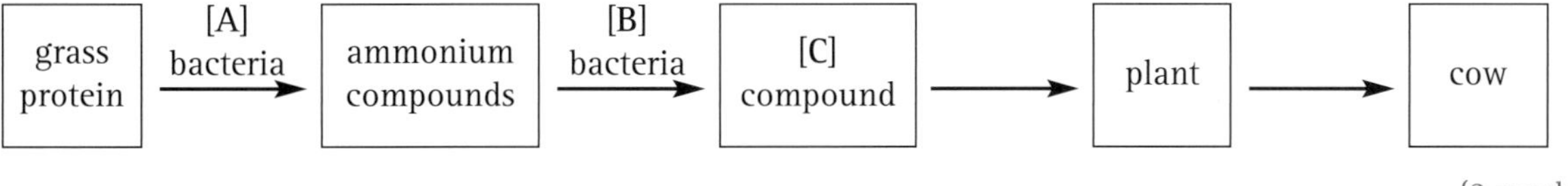

(3 marks)

3 Sewage is accidentally washed into a river after heavy rainfall. Explain each of the following observations. (*Note that there are two marks for each of the following questions so give a fact and reason for each answer.*)

a) A week later the water downstream seems very green.

b) Some of the rooted plants have begun to die.

c) The water soon begins to smell musty and is going brown.

d) Fish are seen gasping for air at the surface. (8 marks)

4 Theoretically, if the amount of carbon dioxide produced by respiration is balanced by the amount used for photosynthesis, then the carbon dioxide content of the air should remain constant.

Copy and complete the table, explaining how each of the following actions upsets the balance.

Action	Increases or decreases CO_2	Explanation
more cars on the road	increases	
planting more trees		
increasing the number of gas fired power stations		
increasing the proportion of electricity produced by wind generators		

(7 marks)

5 Acid rain is a growing environmental concern.

a) Explain how acid rain is formed.

b) Give three ways in which the problem could be reduced.

c) The increasing human population causes the problems of acid rain and the greenhouse effect. Give two other problems resulting from the increase in human population.

(8 marks)

Total: 30 marks

INHERITANCE AND SELECTION

MODULE 4

Types of reproduction

There are two methods of reproduction:

1 Asexual reproduction

Asexual reproduction involves only *one* parent. Offspring or new cells are formed by normal cell division.

This is called mitosis and the offspring are genetically identical, i.e. clones. Before each cell division a copy of the chromosomes is made. The chromosomes are paired and one of each pair goes to each new cell.

This can be seen in plants that have runners.

REMEMBER – Cloned individuals have no genetic variation.

2 Sexual reproduction

Sexual reproduction requires *two* parents.

Specialised cells in the testes and ovaries undergo reduction division, or meiosis, to form haploid gametes. In meiosis copies of all the chromosomes are made, and the cell then divides twice. At the first division the chromosomes separate into two cells, each with 46 chromosomes. In the second division the chromatids separate. So each of the four cells formed has a single set of 23 chromosomes.

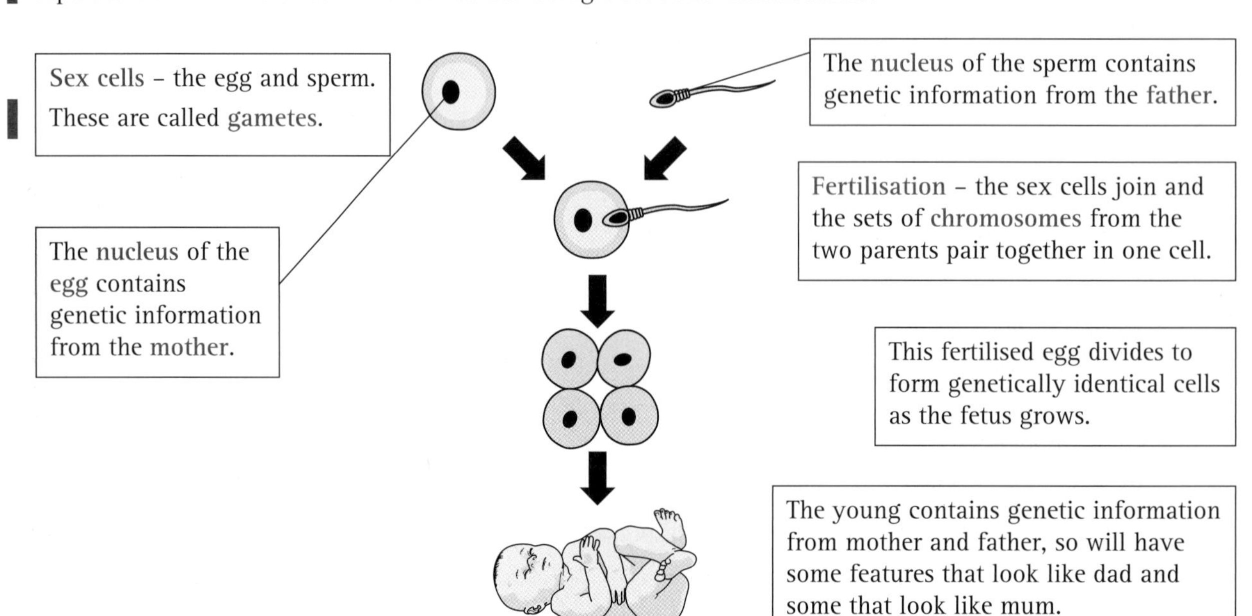

FIGURE 4.1 The process of sexual reproduction

Sexual reproduction gives rise to variation because:

1 Each gamete has a random assortment of chromosomes – one from each pair.

2 Each gamete has different sets of alleles.

3 The alleles from each parent pair, giving new combinations of characters.

Environmental factors, such as light, nutrients and water, can cause differences in the appearances of plants and animals produced by sexual or asexual reproduction.

Variation within a species

The nucleus of a sex cell contains one set of chromosomes.

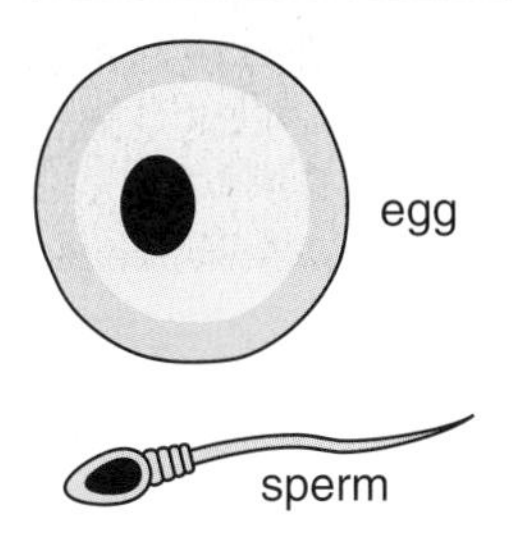

FIGURE 4.2 Sex cells

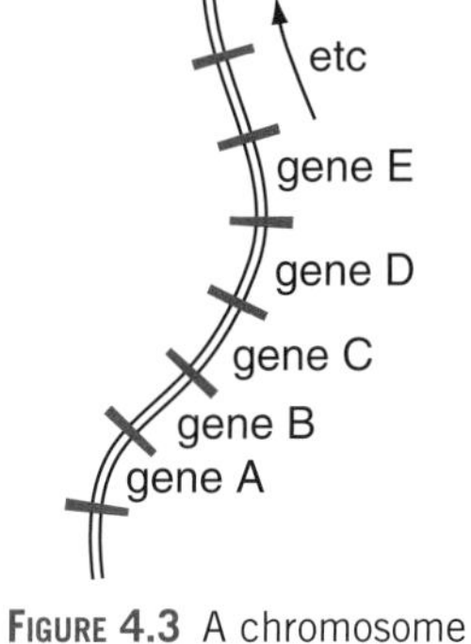

FIGURE 4.3 A chromosome

Each chromosome carries a line of many genes.

Different genes control the development of different characteristics.

There are different forms of some genes and these are called alleles, e.g. the eye colour gene has alleles for blue eye colour, brown eye colour and green eye colour.

Remember – Genetic variation comes from sexual reproduction. No two offspring are alike unless they are identical twins.

In sexual reproduction the young receive a random selection of alleles from both parents so each individual has a unique set. When the chromosomes with their alleles from mother and father pair, only the dominant allele is expressed, so the offspring will show some features from dad and some from mum. (More detail on pages 40–41.)

CHECK YOUR UNDERSTANDING

1. Complete the following sentences:
   a) Male sex cells are called (i) sperm______ and female sex cells are called (ii) eggs______.
   b) __________ is the joining together of the nuclei of male and female gametes.
   c) A chromosome carries a line of __________.
   d) After fertilisation the new cell that is formed divides by ____________ to form the fetus.
2. What two factors could cause two plants of the same species to look different?
3. Identical twins have the same genetic information. Why might they look different when they are older?

Producing plants and animals with desirable characteristics

Taking cuttings

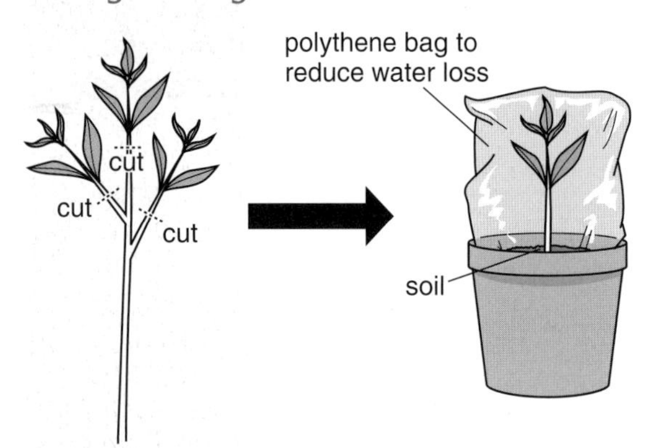

Take young shoots from a plant and insert into a pot of soil.

The cuttings will grow roots and form a new plant genetically identical to the parent plant.

Figure 4.4 Growing from a cutting

Modern cloning techniques

Cloning plants using tissue culture

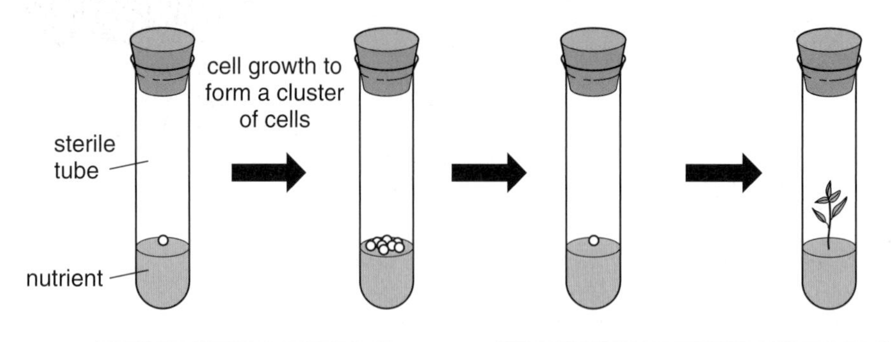

Each cell grows roots and shoots and forms a miniature plant. These can be grown on to full size plants.

A cell is removed from the stem and placed on nutrient in a sterile tube.

Cells are separated and placed on new sterile nutrient with growth hormones. They are placed in warm, light conditions.

Figure 4.5 Tissue culture

Cloning animals by nuclear transfer

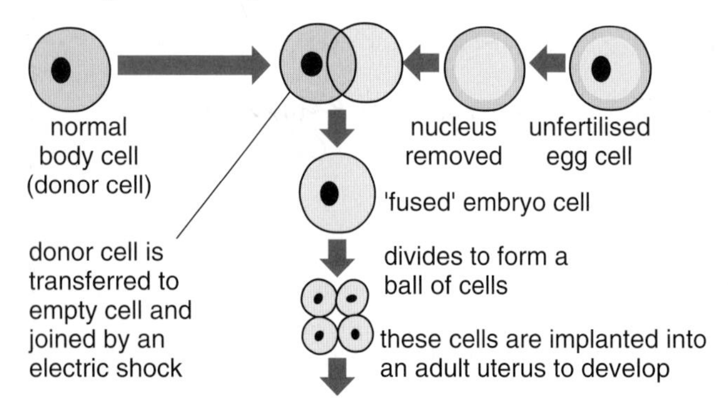

Figure 4.6 Nuclear transfer

Selective breeding

Selective breeding is a way of creating plants and animals which display a particular characteristic. For example, in cereal breeding we might choose 'large numbers of seeds' from one strain and 'drought resistance' from another strain. They could be cross pollinated in the hope of producing a strain that produced a large number of seeds even during a very dry summer.

Remember – For selective breeding to be possible there must be genetic variation in the population to provide the alternative alleles so the breeder can select the useful characteristics. We need 'gene banks' which are collections of living plants and seeds which contain all the genetic variations.

Selective breeding creates problems by reducing the variety of alleles in a population. As a result,

- there is less variety of alleles in the gene pool for further selective breeding
- the new strain produced may not survive if the environmental conditions change, i.e. wetter summers.

Genetic engineering

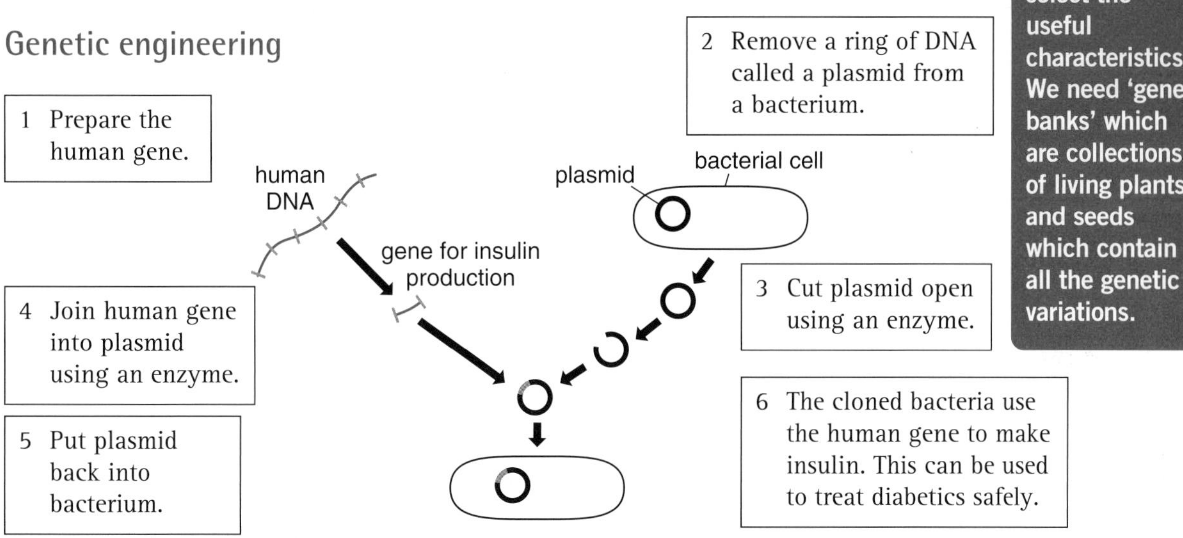

FIGURE 4.7 Using genetic engineering to produce human insulin

Using the human insulin gene in the bacteria means that the insulin produced is a copy of human insulin and so is both safe to use and cheap to produce.

CHECK YOUR UNDERSTANDING

1. Describe the flowers you would expect to grow if cuttings were taken from a red-flowered plant.
2. If a cell is taken from a plant and many are cloned using tissue culture, would you expect to see variation?
3. What problems arise from selective breeding?
4. What are the advantages of selective breeding?
5. Insulin produced by genetic engineering saves many lives. What are the advantages of producing it this way? safe, cheap

The theory of evolution

Fossils

If environmental conditions change, some plants or animals may not be able to survive in the new conditions (see page 24) and may become extinct. Traces of some animals that died millions of years ago can be found as fossils but the majority would have been eaten or decomposed, leaving no trace.

How did some organisms become fossils?

- Some hard remains such as bones or teeth were buried in layers of mud.
- Organisms falling into peat-bogs did not decompose because decomposing bacteria could not survive in such anaerobic, low pH conditions.
- Sometimes the remains of whole organisms became impregnated with mineral salts and formed stone – for example, fossilised trees.
- Evidence also exists in prints – for example, dinosaur footprints left in mud, and insects trapped in resin/amber.

The theory of evolution states that all species of living things which existed in the past and those still present today evolved from simple water life forms which first developed more than 3 billion years ago.

What evidence do fossils provide?

Fossils show the order in which organisms evolved. Going up a cliff face the rocks contain different fossils in different layers:

- The oldest rocks are in the deepest layers and these only contain simple marine life form fossils.
- Marshy land plants with no vascular bundles appear in the next layer up.
- Insects are found in layers 350 million years old.
- Going on upwards, the rock layers contain fish, reptiles, dinosaurs, birds, mammals and flowering plants in that order.

There are no living forms of some of the fossils and so these are said to be extinct, for example dinosaurs and woolly mammoths. They may have become extinct due to changes in the climate, more successful new competitors, new predators or new diseases.

How do new species of plants and animals develop?

If changes occur to the DNA, this alters genes which in turn can change characteristics. If these alterations make the animal better adapted to the environment, the genetic differences may result in evolution of a new species after many generations and a long period of time.

What drives evolution?

Charles Darwin suggested that evolution is driven by natural selection which can work in the following way:

- Organisms produce more young than the environment can support so there is competition for food etc. (see page 25). Many organisms do not survive.
- There is variation in the population because individuals have different alleles. Some of these genetic differences result from mutations.
- Individuals with those alleles that give them the best adaptations to the environment survive, reproduce and pass the beneficial alleles on to the next generation.
- Well-adapted individuals rear more young.

Darwin's theory was based on careful observations, but at that time there was no knowledge of Mendelian genetics to explain variation and inheritance. Darwin could not explain big changes shown by the fossil record, and his theory conflicted with the story of creation in the Bible.

Lamarck had a different explanation for evolution. He suggested that a need for change caused a change to happen in an organism and that this characteristic would be passed onto the offspring. This would mean that a weightlifter develops big muscles so his son would have big muscles. Do you think this is correct?

Revise Lamark's ideas about giraffe evolution on page 107 of AQA GCSE Biology.

Mutations

Mutations result from changes to the DNA resulting in new alleles. Some environmental factors can increase the mutation rate. These include exposure to ionising radiation, UV sunlight, powerful X-rays and certain chemicals. UV light can cause mutations in skin cell DNA resulting in skin cancer.

Most mutations are harmful. Strong X-rays can cause mutations in the sex cells and these mutations are then passed on to the offspring, which may develop abnormally or die during their development.

Some mutations can be beneficial giving the offspring an advantage in the environment. The mutation is passed on to the next generation, and after many generations a new species may arise.

Mutation and natural selection

Bacteria can be used to demonstrate 'speeded up evolution'.

- Bacteria can reproduce rapidly in ideal conditions, giving many generations in a single day.
- Mutations can occur as the DNA replicates for cell division, i.e. during mitosis.
- Some mutations change the bacterial enzymes and the bacteria are able to break down certain antibiotics, i.e. the bacteria destroy the antibiotic rather than the antibiotic destroying them.
- Overuse of one antibiotic increases the likelihood that a clone of bacteria resistant to that antibiotic will arise by natural selection over many generations.

CHECK YOUR UNDERSTANDING

1. What might animals compete for?
2. Will the oldest fossils be found at the top or the bottom of a cliff?
3. Sunburn may result in skin cancer. What has changed inside the cells to cause this?
4. A strain of bacteria has become resistant to the antibiotic penicillin.
   a) What does this mean?
   b) What is the consequence of 'bacterial resistance'?
5. Suggest why woolly mammoths became extinct.
6. Explain in terms of natural selection why giraffes have long necks.

Chromosomes and genes

- A chromosome is a long molecule of DNA.
- The DNA molecule is divided into many genes.
- A gene may control a characteristic.
- Some genes have alternative forms called alleles. For example B and b are the alleles for black and brown fur in mice.
- An allele which controls the development of a characteristic when it is present on only one chromosome of a pair is a dominant allele. This is shown by a capital letter, e.g. B.
- If two matching alleles have to be present for a characteristic to show, one on each chromosome of the pair, the allele is recessive. This is shown by a small letter, e.g. b.
- When both chromosomes of the pair have the same allele the individual is said to be homozygous, (genotype BB or bb). If the alleles are different, e.g. Bb, the individual is heterozygous.

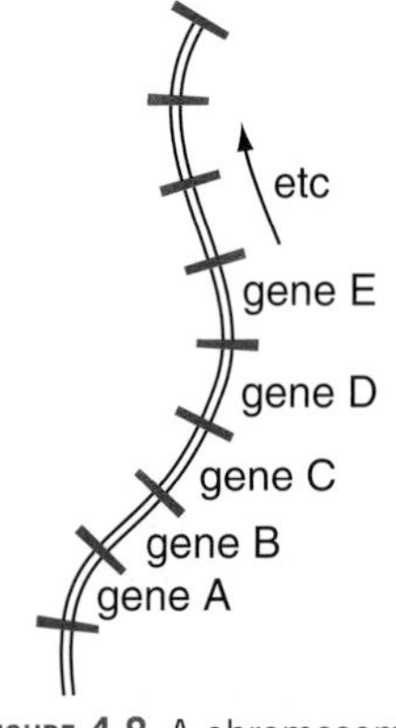

FIGURE 4.8 A chromosome with genes shown

DNA is made of two long strands containing four bases in a linear sequence. A sequence of three bases (a triplet) codes for one amino acid. Therefore, the linear order of bases codes for the order in which the amino acids are assembled to form each protein or enzyme.

Gender determination

Human body cells have 23 pairs of chromosomes. One pair is the sex chromosomes that control your gender. Females have two X chromosomes; males have a non-matching pair of one X and one Y chromosome.

	Father		Mother	
	XY		XX	
Sperm gametes will contain →	(X) or (Y)		(X)	← All mother's eggs contain
Offspring (when sperm joins egg)	XX	or	XY	
which gives	50% females	and	50% males.	

Genetic diseases

Huntington's disease

Huntington's disease is a disorder of the nervous system caused by a dominant allele, H. The normal allele, h, is recessive.

	Parent suffering from Huntington's	Parent with normal alleles
	Hh	hh
Gametes (sperm or egg)	(H) or (h)	(h)
Children	50% Hh (sufferers)	50% hh (normal)

Only the parent with the dominant allele could pass the disease on to the children.

Cystic fibrosis

Cystic fibrosis is a disorder of the cell membranes and causes very sticky mucus all the time, resulting in breathing problems. To have this condition, the child must have two recessive alleles, so one must come in the sperm and the other in the egg. This means that father and mother are both heterozygous Cc – they carry the recessive allele, c, but it is hidden by the dominant normal allele, C.

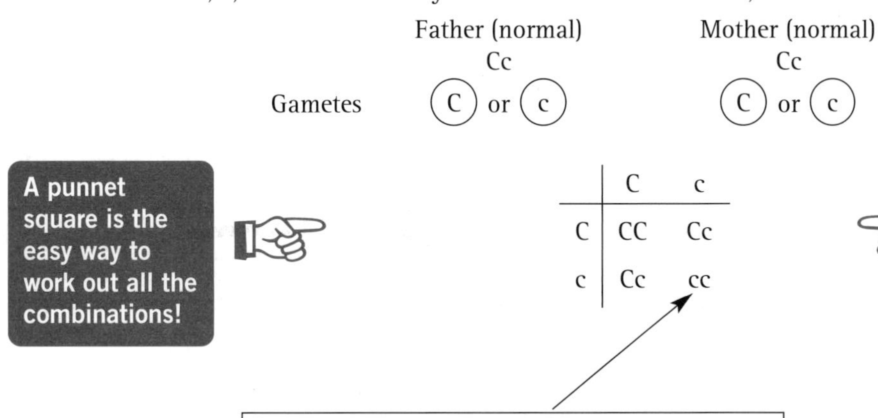

1 in 4 of the children will receive two recessive alleles (and therefore be homozygous recessive) and will suffer from cystic fibrosis.

If you have to use a letter where capital and small can look the same, do make sure that there is a difference when you write them for dominant and recessive alleles.

Sickle cell anaemia

Sickle cell anaemia is a disorder of the red blood cells which reduces the oxygen-carrying capacity of the blood. The red blood cells become the shape of a new moon or sickle.

- A person who has two dominant alleles has normal oxygen transport but is likely to catch malaria.
- A person who has two recessive alleles has very poor oxygen transport and their muscles feel painfully 'cramped' when they use them.
- A person who has one dominant and one recessive allele can transport enough oxygen without pain and is less likely to catch malaria. But having both dominant and recessive alleles is an advantage only if you live near a tropical malarial swamp.

CHECK YOUR UNDERSTANDING

1. Which pair of alleles would give you an advantage if you lived in a region where malaria was common?
2. For a given gene, if one parent is heterozygous and the other homozygous recessive, what proportion of the offspring would you expect to show the dominant allele in their phenotype?
3. What does the term 'linear sequence' mean?
4. What proportion of the offspring would be homozygous recessive from two heterozygous parents?

3 a sequence of anything in a line

Controlling fertility

Menstrual cycle

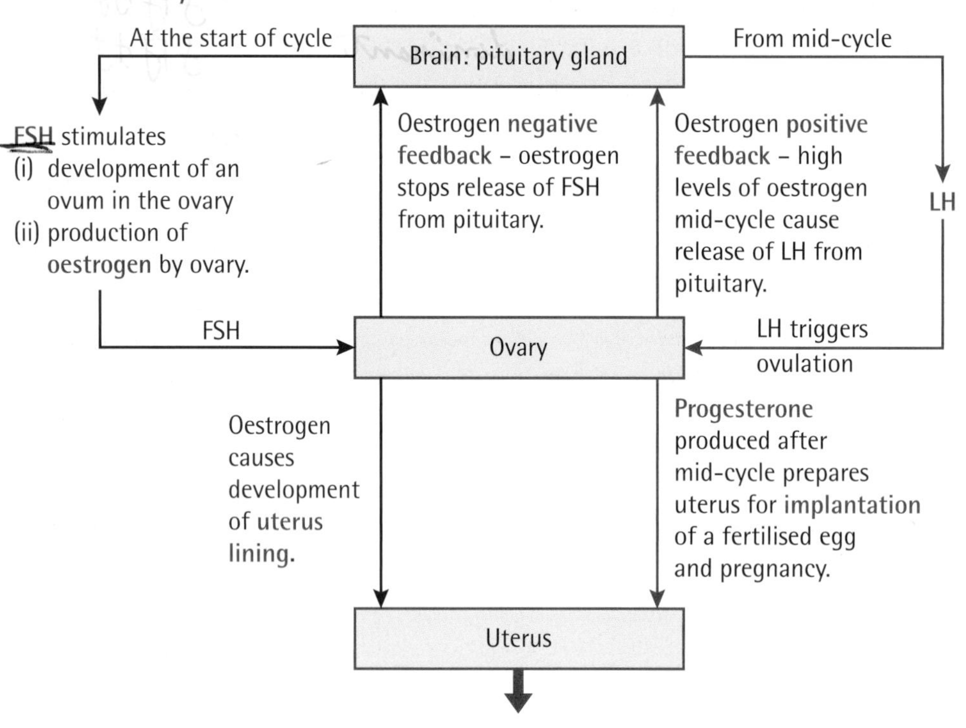

Figure 4.9 The hormones involved in the menstrual cycle

Controlling fertility using artificial hormones

If the pituitary gland produces too little of the hormone FSH, an artificial form can be given to stimulate more ova to mature in the ovary. This increases the chance of an ovum being fertilised but there is more risk of having more than one baby.

To prevent a pregnancy oral contraceptives (the birth pill) can be given.

The pill contains high levels of oestrogen, which inhibits the production of FSH in the pituitary so ova do not mature and so cannot be released.

The pill does not protect against sexually transmitted infections (STIs).

CHECK YOUR UNDERSTANDING

1. The brain produces a hormone at the start of the menstrual cycle – what does the hormone do?
2. What causes ovulation?
3. Which hormone prepares the uterus lining for a fertilised egg?
4. What is the risk of taking a hormone to increase female fertility?

Topic Test

1 A person who has freckles marries a non-freckled person. All their children have freckles.

a) Do you think the freckle gene is dominant or recessive? dominant

b) (i) Use a genetic cross diagram to show the result expected if one of the freckled children marries a non-freckled person.

(ii) If this couple have six children how many would you expect to have freckles? 3

(5 marks)

2 Copy and complete the following sentences.

Chromosomes are found in the ____________ of cells. A chromosome is made up of ____________ wound around a protein backbone. Chromosomes contain a sequence of ____________ . The code for an amino acid is a sequence of ____________. Each gene code sequence has the instructions for making proteins such as ____________ or ____________ . (6 marks)

3 Look at Figure 4.6, the cloning of animals by nuclear transfer, on page 36.

a) Is the nucleus of the donor cell diploid or haploid? (1 mark)

b) When the two cells are fused is the resulting cell diploid or haploid? (1 mark)

c) The fused cell divides. What type of division is this? (1 mark)

d) State which of these mothers the offspring would look like, and explain your answer.

the owner of the uterus in which it developed
or the donor cell mother
or the mother of the unfertilised egg (2 marks)

4 If a bird dies in a field today why is it unlikely to form a fossil? (2 marks)

5 Read the following information and then answer the questions.

An area of land was contaminated with waste water from a mine containing heavy metal salts. Most of the plants were killed. A year after the flood only a few plants were growing in the area. The site was visited five years later, there were small areas of plants and the rest was bare ground.

a) What was the effect of the waste water on the plants originally growing in the area?

b) Why do you think that a few plants were able to grow the following year?

c) Why were there areas of plants growing after five years?

d) If plants were taken from these areas and planted into the bare ground what would you expect to happen? (4 marks)

6 Copy and complete the following sentences.

Human body cells have ___pairs___ of chromosomes. At the start of the female cycle the hormone ___FSH___ is released from the pituitary gland in the brain to stimulate development of an ovum. Specialised cells undergo ___meiosis___ division to form the _____ploid gamete. At fertilisation the nuclei of the ovum and ___sperm___ join together to form a _____ploid cell. This divides repeatedly by ___mitosis___ to form a ball of cells which implants into the uterus. The uterus is prepared for implantation by release of the hormone ___progesterone___ from the ovary.

(8 marks)

Total: 30 marks

Biology examination questions and model answers

1 a) The question describes the process of photosynthesis.

carbon dioxide + *water* + light energy ⟶ glucose + *oxygen*

i) Write in the names of the two missing substances. *(2 marks)*

> There are two missing substances each worth one mark. So don't write more than one in each gap.

ii) Name the green substance which absorbs the light energy. *(1 mark)*

Chlorophyll.

> There is only one correct answer. Do not write chloroplast, it is not a substance.

b) i) In bright sunlight, the concentration of carbon dioxide in the air can limit the rate of photosynthesis. Explain what this means. *(2 marks)*

There is enough light to make photosynthesis go faster but there is not enough carbon dioxide in the air to speed photosynthesis up. Both are needed.

> Mention the need for both light and carbon dioxide.

ii) Give one environmental factor, other than light intensity and carbon dioxide concentration, which can limit the rate of photosynthesis. *(1 mark)*

Temperature.

> Rainfall would be an acceptable alternative answer.

2 The table shows the concentration of some substances in human blood plasma, in the filtrate produced by the kidney and in the urine.

Substance	Concentration in grams per dm^3		
	Blood plasma	Filtrate	Urine
Glucose	1.0	1.0	0.0
Amino acids	0.5	0.5	0.0
Urea	0.3	0.3	20.0
Protein	80.0	0.0	0.0
Ions	7.2	7.2	15.0
Water	912.0	990.0	970.0

a) Explain why:

i) the concentration of glucose in the filtrate is the same as in the blood plasma; *(1 mark)*

Glucose is forced from the blood by the high pressure in the blood capillaries.

> You must explain and not simply describe the differences.

ii) there is no glucose present in the urine. *(1 mark)*

Glucose is reabsorbed into the blood capillaries surrounding the tubule before it reaches the urine.

> Only one mark, so make one clear statement.

b) Suggest why there is no protein in either the filtrate or the urine. *(1 mark)*

Protein molecules are too large to pass from the capillaries into the filtrate and everything in the urine comes from the filtrate.

> Use the terms protein, filtrate and urine given in the question. Do not use 'it' or 'they' as this often gives an ambiguous answer.

c) The volume of water removed in the urine is variable. Explain how the human body reduces the volume of urine produced when less water is consumed. *(3 marks)*

Pituitary gland produces hormone called ADH. This travels in the bloodstream to the kidney where it makes the tubules more permeable to water. So more water is reabsorbed into the bloodstream and less is left in the urine.

> There are more than 3 marks worth in this answer, you do not have to put everything down to get full marks. Do not write about the situation when there is too much water in the blood, as this will gain you no more marks. Just answer the question.

METALS

Metals in the Periodic Table

The chemical elements can be arranged in order of their relative atomic mass (A_r). (Potassium (K) and argon (Ar) have been reversed to improve the 'fit'.)

Symbol	H	He	Li	Be	B	C	N	O	F	Ne	Na	Mg	Al	Si	P	S	Cl	Ar	K	Ca
A_r	1	4	7	9	11	12	14	16	19	20	23	24	27	28	31	32	35.5	40	39	40

This can be rearranged to form the Periodic Table.

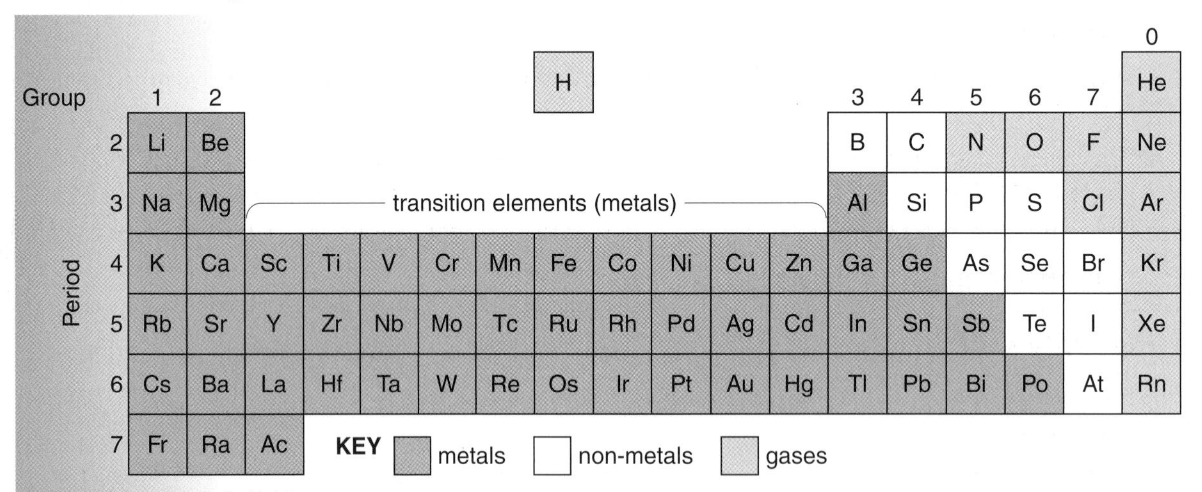

FIGURE 5.1 The Periodic Table

The table below compares some of the properties of two groups of metals – the alkali metals and the transition metals.

	Group 1 metals (alkali metals)	Transition metals
Properties common to all metals	Good conductors of heat Good conductors of electricity Easy to bend or hammer into shape	
Physical properties	Low melting point (Na = 98°C) Low density (Li, Na and K float on water) Soft, easily cut with a knife	High melting point (except mercury which is a liquid at room temperature) (Fe = 1539°C) High density Hard, strong, tough

	(Group 1 metals)	(Transition metals)
Chemical properties	Very reactive Form ionic compounds with non-metals (e.g. Li_2O, NaCl) Compounds are white solids, they dissolve in water to give colourless solutions React with water (metal + water → hydrogen + metal hydroxide)	Not very reactive Do not corrode easily in air or water, so they are used as structural materials (e.g. steel) and for electrical wiring (e.g. copper) Form coloured compounds, so they are used as glazes to colour pottery Used as catalysts (e.g. iron in the manufacture of ammonia and platinum to make nitric acid from ammonia)

CHECK YOUR UNDERSTANDING

1. What does the symbol A_r represent?
2. With which element could the symbol A_r be confused?
3. Approximately what percentage of the elements are metals?
4. Give three ways in which the physical properties of the Group 1 metals differ from those of the transition metals.
5. Give three ways in which the chemical properties of the Group 1 metals differ from those of the transition metals.

Extraction of metals from their ores

The reactivity series

Metals can react:

1 with air to give metal oxides
2 with water (cold, hot or as steam) to produce metal oxides (or hydroxides) and hydrogen gas
3 with acids to produce metal salts and hydrogen gas.

From observing such reactions, we can draw up a reactivity series of metals as shown in Figure 5.2.

Once we have this information, we can use it to make predictions about the outcome of reactions, as a more reactive metal (and the non-metals carbon and hydrogen) can displace a less reactive metal from its compounds.

So:

magnesium + copper oxide → magnesium oxide + copper
$Mg + CuO \rightarrow MgO + Cu$

sodium + water → sodium hydroxide + hydrogen
$2Na + 2H_2O \rightarrow 2NaOH + H_2$

iron + copper sulphate → iron sulphate + copper
$Fe(s) + CuSO_4(aq) \rightarrow FeSO_4(aq) + Cu(s)$

But:

gold + water → NO REACTION
silver + copper oxide → NO REACTION

potassium
sodium
calcium
magnesium
aluminium
carbon*
zinc
iron
tin
lead
hydrogen*
copper
silver
gold
platinum

↑ Increasing reactivity with air, water or acids

FIGURE 5.2 The reactivity series of metals
*Carbon and hydrogen are not metals but are included for comparison

Metals are found in rocks in the Earth's crust. Some unreactive metals like gold occur as the metal itself. Most metals are found as metal compounds – usually metal oxides. Most metal ores are oxides (or substances that can easily be changed into metal oxides). To extract a metal from its oxide, the oxygen must be removed. This is an example of reduction.

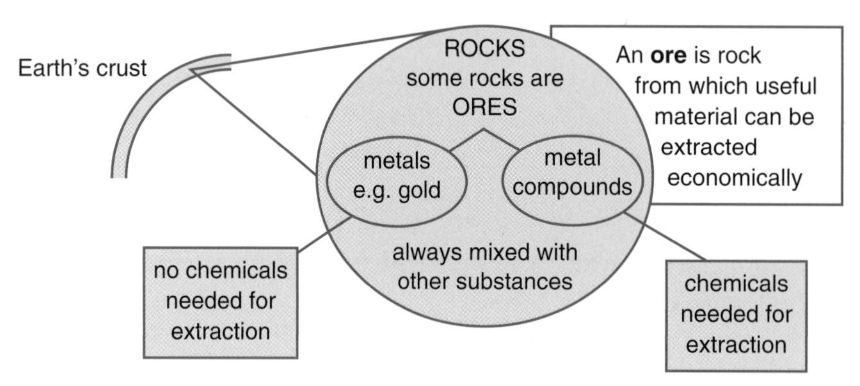

FIGURE 5.3 Extracting metals from the Earth's crust

How a metal is extracted from its ore depends on the position of the metal in the reactivity series. Many metals can be extracted from their compounds by using a more reactive 'metal'. To be cost effective the substance used must be cheap and available. So carbon is used to extract metals (like iron) that are lower down the reactivity series. The process is called smelting.

Position of metal in reactivity series	Method of extraction
Metals at the bottom e.g. gold	Occur uncombined in Earth's crust
Metals below carbon e.g. iron	Heating with carbon
Metals above carbon e.g. aluminium	Electrolysis

CHECK YOUR UNDERSTANDING

❶ Copy and complete these word equations. (*Hint*: Not all will react.)
a) zinc + lead oxide
b) tin + aluminium chloride solution
c) hydrogen + copper oxide

❷ What is the difference between a rock and an ore?

❸ Why is carbon used to extract metals like iron rather than using a more reactive metal like magnesium?

Extracting iron

Iron is extracted from its ore in the blast furnace by heating it with carbon (coke).

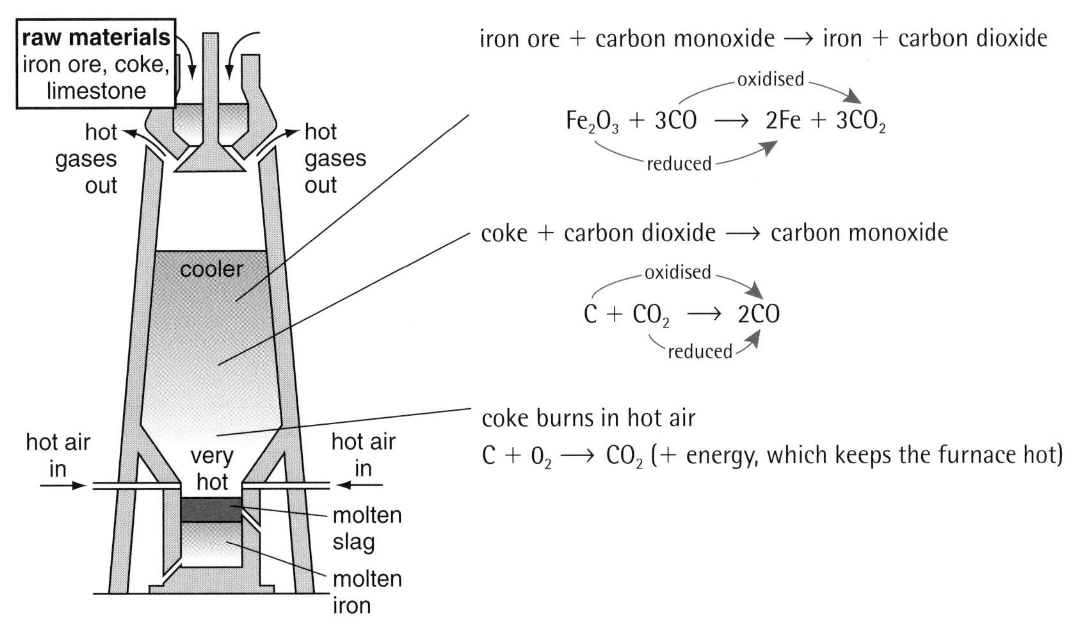

FIGURE 5.4 The reactions in a blast furnace

In the blast furnace coke burns in the hot air blast, producing carbon dioxide. The reaction gives out a lot of heat. The carbon dioxide then reacts with more carbon to produce carbon monoxide. This carbon monoxide reduces iron ore (iron oxide or haematite) to iron. In this process the carbon monoxide is oxidised to carbon dioxide.

When a substance joins with oxygen, we call it an **oxidation** reaction.

All ores contain impurities. In iron ore the main impurity is sand (silicon dioxide). The impurity must be removed or it would weaken the iron produced. The sand reacts with the limestone added as part of the original charge, producing slag.

$$CaCO_3 + SiO_2 \rightarrow CaSiO_3 + CO_2$$

limestone + sand → slag + carbon dioxide

The slag melts and settles on top of the molten iron at the bottom of the blast furnace.

CHECK YOUR UNDERSTANDING

1. What happens to the oxygen content of iron ore when it is reduced?
2. What happens to the oxygen content of carbon monoxide when it is oxidised?
3. a) Why does the impurity have to be removed from the iron ore?
   b) How is the impurity removed?

Electrolysis

Aluminium is too reactive to be extracted by smelting. A more powerful method is used. The process is called electrolysis.

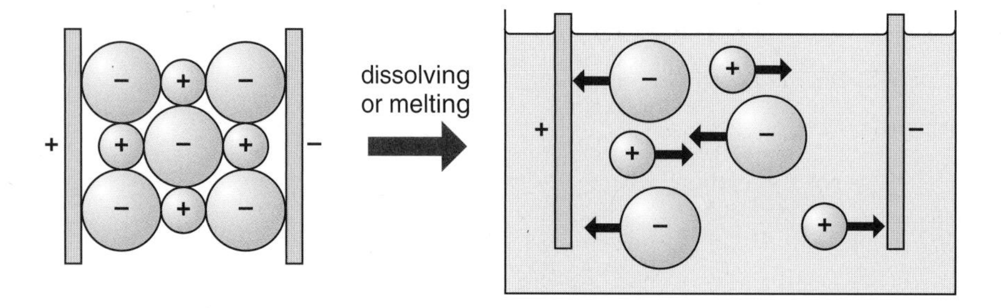

In an ionic solid, the ions are held in place by each other.

Because they cannot move, the solid does not conduct electricity.

When the ionic substance is molten or dissolved in water, the ions are free to move.

They are attracted to the electrode with the opposite charge. Positive ions move towards the cathode (negative electrode) and negative ions move towards the anode (positive electrode).

Because the charges move, the ionic substance now conducts electricity.

FIGURE 5.5 Electrolysis

- When negative ions reach the anode they lose electrons and become atoms.
- When positive ions reach the cathode they gain electrons and become atoms.
- So electrolysis causes ionic substances to break down (decompose). The process can produce gases (mainly at the anode) or metals (at the cathode).
- If the ionic substance is aluminium oxide, the reactions which occur are:

At the anode:
Negatively charged oxide ions lose electrons to become oxygen gas.

At the cathode:
Positively charged aluminium ions gain electrons to become aluminium metal.

Extracting aluminium

Aluminium is extracted by electrolysis using a cell like that in Figure 5.6.

The purified aluminium ore (bauxite) is dissolved in molten cryolite (another aluminium ore). This is because the melting point of bauxite alone is very high.

Aluminium forms at the negative electrode.

The positive aluminium ions gain electrons from the negative electrode.

$$Al^{3+} + 3e^- \rightarrow Al$$

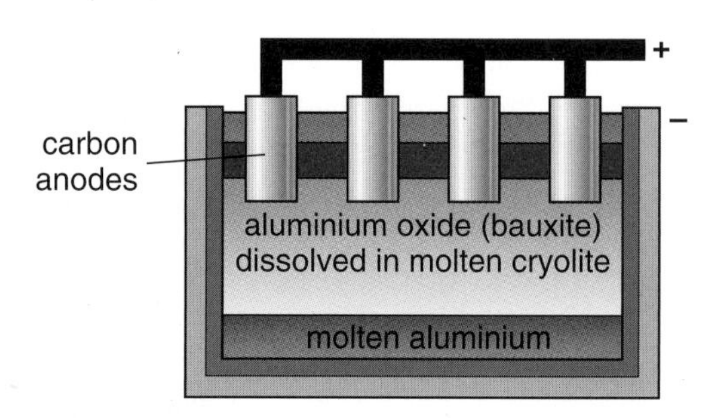

FIGURE 5.6 Extracting aluminium by electrolysis

This is an example of **reduction**. It happens with most positively charged ions when they reach the cathode. The general formula for this is:

$$M^{n+} + ne^- \rightarrow M$$

Oxygen forms on the positively charged carbon electrode.

The negative oxide ions lose electrons to the positive electrode.

$$2O^{2-} \rightarrow O_2 + 4e^-$$

This is an example of **oxidation**. It happens with most negatively charged ions when they reach the anode. The general formula for this is:

$$X^{n-} \rightarrow X + ne^-$$

In the manufacture of aluminium the oxygen reacts with the carbon anode to form carbon dioxide. This causes the anodes to burn away so they have to be replaced frequently.

Redox reactions

Whenever oxidation occurs in chemical reactions, reduction also occurs. Because the two processes always go together reduction/oxidation reactions are called redox reactions.

For example, in the blast furnace iron is reduced by carbon monoxide, and the carbon monoxide is oxidised to form carbon dioxide.

iron ore + carbon monoxide ⟶ iron + carbon dioxide

$$Fe_2O_3 + 3CO \longrightarrow 2Fe + 3CO_2$$

(3CO oxidised → $3CO_2$; Fe_2O_3 reduced → 2Fe)

In electrolysis reactions the two parts of the redox reaction take place in different places. Oxidation occurs at the positive electrode and reduction at the negative electrode. In the example of aluminium oxide:

$$2O^{2-} \longrightarrow O_2 + 4e^- \quad \text{(oxidised)}$$

and

$$Al^{3+} + 3e^- \longrightarrow Al \quad \text{(reduced)}$$

REMEMBER –
Negative electrode
Oxidation
Positive electrode
Q
Reduction

When something is oxidised it loses electrons. When something is reduced it gains electrons.

Remember – OILRIG
Oxidation Is Loss, Reduction Is Gain

Purifying copper

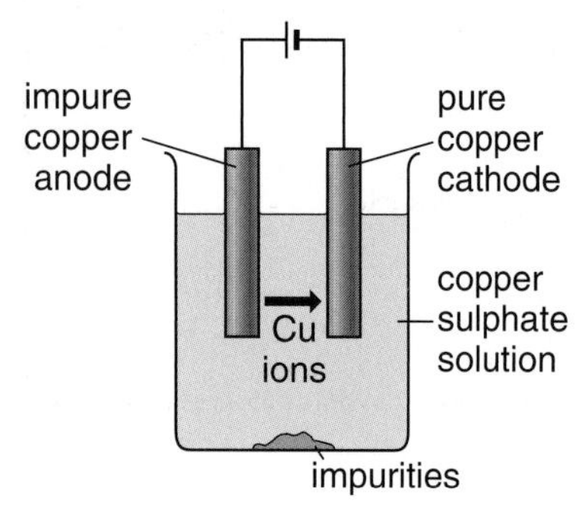

FIGURE 5.7 Purifying copper

- The positive electrode (anode) is impure copper.
- The negative electrode (cathode) is pure copper.
- The solution contains copper ions (positive).
- The copper ions in the solution go to the cathode and become copper atoms.
- The copper atoms join to the pure copper cathode.
- This is a reduction reaction. The equation for this is:

$$Cu^{2+} + 2e^- \rightarrow Cu$$

- The cathode gets thicker.
- The copper in the impure anode forms copper ions which replace those removed from the solution.
- This is an oxidation reaction. The equation for this is:

$$Cu \rightarrow Cu^{2+} + 2e^-$$

- The impure anode gets thinner.
- This is the reverse reaction to that which occurs at the negative electrode. Because both the oxidation and reduction take place together it is an example of a redox reaction.
- Impurities from the anode fall to the bottom of the tank.

CHECK YOUR UNDERSTANDING

1. Why don't solid ionic compounds conduct electricity?
2. Why do ionic compounds conduct electricity when molten or dissolved in water?
3. What is the name and formula of the main ore of aluminium?
4. a) At which electrode in the electrolysis cell does aluminium form?
   b) What forms at the other electrode?
   c) Why does the carbon anode have to be replaced quite often?
   d) i) Write ionic equations for the reactions at each electrode.
      ii) Which ion is oxidised?
      iii) Which ion is reduced?

❺ Write balanced equations for each of the following reactions. Add 'oxidised' and 'reduced' arrows to the equations.

a) Magnesium reacting with copper oxide. One of the products is copper.

b) Hydrogen sulphide (H_2S) reacting with sulphur dioxide to form water and sulphur.

c) Hydrogen reacting with chlorine to form hydrogen chloride.

d) Methane (CH_4) burning to produce carbon dioxide and water vapour.

Preventing corrosion

Iron and steel

Iron and steel corrode (rust) more rapidly than most transition metals. Adding less reactive metals like chromium or nickel can make non-rusting alloys. These alloys are known as stainless steel.

Iron and steel can also be protected by sacrificial protection.

In this process magnesium or zinc is used. Blocks of either metal are fixed to the iron object (e.g. a ship). Because iron is less reactive, the magnesium or zinc corrodes first.

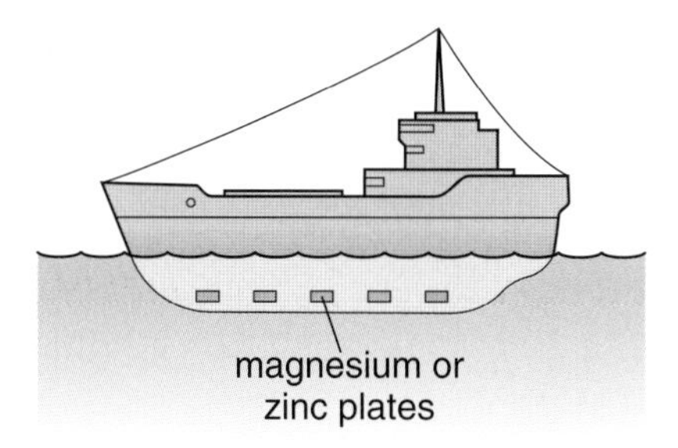

FIGURE 5.8 Sacrificial protection

Aluminium

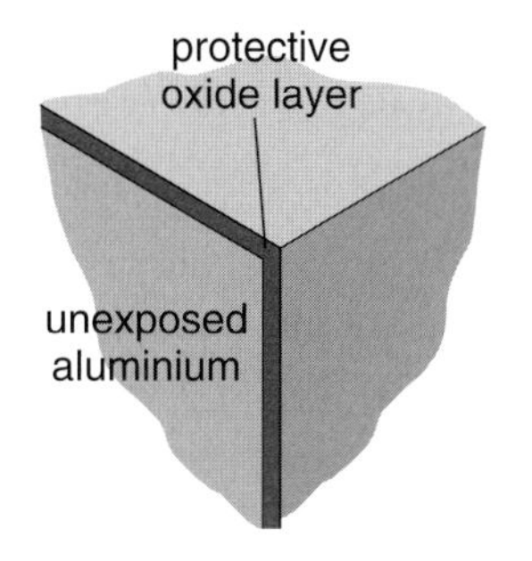

FIGURE 5.9 A section through a block of aluminium

Aluminium is quite high up in the reactivity series. But aluminium does not seem to be very reactive. (You can boil water in aluminium saucepans for years without them corroding.) This is because aluminium reacts with oxygen in the air to form aluminium oxide. The aluminium oxide forms a thin, protective layer on the surface. It seals the unexposed aluminium so that air and water cannot reach it.

Aluminium can be made harder, stiffer and stronger by adding other elements. Magnesium is an element that can be used. These aluminium alloys are useful as structural metals.

CHECK YOUR UNDERSTANDING

❶ What word is used to describe the corroding of iron?

❷ a) Which elements are used to form a non-corroding alloy with iron?
b) What is this alloy called?

❸ a) Which two metals are used to protect iron and steel by being fixed to the surface?
b) What property must these metals have to make this process work?
c) What is the process called?

❹ Why is aluminium less reactive than its position in the reactivity series suggests?

Making metal compounds

Acids and alkalis

All acids contain hydrogen ions (H^+). It is the hydrogen ion that makes the solution acidic. All alkalis contain hydroxide ions (OH^-). It is the hydroxide ion that makes the solution alkaline.

When an acid reacts with an alkali the process is called neutralisation. The products are a salt and water.

acid + alkali → salt + water
(neutral)

LEARN this word equation.

Salts

Salts have a metal 'bit' (from the alkali) and an acid 'bit'. The name of the acid is changed when it forms a salt.

The salt produced depends on the acid used and the metal in the alkali.

Hydrochloric acid produces chloride salts.

sodium hydroxide	+	hydrochloric acid	→	sodium chloride	+	water
$NaOH$	+	HCl	→	$NaCl$	+	H_2O

Sulphuric acid produces sulphate salts.

potassium hydroxide	+	sulphuric acid	→	potassium sulphate	+	water
$2KOH$	+	H_2SO_4	→	K_2SO_4	+	$2H_2O$

Nitric acid produces nitrate salts.

calcium hydroxide	+	nitric acid	→	calcium nitrate	+	water
$Ca(OH)_2$	+	$2HNO_3$	→	$Ca(NO_3)_2$	+	$2H_2O$

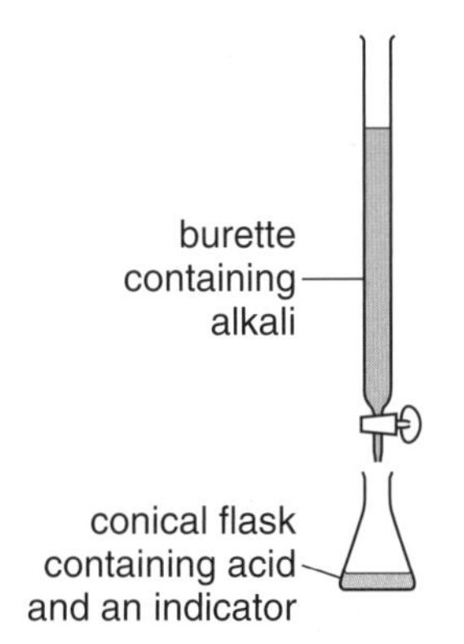

FIGURE 5.10 Neutralising an acid with an alkali

In all these solutions the acid, alkali and salt are ionised.

For the reaction:

$$NaOH + HCl \rightarrow NaCl + H_2O$$

The equation can be written as:

$$Na^+(aq) + OH^-(aq) + H^+(aq) + Cl^-(aq) \rightarrow Na^+(aq) + Cl^-(aq) + H_2O(l)$$

The substances present on BOTH sides of the equation are called spectator ions. These ions are unchanged and can be eliminated.

$$\cancel{Na}^+ + OH^- + H^+ + \cancel{Cl}^- \rightarrow \cancel{Na}^+ + \cancel{Cl}^- + H_2O$$

This leaves just:

$$OH^-(aq) + H^+(aq) \rightarrow H_2O(l)$$

And the equation:

$$2KOH + H_2SO_4 \rightarrow K_2SO_4 + 2H_2O$$

This can also be written as an ionic equation:

$$2K^+(aq) + 2OH^-(aq) + 2H^+(aq) + SO_4^{2-}(aq) \rightarrow 2K^+(aq) + SO_4^{2-}(aq) + 2H_2O(l)$$

If the spectator ions are eliminated the remaining ionic equation is:

$$2OH^-(aq) + 2H^+(aq) \rightarrow 2H_2O(l)$$

This is true of all neutralisation reactions. The only chemical change that takes place is:

$$OH^-(aq) + H^+(aq) \rightarrow H_2O(l)$$

Ammonia (NH_3) also forms alkaline solutions. When neutralised by an acid it forms ammonium salts.

ammonia + hydrochloric acid → ammonium chloride

The oxides and hydroxides of transition metals are not soluble in water. They are called bases. An alkali is also a base, but one that is soluble in water.

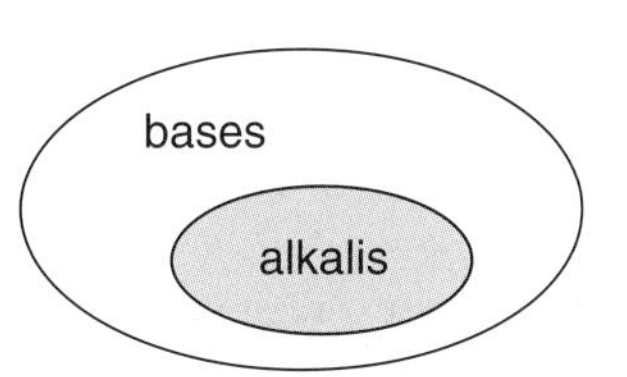

FIGURE 5.11 An alkali is a soluble base

Salts of transition metals can be made by adding the transition metal oxide (or hydroxide) to the acid. The base is added in small quantities until no more will 'dissolve' (this means the reaction is complete). All the acid has now been neutralised. The excess base is filtered off.

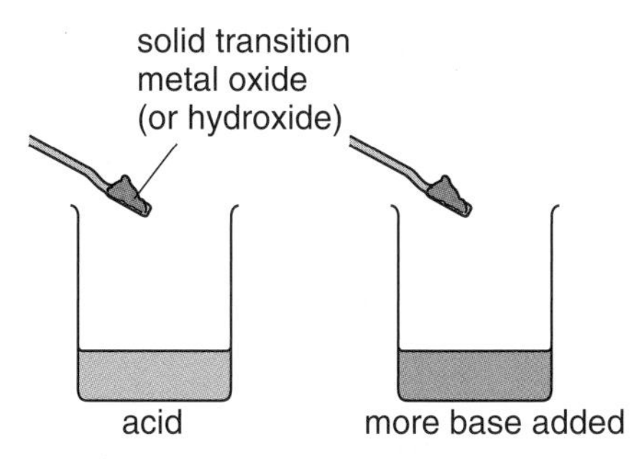

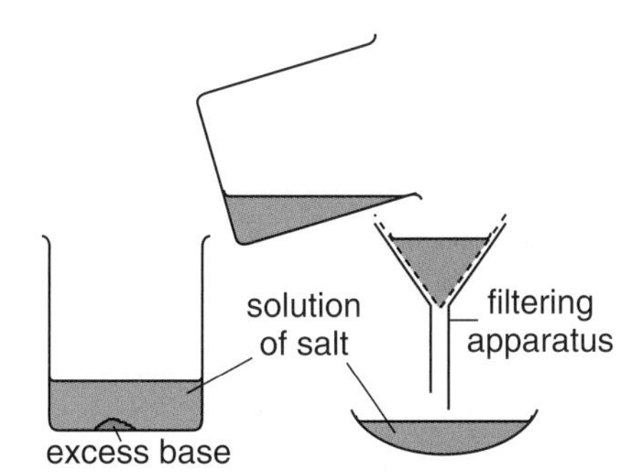

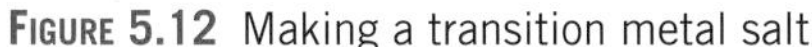

FIGURE 5.12 Making a transition metal salt

CHECK YOUR UNDERSTANDING

❶ When an acid reacts with an alkali a salt is formed. What else is always formed?

❷ What salt is formed in the following reactions?

a) Hydrochloric acid and potassium hydroxide.

b) Lithium hydroxide and nitric acid.

c) Ammonia solution and sulphuric acid.

❸ What is the difference between a base and an alkali?

❹ The equation below is for the reaction between potassium hydroxide and nitric acid.

$$KOH + HNO_3 \rightarrow KNO_3 + H_2O$$

a) Write the equation showing all the ions present. Include state symbols.

b) Underline the spectator ions.

c) What is the ionic equation for the reaction that takes place?

Topic Test

1 Which two of the following symbols represent transition metals?

Mg Mn Pb Rb Ru (2 marks)

2 Which two elements in the box would react with iron oxide?

carbon copper lead magnesium tin

(2 marks)

3 In the blast furnace the following substances are added:

coke hot air iron ore limestone

Use the substances in the list to answer the questions below.

a) Which substance burns to keep the furnace hot?

b) Which substance is not added at the top of the furnace?

c) Which substance is used to convert impurities into slag?

d) Which substance reacts with carbon monoxide in the blast furnace? (4 marks)

4 This question is about electrolysis. Select the correct answer from each box.

a) Ionic compounds conduct electricity when they are molten. When else can they conduct electricity?
   (i) If they are soluble solids.
   (ii) If they are insoluble solids.
   (iii) When they are in solution.
   (iv) Either as a solid or in solution.

b) Electrolysis of a molten ionic substance causes it to
   (i) be neutralised.
   (ii) break down.
   (iii) combine.
   (iv) turn into a solution.

c) At the positive electrode, ions
   (i) deposit as metals.
   (ii) gain electrons.
   (iii) join together.
   (iv) lose electrons.

d) When an ion of element X reaches the negative electrode which of the following reactions take place?
   (i) $X^+ + e^- \rightarrow X$
   (ii) $X^+ \rightarrow X + e^-$
   (iii) $X^- + e^- \rightarrow X$
   (iv) $X^- \rightarrow X + e^-$

(4 marks)

5 For each of the following state if the process uses electrolysis or heating with carbon:
   a) extracting aluminium
   b) extracting iron
   c) purifying copper. (3 marks)

6 Name two ways in which steel can be protected from corrosion. (2 marks)

7 Aluminium is high in the reactivity series yet it can be used to make saucepans. Explain this. (3 marks)

8 Name a substance that would have pH of 4. (1 mark)

9 a) Copy and complete the table.

Acid	Base/Alkali	Salt
sulphuric acid	(ii)	sodium sulphate
hydrochloric acid	potassium hydroxide	(iii)
(i)	copper oxide	copper nitrate

   b) What type of reaction are these?
   c) In each reaction a salt is formed. What else is formed? (5 marks)

10 Look at the table below. The substances in the table are all either strong acids or strong bases. In each case the same volume and the same concentrations of the substances were used. The temperature is measured when the acid and alkali react.

Acid	Alkali	Temperature rise/°C
hydrochloric acid	sodium hydroxide	12.5
nitric acid	potassium hydroxide	12.5

   a) Explain why all the temperature rises are the same.
   b) Ammonia is a weak base. If ammonia is neutralised with hydrochloric acid the temperature rise is lower. Why is the temperature rise lower? (4 marks)

Total: 30 marks

EARTH MATERIALS

Uses of limestone

Limestone is a very common substance, which makes it a relatively cheap material to use.

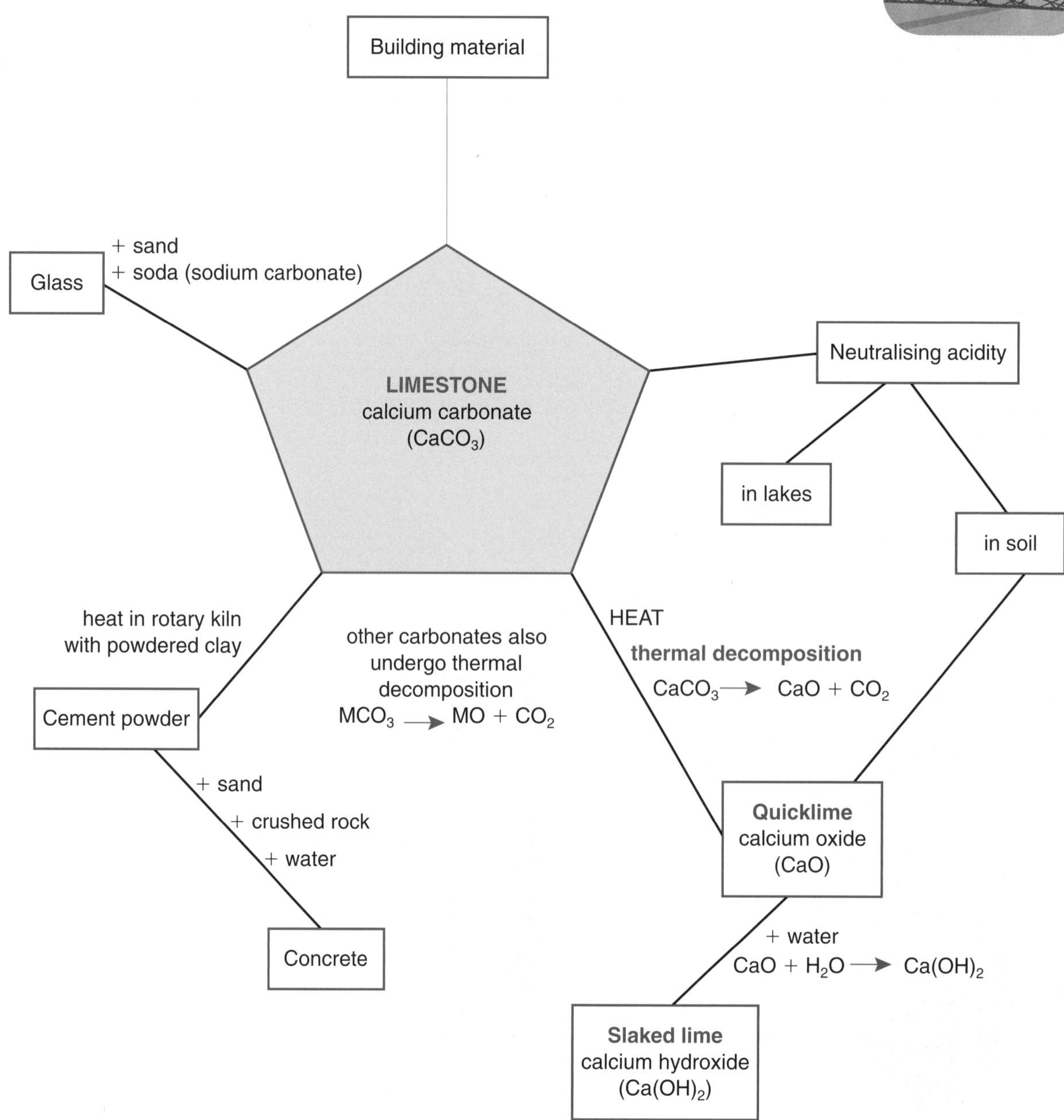

FIGURE 6.1 Uses of limestone

CHECK YOUR UNDERSTANDING

❶ Write word equations for the following reactions of limestone and its products.

a) The thermal decomposition of limestone.

b) The reaction between quicklime and water.

c) The reaction in which limestone neutralises sulphuric acid in lakes.

❷ Why is quicklime not used to neutralise acidity in lakes?

❸ Name one process not included in Figure 6.1 that uses limestone.

Useful products from crude oil

What is crude oil?

Crude oil is a mixture of different hydrocarbons. A hydrocarbon is a compound that contains only carbon and hydrogen. The different hydrocarbons in crude oil are not chemically combined and can be separated by fractional distillation. Within each fraction, the molecules have about the same number of carbon atoms.

The fractional distillation of crude oil

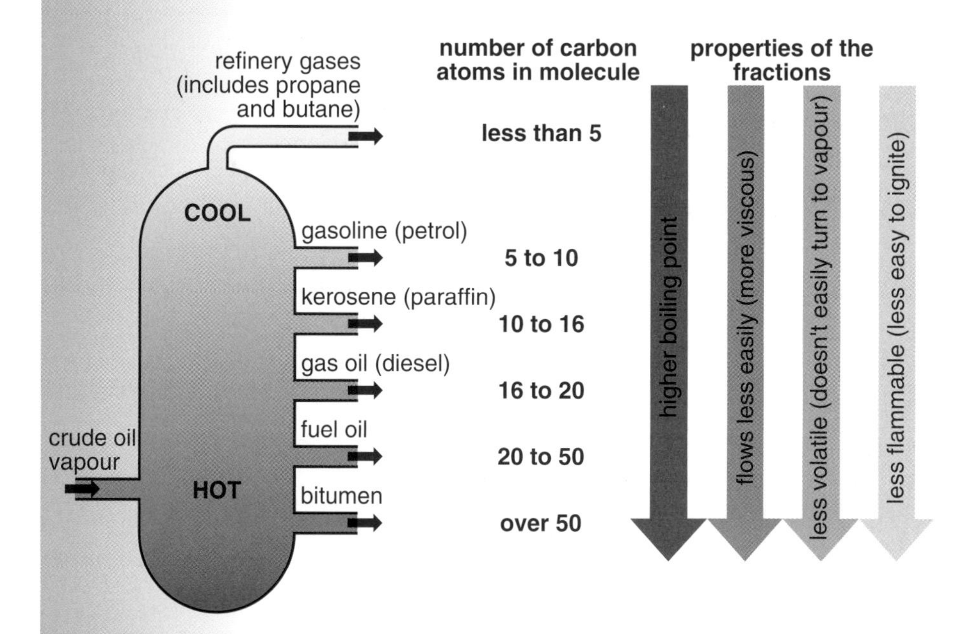

FIGURE 6.2 Separating the fractions of crude oil

The large hydrocarbon molecules are not very useful. They can be broken down into smaller, more useful molecules by cracking.

Cracking

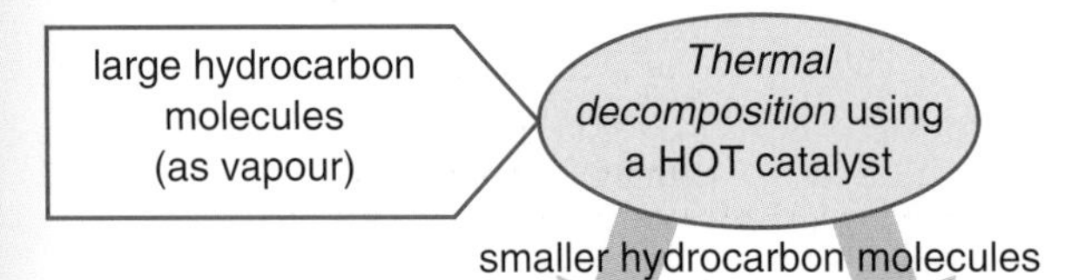

Polymers

Fuels

Cracking is the process that breaks large hydrocarbon molecules into smaller ones.

Polymers	Fuels
Polymers include plastics. Poly(ethene) is used for making plastic bags and bottles. Poly(propene) is used for making crates (e.g. milk crates) and ropes. Most plastics are not biodegradable. This means they are not broken down by micro-organisms. This causes problems if the plastics are buried in landfill sites. Plastics can be recycled or incinerated (burned).	These fuels contain carbon and hydrogen. Sulphur may also be present as an impurity. When the fuel is burned, the following reactions take place: carbon + oxygen → carbon dioxide hydrogen + oxygen → water (vapour) sulphur + oxygen → sulphur dioxide Sulphur dioxide (SO_2) is a pollutant. It causes acid rain. Carbon dioxide (CO_2) is a 'greenhouse' gas.

Hydrocarbons

Hydrocarbons contain chains of carbon atoms. The carbon atoms are linked together by covalent bonds. The hydrogen atoms are also joined to the carbon atoms by covalent bonds.

Alkanes

In alkanes the carbon atoms are joined by single, covalent bonds. Alkanes are called saturated hydrocarbons.

Name	Formula	Structural formula	Arrangement of atoms in molecule
methane	CH_4	H | H–C–H | H	
ethane	C_2H_6	H H | | H–C–C–H | | H H	

Alkenes

In alkenes at least two of the carbon atoms are joined by double covalent bonds. Alkenes are called unsaturated hydrocarbons. This is because they have a double bond that many other substances can attack, as a result alkenes are much more reactive than alkanes.

Name	Formula	Structural formula	Arrangement of atoms in molecule
ethene	C_2H_4	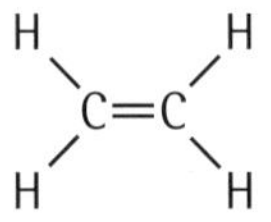 $H_2C{=}CH_2$	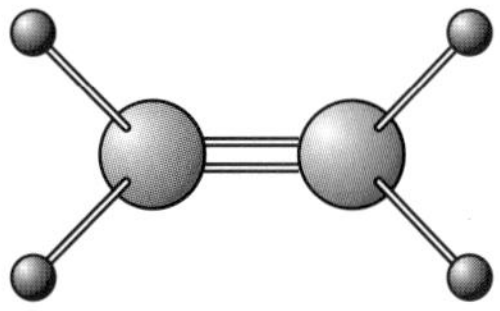

Testing for an alkene

Shake the alkene with a small quantity of bromine water. The yellow-brown bromine water will turn colourless. This is because the bromine reacts with the alkene.

Addition polymerisation

Because alkenes are reactive they can be made to join together to form very long chains. This process is called addition polymerisation and is used to produce polymers. The alkene used in the polymerisation is called a monomer.

Plastics like poly(ethene) (often called polythene) and poly(propene) are polymers. They can be made from the monomers ethene and propene respectively.

The polymerisation can be represented by the equation:

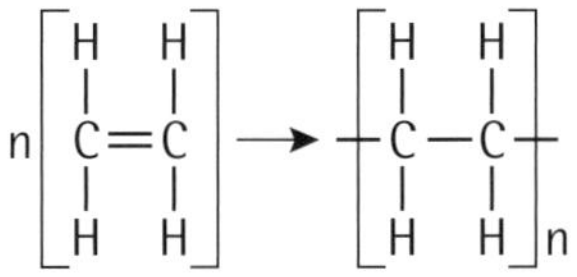

$$n\,[CH_2{=}CH_2] \rightarrow [-CH_2-CH_2-]_n$$

CHECK YOUR UNDERSTANDING

1. What is meant by the word 'hydrocarbon'?
2. What is the process used to separate the different substances in crude oil?
3. List the main fractions into which crude oil is broken down.
4. Give five ways in which the fractions differ from each other.
5. Which fractions of crude oil are the least useful?

6. What is the name of the process that can convert the least useful fractions of oil into more useful products?
7. What are the two main uses of the products formed by cracking?
8. Explain why putting plastic waste into a landfill site is not environmentally friendly.
9. What methods other than landfill are there of disposing of plastics? What are the environmental effects of these methods of disposal?
10. When fuels are burned what are the two main products?
11. Fuels often contain sulphur as an impurity. What are the environmental effects of burning sulphur-containing fuels?
12. What is the difference between a saturated and an unsaturated hydrocarbon?
13. Propane has the formula C_3H_8. Draw the structural formula of propane.

The creation of the Earth's atmosphere

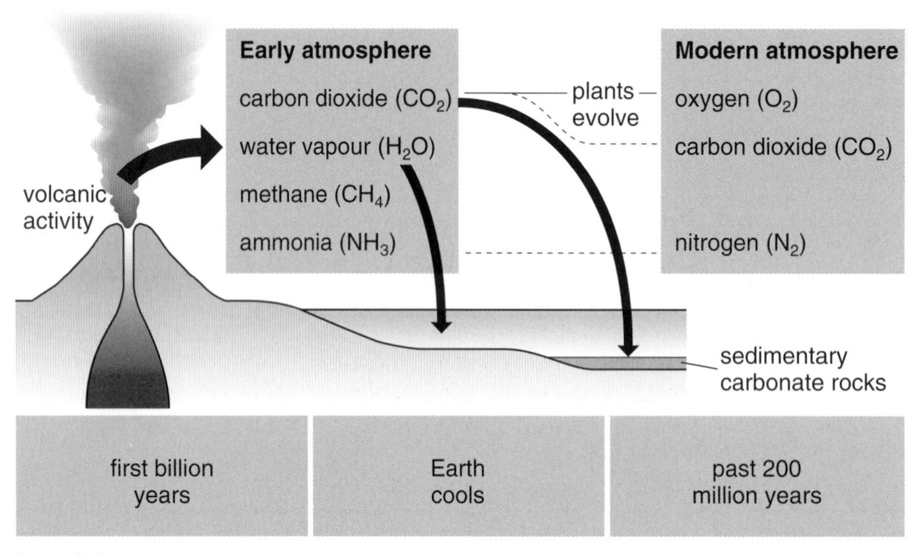

FIGURE 6.3 How the Earth's atmosphere was formed

Intense volcanic activity created the first atmosphere. It contained carbon dioxide, water vapour and small amounts of methane and ammonia. As the Earth cooled, the water vapour formed oceans. Some of the carbon dioxide dissolved in the oceans. Eventually it became 'locked up' in sedimentary, carbonate rocks.

At this stage the atmosphere was similar to that of Venus or Mars today – there was almost no oxygen.

Once green plants evolved, the process of photosynthesis began. Gradually, the plants took up the carbon dioxide and oxygen was released. Many of the micro-organisms on Earth at that stage could not survive in the presence of oxygen. As the Earth became 'polluted' with oxygen, they died.

Some of the plants became fossilised and the carbon was again 'locked up' – this time in the form of fossil fuels. Methane and ammonia reacted with some of the oxygen to form carbon dioxide, water and nitrogen.

But the main source of nitrogen was living organisms, including denitrifying bacteria.

About 200 000 000 years ago the atmosphere reached its present composition. Since then it has not changed very much.

Composition of atmosphere now	
Gas	**%**
nitrogen	80
oxygen	20
other gases (water vapour, noble gases and carbon dioxide)	about 1

Some of the oxygen in the atmosphere was changed into ozone.

$$3O_2 \rightarrow 2O_3$$

Ozone filters out much of the harmful ultraviolet radiation from the Sun. This allowed the evolution of new living organisms.

Carbon dioxide in the atmosphere

Volcanoes still release a lot of carbon dioxide into the atmosphere. This happens because carbonate rocks get moved deep into the Earth by geological activity. The high temperatures cause the carbonate to be thermally decomposed, releasing carbon dioxide.

Burning fossil fuels releases carbon dioxide into the atmosphere. The carbon in fossil fuels has been locked there for many hundreds of millions of years. This results in an increase in the amount of carbon dioxide in the atmosphere.

As the carbon dioxide content of the atmosphere rises, the rate at which it reacts with sea water also increases. This reaction produces insoluble carbonates (mainly calcium carbonate), which are deposited as new sedimentary rocks, and soluble hydrogencarbonates (mainly calcium and magnesium hydrogencarbonate). Although this counteracts the effect of burning fossil fuels to a certain extent, it is not enough to absorb all the extra carbon dioxide released.

CHECK YOUR UNDERSTANDING

1. How was the Earth's original atmosphere formed?
2. When was the Earth's original atmosphere formed?
3. Name four gases present in the original atmosphere. For each gas, explain what happened to it as the atmosphere evolved.
4. What is the composition of the Earth's present atmosphere?

❺ Which two processes were responsible for producing the nitrogen in our atmosphere today?

❻ The diagram shows how carbon is recycled over long periods. Fill in the empty boxes.

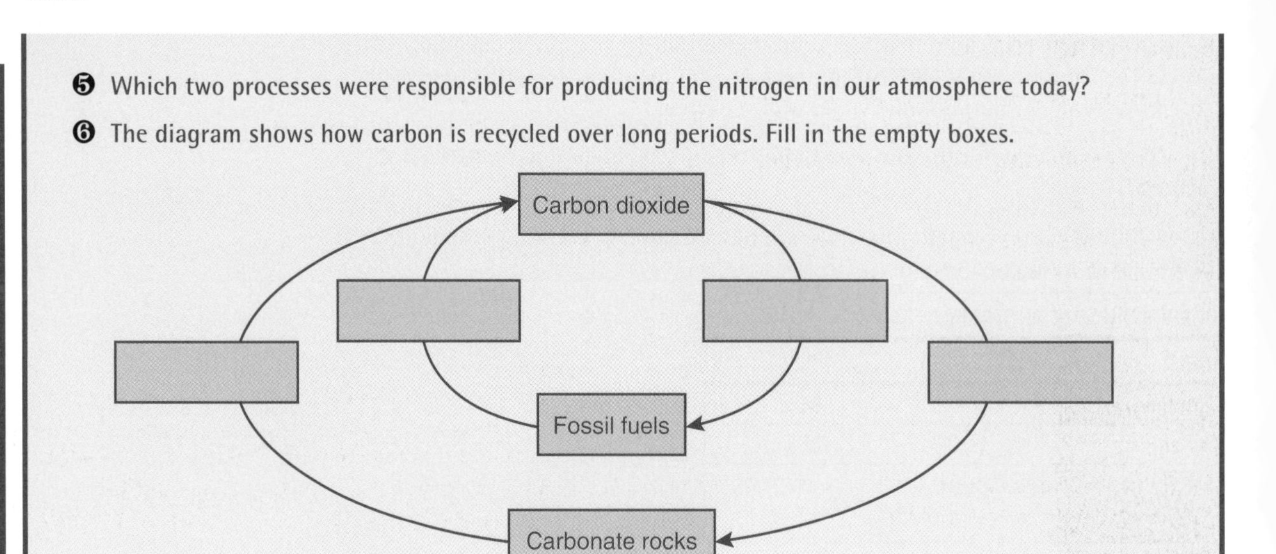

The structure of the Earth

Rocks are continually being recycled. The process is very slow and takes many millions of years to complete.

The crust is very thin – between 10 km and 100 km thick.

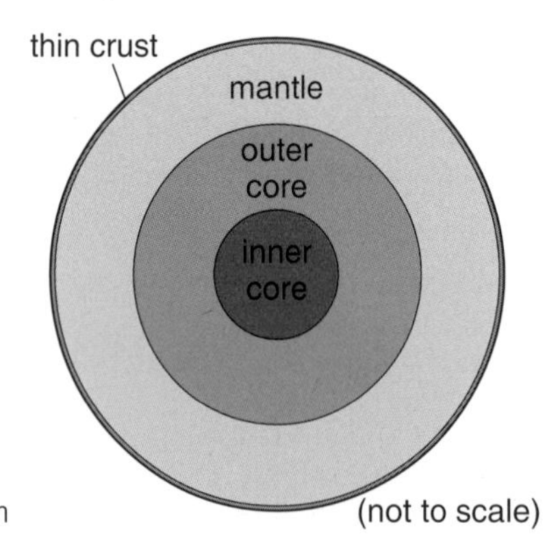

FIGURE 6.4 A section through the Earth

The radius of the Earth's core is just over half that of the Earth. It is made of nickel and iron. The inner core is solid and the outer core is liquid.

The mantle is rock. It has the properties of a solid except that it can flow very slowly (like very thick treacle).

The average density of the Earth (about 5.5 g/cm^3) is much higher than that of the crust (about 2.7 g/cm^3). This means that the Earth's core must have a much higher density (about 11 g/cm^3). This is because the Earth's core is made from a different material from the crust.

CHECK YOUR UNDERSTANDING

❶ Which part of the Earth has the highest density?

❷ a) The Earth's internal structure has four main parts. What are these parts called?

b) Which of these four parts has the largest volume?

❸ What is unusual about the rock material that makes up the mantle?

Sedimentary rocks

Sedimentary rocks form as small fragments of rock (or the shells of dead sea creatures) are deposited on the sea bed. The appearance of the sedimentary rock is evidence of how the fragments were deposited.

The rocks are usually found in layers. These layers formed because the deposits did not settle out in a regular way. In some cases the deposits have ripples that were caused by waves or currents in the sea.

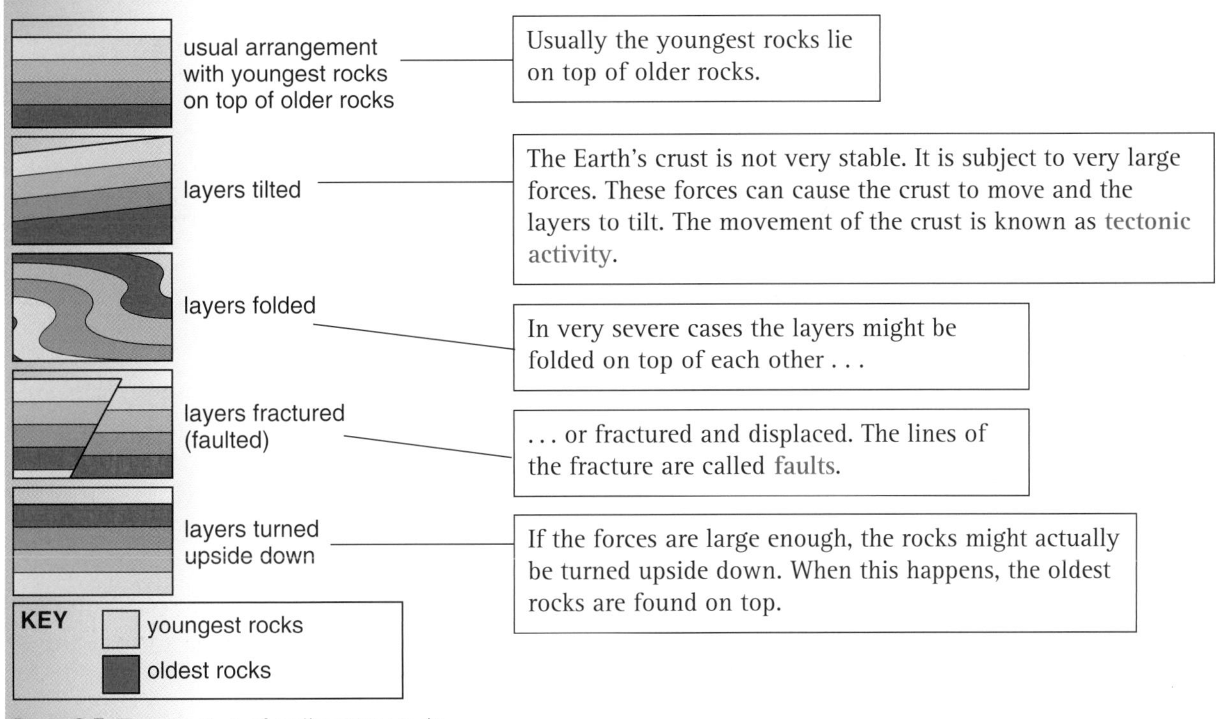

FIGURE 6.5 The structure of sedimentary rocks

When the crust moves, mountain ranges are sometimes formed. The process is very slow – it can take millions of years. These new mountain ranges replace older ones which are being gradually worn down by weathering and erosion.

Metamorphic rocks

Metamorphic rocks are formed when sedimentary rocks are heated to high temperatures and/or put under great pressure. The Earth movements that can distort sedimentary rocks can also cause the temperatures and pressures needed.

CHECK YOUR UNDERSTANDING

1. Name four ways in which sedimentary rocks can be distorted.
2. What name is given to the movement of the Earth's crust?
3. How are metamorphic rocks formed?

Continental drift

The west coast of Africa and east coast of South America are several thousand kilometres apart. But they seem to fit together like pieces in a huge jigsaw. The fossils and rock structures are also similar. These facts suggest that they were once part of the same land mass.

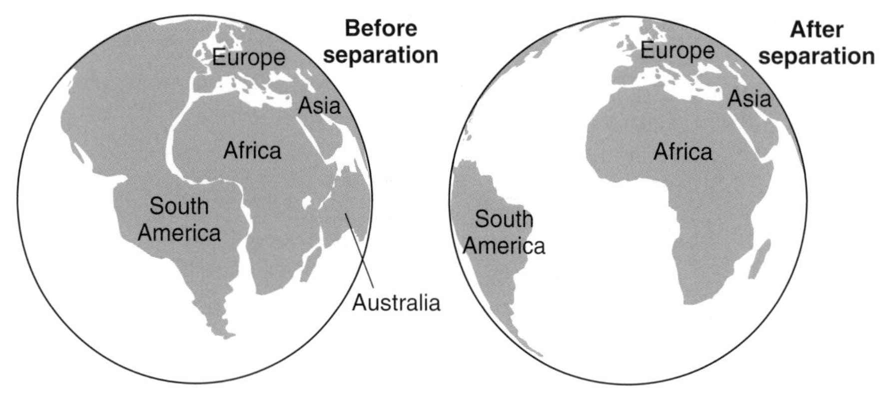

FIGURE 6.6 These maps show how South America and Africa may once have fitted together

In the early part of the twentieth century, Alfred Wegener put forward the idea of continental drift. He thought that the Earth's crust was moving. His ideas were not taken seriously. At that time scientists thought that the Earth was shrinking as it cooled down. They believed that mountains, earthquakes and volcanoes were caused by distortion of the Earth's crust as the core cooled and got smaller.

It was almost 50 years after Wegener proposed his theory before scientists discovered that the Earth's surface is moving. It moves very slowly – just a few centimetres each year. The Earth's lithosphere (the crust and the upper part of the mantle) is made up of a number of large pieces. These pieces are called tectonic plates.

Radioactive processes inside the Earth produce heat. This heat causes convection currents in the mantle. The tectonic plates move because of these convection currents. Earthquakes and volcanic activity occur at the boundaries between the plates.

The movements of the plates are very complex, so scientists are not able to predict exactly when earthquakes and volcanic eruptions will occur.

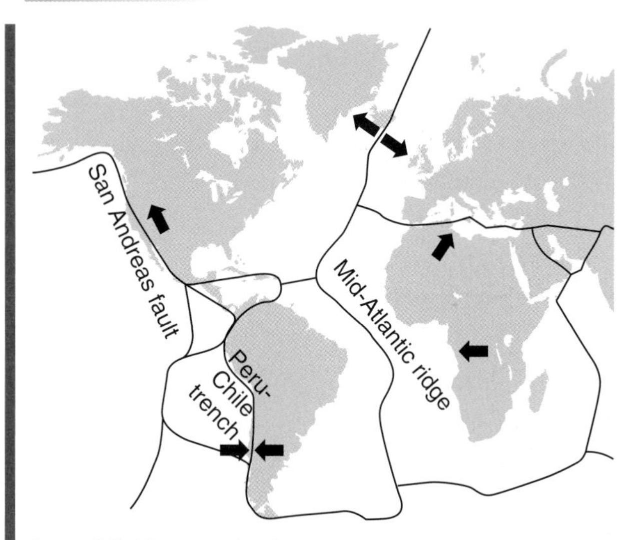

FIGURE 6.7 The tectonic plates

Sliding plates

Along the San Andreas fault in California the plates slide past each other. This causes earthquakes.

Plates moving towards each other

Along the western side of South America the plates are moving towards each other.

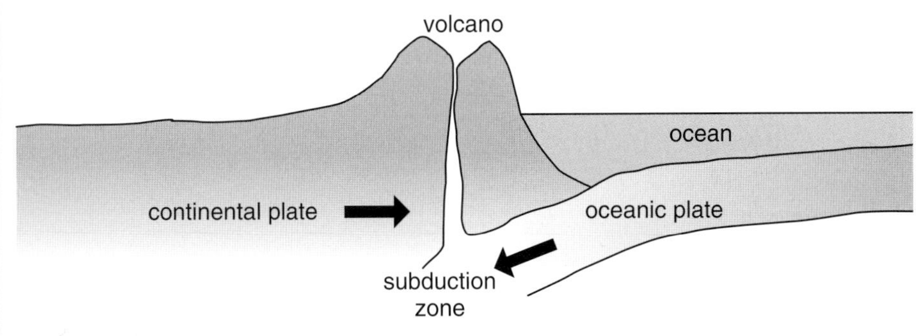

FIGURE 6.8 Plates moving towards each other

When this happens the thinner, denser oceanic plate can be forced down below the thicker, granitic continental plate. This process is called subduction. The continental plate is compressed causing folding and forms mountain ridges, like the Andes in South America. The heat and pressure produced may also turn some of the continental plate into metamorphic rock. The oceanic plate can begin to melt. The magma produced can rise through the continental crust to the surface causing volcanoes. The sliding motion between the plates can also cause earthquakes.

Plates moving away from each other

As the plates move apart fractures occur in the rock. These fractures fill with magma which cools very rapidly under the sea, producing basaltic oceanic crust. The process is called sea floor spreading. This is happening along the mid-Atlantic ridge.

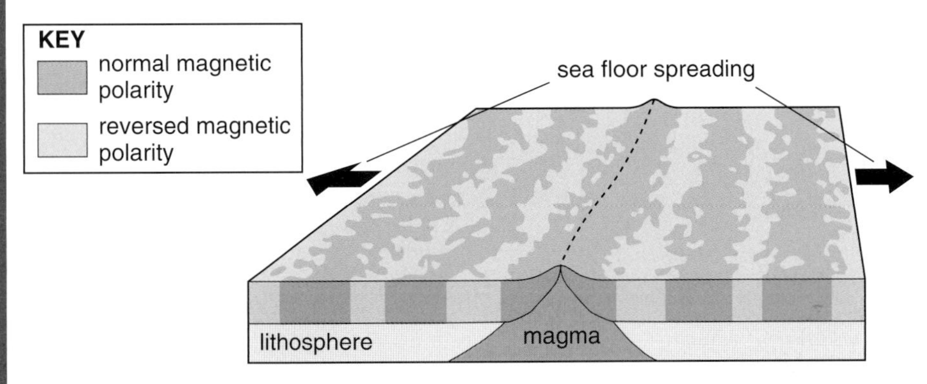

FIGURE 6.9 Sea floor spreading

Magma contains minerals with a high iron content. As the magma solidifies these minerals record the direction of the Earth's magnetic field at the time. Periodically, the Earth's magnetic field reverses. The rocks on either side of the ridge retain a record of these reversals and add support to the concept of sea floor spreading.

CHECK YOUR UNDERSTANDING

1. Name two pieces of evidence that suggested to scientists that South America and Africa were once joined.
2. a) What was Wegener's theory called?
   b) Why was it not accepted until 50 years after he had proposed it?
3. The Earth's lithosphere is made up of a number of plates.
   a) What is meant by the word lithosphere?
   b) What is the general term used to describe the plates?
   c) What causes the plates to move?
4. a) What are the three main ways that plates move?
   b) Name one place in the world where each of these types of movement is occuring.
5. What is meant by:
   a) subduction?
   b) sea floor spreading?

Topic Test

1 This question is about cracking hydrocarbon molecules. For each part pick the correct answer.

a) Cracking is an example of: (i) combustion. (ii) fractional distillation. (iii) neutralisation. (iv) thermal decomposition.	b) Cracking can be used to make substances needed to make plastics. Which of the statements is true? (i) All plastics can be recycled. (ii) Plastics are biodegradable. (iii) Poly(ethene) is used to make milk crates. (iv) Poly(propene) is used to make ropes.
c) In the process of cracking: (i) large molecules are broken down into smaller ones. (ii) large molecules are combined to make polymers. (iii) small molecules are broken down into carbon atoms. (iv) small molecules are combined to make polymers.	d) Cracking can also produce fuels. Which statement is NOT true? (i) The fuels contain hydrogen and carbon. (ii) The products of combustion include carbon dioxide and water vapour. (iii) Sulphur may be present as an impurity. (iv) Sulphur burns to produce sulphur dioxide which can make rain alkaline.

(4 marks)

2 a) What word is used to describe fractures in layers of rock?
b) What is meant by 'tectonic activity'?
c) What is the Earth's 'lithosphere'? (3 marks)

3 The Earth's lithosphere is made up of a number of plates. These plates move. Explain why the plates move. (2 marks)

4 Which two of the following are true for an alkene, but NOT true for an alkane?
A They are flammable.
B They are hydrocarbons.
C They decolourise bromine water.
D They contain C=C bonds.
E They contain C–H bonds. (2 marks)

5 Copy and complete the equation below showing the polymerisation of propene.

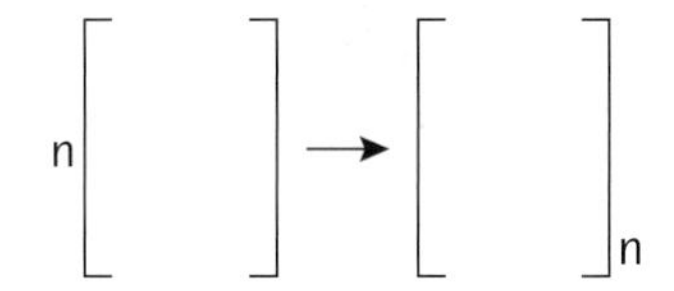

(2 marks)

6 This question is about changes in the oxygen content of the atmosphere. For each part pick the correct answer.

a) Atmospheric oxygen was formed by: (i) animals. (ii) animals and plants. (iii) plants. (iv) volcanic activity.	b) The oxygen reacted with the methane in the atmosphere. What were the products? (i) Carbon dioxide and hydrogen. (ii) Carbon dioxide and water. (iii) Carbon monoxide and hydrogen. (iv) Carbon monoxide and water.
c) Oxygen also reacted with ammonia in the atmosphere. Which of the following equations is correct? (i) $2NH_3 + 2O_2 \rightarrow 2NO_2 + 3H_2$ (ii) $2NH_3 + O_2 \rightarrow 2NO + 3H_2$ (iii) $4NH_3 + 2O_3 \rightarrow 2N_2 + 6H_2O$ (iv) $4NH_3 + 3O_2 \rightarrow 2N_2 + 6H_2O$	d) Some of the oxygen was converted into ozone. What useful purpose does ozone serve? (i) It removes some of the heat from the Sun. (ii) It removes some of the infrared radiation from the Sun. (iii) It removes some of the radio waves from the Sun. (iv) It removes some of the ultraviolet radiation from the Sun.

(4 marks)

7 Sea floor spreading occurs along the mid-Atlantic ridge.
a) What causes sea floor spreading?
b) What type of new rock does sea floor spreading produce? (3 marks)

Total: 20 marks

PATTERNS OF CHEMICAL CHANGE

Hazard symbols

The hazard symbols are used to label chemicals to show how dangerous they are.

Oxidising
These substances provide oxygen which allows other materials to burn more fiercely.

Highly flammable
These substances easily catch fire.

Toxic
These substances can cause death. They may have their effects when swallowed, breathed in or absorbed through the skin.

Corrosive
These substances attack and destroy living tissues, including eyes and skin.

Harmful
These substances are similar to toxic substances but are less dangerous.

Irritant
These substances are not corrosive but can cause reddening or blistering of the skin.

FIGURE 7.1 Hazard warning symbols

Chemical reactions

LEARN what happens during chemical reactions.

Here are the main features of a chemical reaction:

1 Chemical reactions make new substances.
2 The starting materials are called reactants and the new substances made are called products.
3 Before a chemical change can start, the reactants must be mixed so that the particles in them can collide.
4 When the particles collide, the energy of the collision must be enough to break the chemical bonds in the reactants.
5 The least amount of energy needed to do this is called the activation energy.
6 Once the reactants have decomposed, the particles released join together in a different way to make the new substances – the products.

Chemical reactions can be represented using different types of equation.

- General equations show the types of substances involved in the reaction.

  e.g. acid + alkali → salt + water

- Word equations show the names of all the reactants and products.

  e.g. hydrochloric acid + sodium hydroxide → sodium chloride + water

- Symbol (or formula) equations show the chemical symbols or formulae of the reactants and products.

  e.g. $HCl + NaOH \rightarrow NaCl + H_2O$

- Balanced chemical equations must always be written. This means that there must be equal numbers of atoms of each element on each side of the equation.

  e.g. $H_2SO_4 + 2NaOH \rightarrow Na_2SO_4 + 2H_2O$

  Chemical equations can be used to calculate the amounts of reactants and products involved in a chemical reaction (see page 80).

Rates of reaction

Some chemical reactions can be very fast, like explosions, but some can be quite slow, like the fermentation of sugar in grapes to make wine, or the rusting of iron. Figure 7.2 shows some ways of following the rate of chemical reactions.

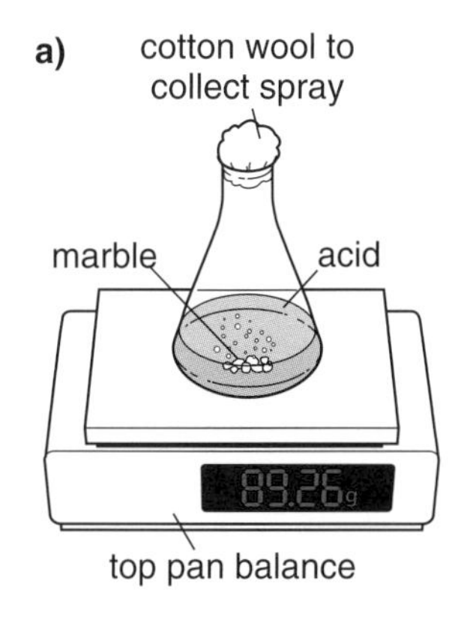

Record the mass each minute as the gas escapes.

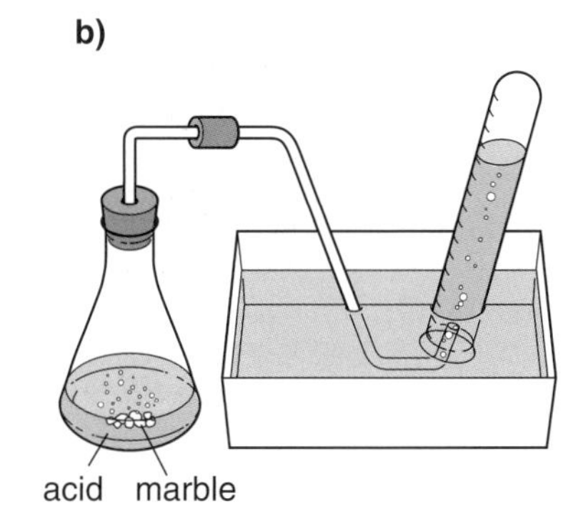

Record the total volume of gas collected each minute.

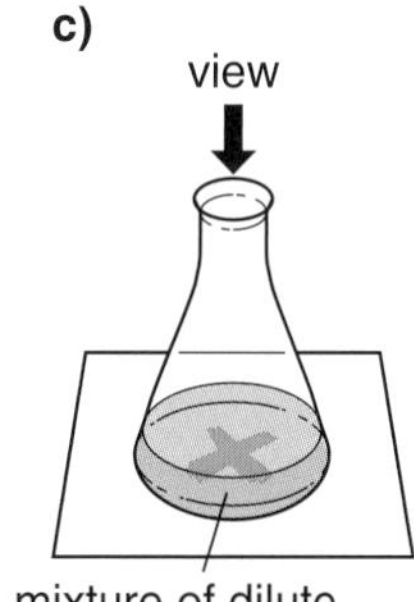

Measure how long it takes for the X to disappear as the liquid goes cloudy.

FIGURE 7.2 Measuring the rate of reaction

Once a set of readings has been taken, a change is then made (e.g. raising the temperature), and the experiment is repeated. The readings taken can be displayed on a graph. The graph for experiment (a) above would look something like Figure 7.3.

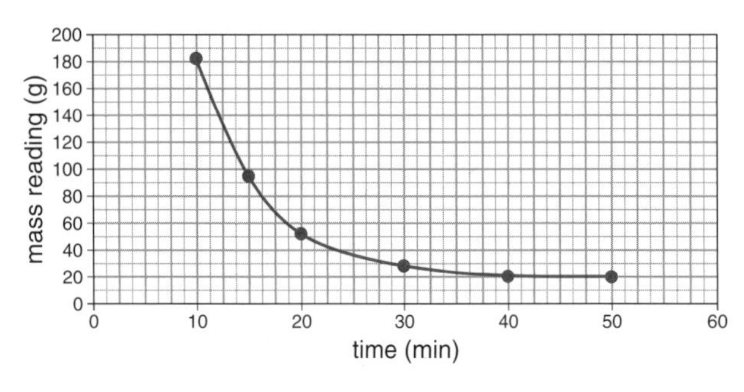

Note that as the reaction takes place, the rate slows down – the graph becomes less steep, and eventually it levels off because the reaction is complete. The reaction stops when one of the reactants is used up.

FIGURE 7.3 A graph of results for experiment (a)

The graph for experiment (b) would look something like Figure 7.4.

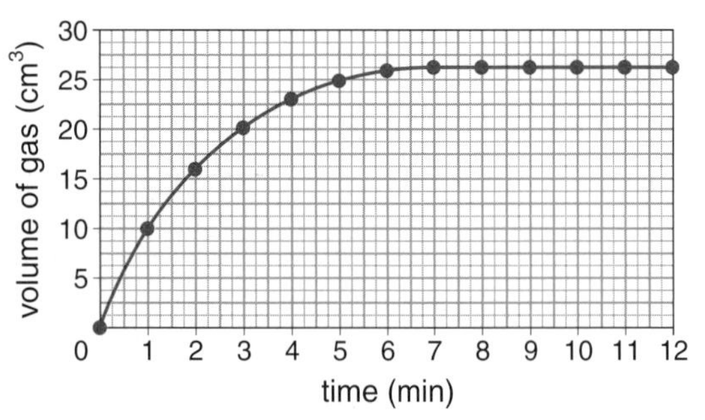

Note once again that the graph is quite steep at the beginning and then becomes less steep as the reaction rate slows down. This is because the reactants are slowly being used up and their concentration is decreasing. Eventually no more gas is given off because one of the reactants has been used up.

FIGURE 7.4 A graph of results for experiment (b)

CHECK YOUR UNDERSTANDING

❶ Give the name of a piece of apparatus that could be used, instead of the graduated gas measuring tube, for collecting and measuring the volume of gas produced in experiment (b) above.

❷ Why do both graphs, in Figure 7.3 and Figure 7.4, eventually level off?

Changing reaction rates

There are several ways of changing the rate of a reaction. Here is a summary with explanations.

Change	What it does	How it does it
Temperature	Reactions go faster at higher temperatures.	Raising the temperature increases the speed of the reacting particles so that they collide more often and with greater energy, so there is more chance that they will react.
		Also more reactant particles are likely to reach the activation energy for the reaction (see page 70).
Concentration	Concentrated solutions react faster than dilute solutions.	Increasing the concentration of a solution puts the reactants closer together so that they are likely to collide more often. Also they don't have so far to travel before they can collide.

Pressure	Changing the pressure only affects reactions involving gases. Gas reactions go faster at high pressures.	Increasing the pressure on a gas reaction has exactly the same effect as increasing the concentration of a solution. The reacting particles are closer together and more likely to collide and react.
Particle size	Small particles react faster than large ones.	Smaller particles have a greater surface area than the same amount of larger particles. This means that more solid reactant becomes exposed and there is more chance of a reaction taking place.
Use of a catalyst	Catalysts speed up chemical reactions but do not get used up. They can be used over and over again.	Catalysts provide an easier route from reactants to products, by lowering the activation energy for the reaction. Different reactions usually need different catalysts. Some reactions are not affected by catalysts.

It is important to be able to control the rate of a reaction in industry.

- Too fast a reaction rate could be dangerous and difficult to control.
- Too slow a reaction rate could be costly because it takes too long to make the product.

LEARN what can be done to change the reaction rate.

CHECK YOUR UNDERSTANDING

❶ Suggest three ways of making some marble lumps dissolve as quickly as possible in hydrochloric acid.

❷ Give two reasons why raising the temperature increases the rate of chemical reactions.

❸ Why does 1 kg of sawdust burn faster than a 1 kg log of wood?

Rate of reaction and amount of reaction

The rate of reaction tells you how fast the reaction is going and depends on the factors shown in the table above.

The amount of reaction tells you how much reaction is taking place and the amount of product made. This depends on the amounts of reactants used in the reaction. The greater the amount of starting materials, the greater the amount of products formed. The graphs in Figure 7.5 show the differences.

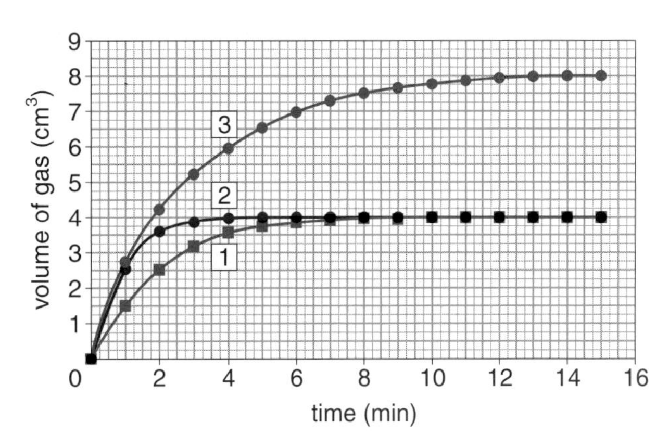

FIGURE 7.5

Graphs 1 and 2 in Figure 7.5 are for two experiments that have used the same amounts of reactants, e.g. 50 cm^3 of acid and a small (1 cm) piece of magnesium. In both experiments there is enough acid to dissolve all the magnesium. So the reaction stops when all the magnesium has dissolved.

However, the acid used in experiment 2 is more concentrated than the acid used in experiment 1, so graph 2 is steeper than graph 1. The more concentrated acid is dissolving the magnesium faster but the same total amount of gas is being made in each experiment.

Graph 3 shows what happens if a larger amount of magnesium (e.g. 2 cm) is added to 50 cm^3 of acid and left until it completely dissolves. The greater amount of magnesium helps to make more gas than in the other two experiments.

Enzymes

Some important points to remember about enzymes:

1 Enzymes are catalysts that are produced by living things.

2 Enzymes are very important because they allow chemical reactions to take place quickly at ordinary temperatures and pressures, reducing fuel costs.

3 Enzymes work best in warm conditions rather than hot. This is because they are protein molecules which are usually damaged (or denatured) by temperatures above 40 °C.

4 Enzymes are affected by the pH value of their surroundings. Different enzymes work best at different pH values.

Reactions that use enzymes to help them work faster

Making beer and wine	This process is called fermentation. The enzymes in yeast cells help to convert sugar into alcohol and carbon dioxide.
Making bread dough rise	This is also fermentation. The carbon dioxide gas produced helps the bread dough to rise.
Making yoghurt	Enzymes in bacteria convert the sugar in milk (called lactose) into yoghurt (which contains lactic acid).
Using detergents	Biological detergents may contain enzymes. These help to digest protein-based stains and fat-based stains. They work at low temperatures.
In some baby foods	Some baby foods contain enzymes that help to start the process of digesting proteins, making it easier for the baby.

Making sugar syrup	Starch syrup from plants is converted into a sugar syrup containing the sweet sugars glucose and maltose. These can be used in the brewing industry and for sweetening drinks.
Making sweeteners	The enzyme isomerase changes glucose into a sweeter sugar called fructose. This means less sugar is needed to sweeten foods and drinks.

Using enzymes in industrial processes

Industry prefers to use continuous processes rather than batch processes.

A continuous process is where there is an uninterrupted production of product. A batch process is where there is a period of time when the process has to be stopped so that the product can be removed and new reactants added. Enzyme catalysts enable industry to use continuous processes.

For a continuous process the enzyme must be stabilised so that it can continue to work for as long as possible, this requires continuous monitoring of the environment in which the enzyme is working. The enzyme also needs to be immobilised. This is done by trapping it on an inert support (e.g. alginate beads) enabling the reactants to come into contact with it.

Energy changes

When chemical reactions take place, energy changes often occur. Sometimes energy is given off in the form of heat and/or light, but sometimes heat energy has to be added to make the reaction take place.

When a fuel (e.g. coal, coke, oil, natural gas, petrol, etc.) burns, heat and light energy are released and the surroundings become warmer. When energy is released in this way, the reaction is said to be exothermic. These are the most common types of reaction and some other examples are:

- Adding a fairly reactive metal (e.g. magnesium) to an acid.
- Reacting an acid with an alkali (e.g. adding hydrochloric acid to sodium hydroxide).
- Adding water to some white anhydrous copper sulphate turns the white powder to blue. This reaction can be used to show that water is present.
- Adding very reactive metals (e.g. sodium and potassium) to water.

FIGURE 7.6 An exothermic change

When a plant is in sunlight, the process called photosynthesis takes place and the plant absorbs energy from the Sun.

When energy is absorbed in this way, the reaction is said to be endothermic. This type of reaction is not quite so common, but there are other examples. If a chemical compound needs to be heated to decompose it, then an endothermic change is taking place. Here are some more examples:

- Heating copper carbonate to make copper oxide and carbon dioxide.
- Heating blue copper sulphate crystals to make white anhydrous copper sulphate.

FIGURE 7.7 An endothermic change

The reason why energy is involved in chemical reactions is quite simple.

1. The chemical bonds holding the elements together in the reactants have to be broken before any new substance can be made.
2. This means heat energy must be added (i.e. this stage is an endothermic process).
3. When new chemical bonds are made in the products, heat energy is given out (i.e. this stage is an exothermic process).

4 If more energy is given out making new bonds than is added to break existing bonds, then the reaction is exothermic. The difference between the energy put in and the energy released is given out, usually as heat energy, so the reaction mixture gets hotter.

5 If less energy is given out making new bonds than is added to break existing bonds, then the reaction is endothermic and the reaction mixture gets colder.

The overall energy change in a reaction can be calculated using bond energy values. The bond energy is the amount of energy (in kilojoules) that is liberated when one mole of a chemical bond is formed. It is also the amount of energy that has to be put in to break one mole of the bond, so the larger its value the stronger the bond. Typical values are:

O–H = 464 O=O = 497 C=O = 745

H–Br = 366 H–H = 436 Br–Br = 193

Consider the reaction $H_2 + Br_2 \rightarrow 2HBr$

Bonds to break (energy put in)		**Bonds made (energy given out)**	
H–H	1 × 436 = 436	2 × H–Br	2 × 366 = 732
Br–Br	1 × 193 = 193		
Total energy put in	= +629 kJ	Total energy given out	= −732 kJ

More energy is given out than put in so the reaction is exothermic, releasing 103 kJ.

These energy changes can be shown using an energy diagram.

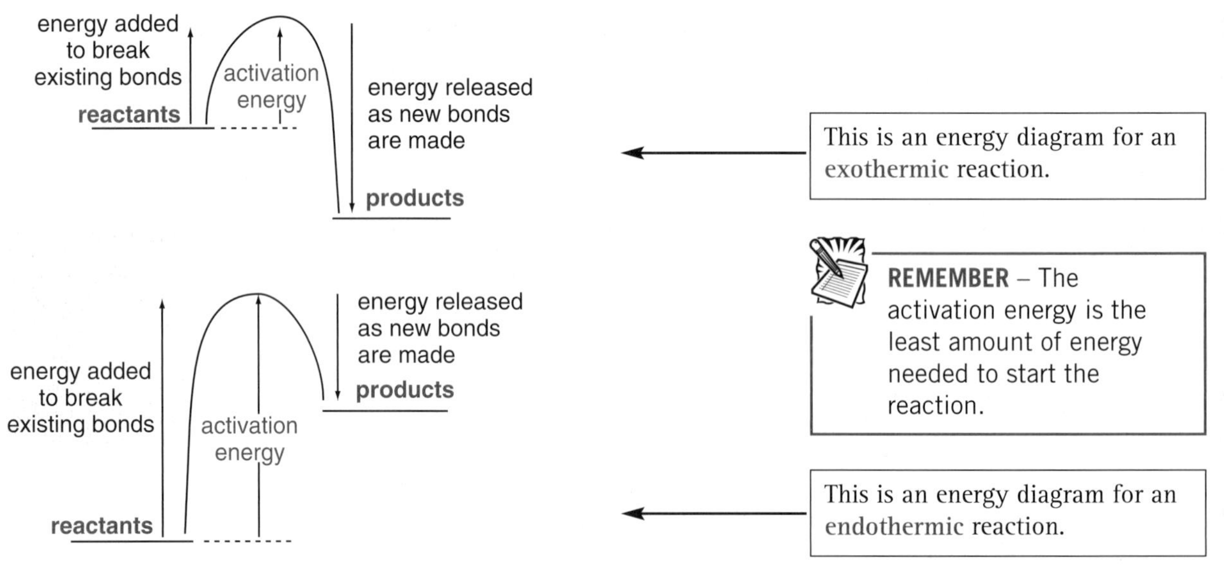

This is an energy diagram for an exothermic reaction.

REMEMBER – The activation energy is the least amount of energy needed to start the reaction.

This is an energy diagram for an endothermic reaction.

FIGURE 7.8 Energy diagrams

Reversible reactions

Some reactions are called reversible reactions, and are shown in chemical equations using a special sign between reactants and products rather than an arrow.

Reactants $\rightleftharpoons$ Products

This sign shows that the reaction can take place both in the forward and the reverse directions depending on the conditions chosen.

One common example is when ammonium chloride solid is heated and the products are cooled.

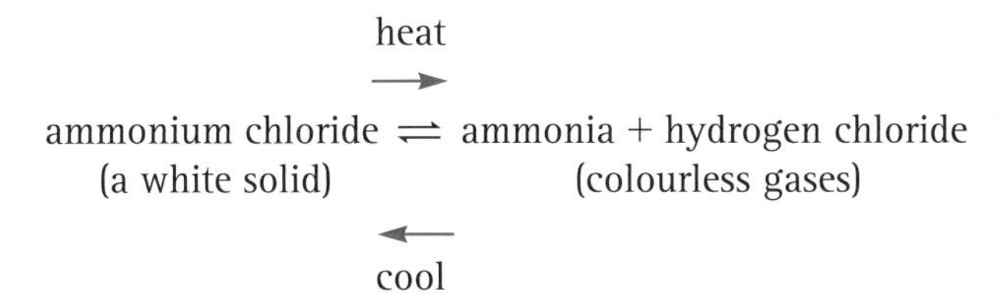

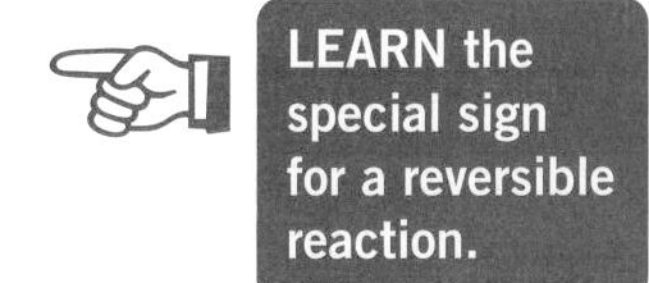

The forward reaction needs heat energy to make it work so, it is endothermic.

The reverse reaction gives out heat energy so it is exothermic.

Another example is the action of heat on blue copper sulphate crystals to make white anhydrous copper sulphate and water. Heat is needed to change the blue crystals into the white powder but heat is released when water is added back to the white powder.

Any reversible reaction that is exothermic in one direction is endothermic in the other.

If a reversible reaction is carried out in a closed vessel, so that nothing can enter or escape, a point is reached where the forward reaction is making products at the same rate as the reverse reaction is reforming the reactants. At this point a dynamic equilibrium exists. The relative amounts of reactants and products present in the equilibrium mixture depends on the conditions of the reaction. These conditions have to be very carefully controlled in industry to produce the best yield of product.

The table is a summary of the effects of different conditions on the position of equilibrium.

Nature of forward reaction	Change made at equilibrium	Effect of change
Exothermic	Increasing the temperature	The yield of products is decreased, but the reaction rate increases. The decrease in yield is due to the product decomposing at the higher temperature.
	Lowering the temperature	The yield of products is increased but the reaction rate decreases.
Endothermic	Increasing the temperature	The yield of products is increased because the higher temperature helps to make up the energy shortfall. The reaction rate also increases.
	Lowering the temperature	The yield of products is decreased and the reaction rate also decreases.
Gaseous reaction	Increasing the pressure	This favours the reaction direction in which there is a **reduction in the number of molecules** as the reaction proceeds. (See the Haber process on pages 78–79.)

These are important points to consider for industrial processes.

Some important industrial processes

The air around us is a mixture of gases including nitrogen, oxygen, noble gases, carbon dioxide and water vapour. About 80% of the air is nitrogen gas and this is an essential element needed to make plants grow. Unfortunately few plants can use the nitrogen directly from the air and it is often necessary to add extra nitrogen to crops in the form of nitrogen-based fertilisers. These are manufactured from a compound called ammonia (NH_3) which contains nitrogen. Here are some advantages and disadvantages of using artificial fertilisers:

Advantages	Disadvantages
1 Crop yields are improved.	1 If too much fertiliser is added, some gets washed off the land into streams and rivers and the water becomes contaminated.
2 The land used for growing crops can be used every year for growing more crops instead of leaving it every so often to recover.	2 The fertiliser in the water encourages water plants and algae to grow. The surface becomes covered in green algae which are decomposed by bacteria using up oxygen dissolved in the water. Fish are then starved of essential oxygen.
	3 The nitrates in fertilisers get into drinking water and these nitrates are converted by the body into harmful chemicals.

The Haber process for making ammonia

Ammonia (NH_3) is manufactured from nitrogen and hydrogen in the Haber process.

The reaction is a reversible one. It is exothermic in the forward reaction.

$$\text{nitrogen} + \text{hydrogen} \rightleftharpoons \text{ammonia}$$
$$N_2 + 3H_2 \rightleftharpoons 2NH_3$$

Only small amounts of the nitrogen and hydrogen in the mixture actually combine. The mixture leaving the chamber is cooled and the ammonia gas condenses to liquid ammonia. The unchanged nitrogen and hydrogen are then recycled back through the catalyst chamber.

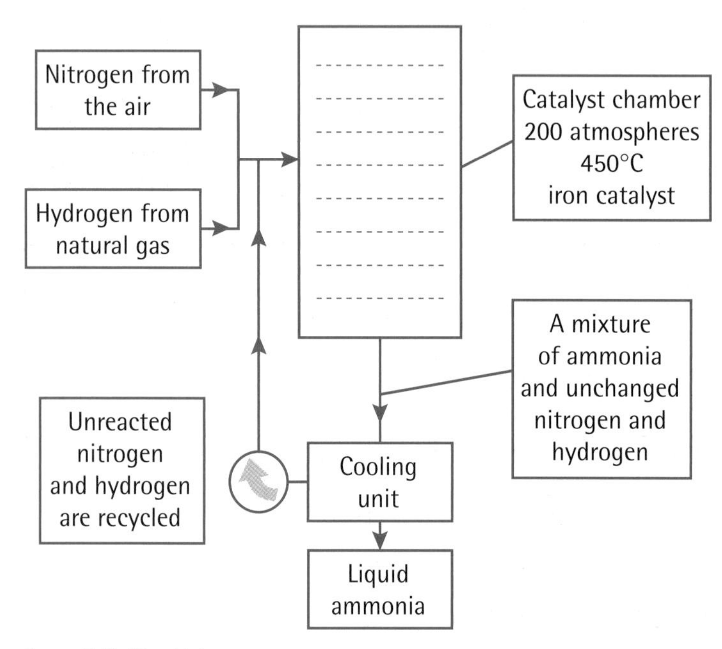

FIGURE 7.9 The Haber process

Feature	What you need to know
What are the raw materials?	Nitrogen from the air and hydrogen obtained from natural gas.
How are they combined?	They are first purified and are then passed over a catalyst at a moderate temperature and a high pressure.
What pressure is used and why?	A high pressure of about 200 atmospheres is used. High pressures increase the rate of this reaction because the gases become more concentrated. The yield is increased because there is a reduction in the number of molecules (from 4 to 2) as the forward reaction occurs.
What temperature is used and why?	A moderate temperature of about 450°C is used. A very high temperature would speed up the reaction but it would also make the ammonia decompose back into nitrogen and hydrogen. Low temperatures make the reaction too slow. The moderate temperature is used as a compromise.
Which catalyst is used?	A catalyst of iron is used.

LEARN these main features of the Haber process.

Changing the ammonia into fertiliser

Stage	What happens
1	A mixture of ammonia and air is passed over a platinum catalyst at 900°C. The ammonia is oxidised to nitrogen monoxide (NO) and water (H_2O).
2	The nitrogen monoxide is cooled and reacted with more oxygen to make nitrogen dioxide (NO_2).
3	The nitrogen dioxide then reacts with oxygen and water to make nitric acid (HNO_3).
4	The nitric acid can then be reacted with ammonia to make the fertiliser called ammonium nitrate which has the chemical formula NH_4NO_3. $NH_3 + HNO_3 \rightarrow NH_4NO_3$

CHECK YOUR UNDERSTANDING

1. What is meant by a reversible reaction?
2. Describe a simple test you could do to show that a liquid contains water. Give the result of the test.
3. Using the bond energy values from page 76, calculate the energy change for the burning of hydrogen:
   $2H_2 + O_2 \rightarrow 2H_2O$ (there are two O–H bonds in water)
4. Make a list of the important reaction conditions used in the Haber process.

Simple calculations

Every substance is made from elements and each element is made of atoms. Atoms of different elements have different masses. The masses of individual atoms are too small for us to consider so we need to know how the masses of different elements compare with each other. This is done by using relative atomic masses (the symbol for which is A_r, see page 46).

Relative atomic mass (A_r)

Values of relative atomic masses will be given in an examination question.

$H = 1 \quad C = 12 \quad O = 16 \quad Na = 23 \quad Mg = 24 \quad S = 32 \quad Cl = 35.5$

These numbers compare the masses of atoms of different elements with each other. For example, Mg = 24 and C = 12 tells us that a magnesium atom is twice as heavy as a carbon atom. C = 12 and H = 1 tells us that carbon atoms are twelve times heavier than hydrogen atoms.

Relative formula mass (M_r)

Atoms are rarely found on their own, they are nearly always combined together. Sometimes identical atoms join together to make molecules of elements, e.g. H_2. Atoms of different elements join together to make compounds, e.g. H_2SO_4. To find out how the masses of these substances compare, we must use relative formula masses (the symbol for which is M_r).

Relative formula masses are calculated by adding together the masses of **all** the atoms of each element shown in the chemical formula.

Example 1: What is the relative formula mass of carbon dioxide (CO_2)?

$$C = 12 \quad O = 16$$

The formula (CO_2) tells us that there is one carbon atom and two oxygen atoms.

So: CO_2 has a relative formula mass of 12 + 16 + 16 = 44.

Example 2: What is the relative formula mass of sulphuric acid (H_2SO_4)?

$$H = 1 \quad S = 32 \quad O = 16$$

The formula (H_2SO_4) tells us that there are two hydrogen atoms, one sulphur atom and four oxygen atoms.

So: H_2SO_4 has a relative formula mass of (1 + 1) + 32 + (16 + 16 + 16 + 16) = 98.

To calculate the percentage of an element in a compound from its formula, follow the steps in this example:

Example: What is the percentage of magnesium (Mg) in magnesium sulphate ($MgSO_4$)?

1. Calculate the relative formula mass, e.g. $MgSO_4$ is 24 + 32 + 16 + 16 + 16 + 16 = 120.
2. Calculate the fraction of the element present in this compound, e.g. for magnesium 24 ÷ 120.
3. Convert this to a percentage, e.g. for magnesium 24 ÷ 120 × 100 = 20%.

To determine the formula of a compound from its percentage composition, follow the steps in this example.

Example: A compound contains 0.8 g calcium, 0.64 g sulphur and 1.28 g oxygen. What is its formula? (Ca = 40 S = 32 O = 16)

	Ca	S	O
Amount of element (g)	0.8	0.64	1.28
Divide by relative atomic mass	$0.8 \div 40 = 0.02$	$0.64 \div 32 = 0.02$	$1.28 \div 16 = 0.08$
Divide by smallest number to get a whole number ratio	$0.02 \div 0.02 = 1$	$0.02 \div 0.02 = 1$	$0.08 \div 0.02 = 4$

Simplest formula is $CaSO_4$

To calculate reacting masses and volumes from equations, follow the steps in this example.

Example: Calculate a) the mass of sodium carbonate (Na_2CO_3) that would react with 4.9 g of sulphuric acid (H_2SO_4) and b) the volume of carbon dioxide (CO_2) evolved.

Na = 23 C = 12 O = 16 H = 1 S = 32

The volume of 1 mole of a gas is 24 dm^3 under room conditions.

$$H_2SO_4 + Na_2CO_3 \rightarrow Na_2SO_4 + H_2O + CO_2$$

a) Only H_2SO_4 and Na_2CO_3 are needed here. One mole of substance is its relative mass in g.

The equation shows that 1 mole of H_2SO_4 reacts with 1 mole of Na_2CO_3.

i.e. (2 + 32 + 64) = 98 g H_2SO_4 reacts with
(46 + 12 + 48) = 106 g Na_2CO_3

4.9 is 1/20th of 98, therefore 4.9 g H_2SO_4 would react with 1/20th of 106 g = 5.3 g Na_2CO_3

b) The equation shows that 1 mole of H_2SO_4 produces 1 mole of CO_2 = 24 dm^3.

98 g H_2SO_4 produces 24 dm^3 CO_2, therefore 4.9 g H_2SO_4 produces 1/20th of 24 dm^3 of CO_2 = 1.2 dm^3

Topic Test

1 Explain why magnesium dissolves faster in concentrated acid than in dilute acid. (2 marks)

2 What is a catalyst and what does it do to the rate of a chemical reaction? (2 marks)

3 Why do most chemical reactions become slower as the reaction proceeds? (3 marks)

4 Why do chemical reactions eventually stop? (1 mark)

5 Why are many industrial chemical reactions involving gases carried out at quite high pressures? (2 marks)

6 What are the disadvantages of using very high pressures in industry? (1 mark)

7 What are the main advantages of using enzymes in industry? (1 mark)

8 What steps are taken in industry to make sure that enzymes keep working for a long time? (2 marks)

9 Why don't enzymes work at high temperatures? (1 mark)

10 Some reactions are described as being exothermic and some as endothermic. Explain the terms exothermic and endothermic. (2 marks)

11 What name is given to the minimum amount of energy that must be given to the reacting substances to start a chemical reaction? (1 mark)

12 Describe a simple test for the gas carbon dioxide. (2 marks)

13 Give one advantage and one disadvantage of using fertilisers. (2 marks)

14 Ammonia is made industrially from nitrogen and hydrogen. Where are these two gases obtained from for this process. (2 marks)

15 List the essential conditions of temperature and pressure used in the Haber process for manufacturing ammonia. (2 marks)

16 Which catalyst is used in the Haber process? (1 mark)

17 Why is a very high temperature not used in the Haber process? (1 mark)

18 The formulae of two fertilisers are a) NH_4NO_3 and b) $(NH_4)_2SO_4$. For each fertiliser calculate the relative formula mass and the percentage of nitrogen present.
(Use the following relative atomic masses: H = 1; N = 14; O = 16; S = 32) (4 marks)

19 Calculate the formula of a compound that contains 27.4% sodium (Na); 1.2% hydrogen (H); 14.3% carbon (C); and 57.1% oxygen (O). Na = 23; H = 1; C = 12; O = 16. (4 marks)

20 Calculate the mass of magnesium oxide (MgO), needed to destroy 2.1 g of nitric acid (HNO_3).
The equation for the reaction is:

$$MgO + 2HNO_3 = Mg(NO_3)_2 + H_2O$$

Mg = 24; H = 1; N = 14; O = 16 (4 marks)

Total: 40 marks

STRUCTURES AND BONDING

MODULE 8

The atom

Some important points about atoms:

- All substances are made from atoms.
- If all the atoms in a substance are the same, the substance is an element.
- If the atoms in a substance are different and are joined together, the substance is a compound. (If they are not joined together it is a mixture.)
- Atoms have a small central part called the nucleus. This contains positively charged protons, together with neutrons that have no electrical charge.
- All atoms of a particular element have the same number of protons.
- Atoms of different elements have different numbers of protons.
- Atoms of the same element can have different numbers of neutrons. These atoms are called isotopes.
- Nearly all the mass of the atom is in its nucleus.
- The nucleus is surrounded by a series of shells or energy levels. These contain negatively charged electrons.
- Electrons have almost no mass.
- In an atom, the number of protons in the nucleus equals the number of electrons in the energy levels. Atoms have no overall electrical charge.
- The number of protons in an atom is called the atomic number.
- The total number of protons and neutrons in an atom is called the mass number.

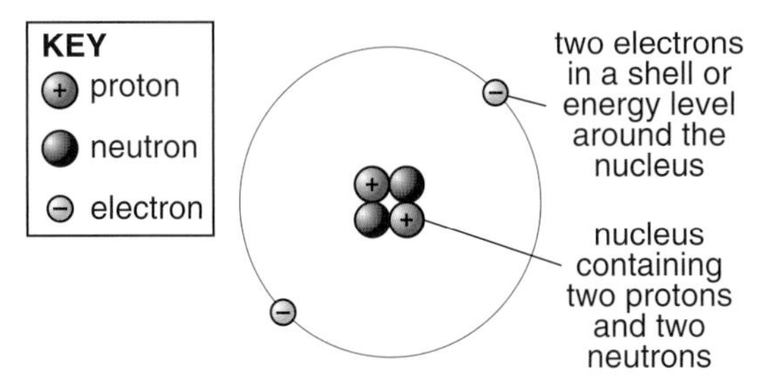

FIGURE 8.1 An atom of helium

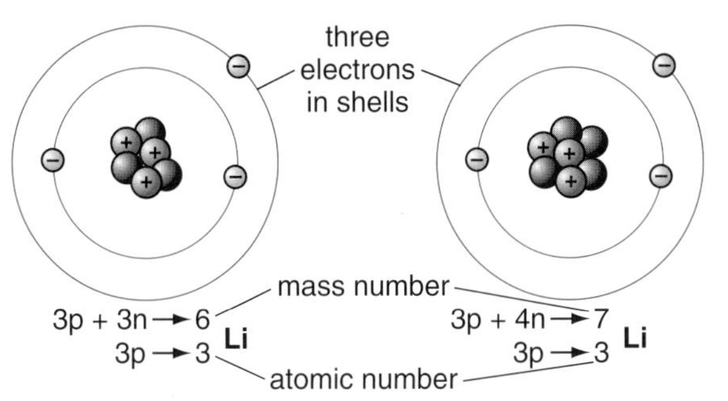

FIGURE 8.2 Isotopes of lithium – element number 3

The relative masses and charges of protons, neutrons and electrons:

	Mass	Charge
Proton	1	+1
Neutron	1	0
Electron	negligible	−1

REMEMBER – **Isotopes** are atoms of the same element with the **same number** of **protons** but **different numbers** of **neutrons**.

Atomic numbers and **mass numbers** are shown as follows: for sodium

mass number 23
Na
atomic number 11

The outer part of the atom

Each electron occupies a particular energy level (or shell). Where there are several energy levels available, the electron occupies the level with the lowest energy.

The electronic structures of elements can be shown in the form of a diagram (see Figure 8.3) or a table.

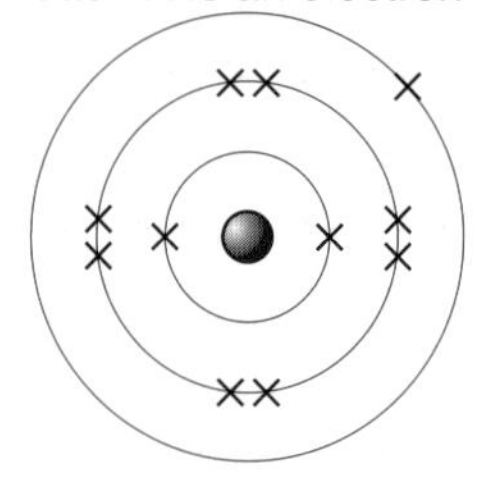

FIGURE 8.3 An atom of sodium 2,8,1

Some important points to note:

1. The first energy level (the one closest to the nucleus) can only hold a maximum of **2** electrons.
2. The second shell can hold a maximum of **8** electrons.
3. The third shell is stable when it has **8** electrons in it.
4. When the shells in an atom are full, the atom is stable.
5. The electronic structure shown in Figure 8.3 (2,8,1) shows the numbers of electrons in each energy level starting with the ones closest to the nucleus.

The electronic structures of the first 20 elements in the Periodic Table are shown in the table below.

Atomic number	Name	Symbol	1st energy level	2nd energy level	3rd energy level	4th energy level
1	hydrogen	H	1			
2	helium	He	2	1st energy level now full		
3	lithium	Li	2	1		
4	beryllium	Be	2	2		
5	boron	B	2	3		
6	carbon	C	2	4		
7	nitrogen	N	2	5		
8	oxygen	O	2	6		
9	fluorine	F	2	7		
10	neon	Ne	2	8	2nd energy level full	
11	sodium	Na	2	8	1	
12	magnesium	Mg	2	8	2	
13	aluminium	Al	2	8	3	
14	silicon	Si	2	8	4	
15	phosphorus	P	2	8	5	
16	sulphur	S	2	8	6	
17	chlorine	Cl	2	8	7	
18	argon	Ar	2	8	8	3rd level full
19	potassium	K	2	8	8	1
20	calcium	Ca	2	8	8	2

CHECK YOUR UNDERSTANDING

❶ Using an x to represent each electron, draw diagrams similar to Figure 8.3 to show how the electrons are arranged in atoms of a) silicon and b) argon.

❷ How many protons, neutrons and electrons are there in an atom of the isotope of chlorine that has an atomic number of 17 and a mass number of 35?

Electronic structures give us lots of important information. Check the points below by looking at the table on page 84 and a copy of the Periodic Table.

1. The **noble gas** elements have all their energy levels **full**.
2. The number of electrons in the outermost energy level tells us the **Group number** to which the element belongs. For example, sodium (2,8,1) is in Group 1; fluorine (2,7) is in Group 7. The group number is the number at the top of each vertical column in the Periodic Table.
3. The rows in the Periodic Table are known as **periods**. The period number tells us the number of the energy level being filled. For example, magnesium is in the third period because the third energy level is being filled.
4. Metal elements usually have one, two or three electrons in their outer energy level.
5. Non-metal elements usually have four, five, six or seven electrons in their outer energy level.
6. Noble gases usually have eight electrons in their outer energy level (except helium that has only two).
7. It is also important to know that when atoms combine, they do so to obtain the same electronic structure as the nearest noble gas (see pages 86–87).

Organising elements

Early attempts at arranging the elements into order made use of relative atomic masses (A_r) (see page 46). The elements were arranged in order of their relative atomic masses, and for most elements this placed them in groups with very similar chemical properties. This had some problems, for example argon atoms have a greater relative atomic mass than potassium atoms but argon is better placed before potassium in the Periodic Table. The modern Periodic Table arranges the elements in order of their atomic number (i.e. the number of protons in the nucleus). Arranging them this way puts each element into its correct group. Note that there are more metals than non-metals.

Period \ Group	1	2											3	4	5	6	7	0
								H										He
2	Li	Be											B	C	N	O	F	Ne
3	Na	Mg	transition elements (metals)										Al	Si	P	S	Cl	Ar
4	K	Ca	Sc	Ti	V	Cr	Mn	Fe	Co	Ni	Cu	Zn	Ga	Ge	As	Se	Br	Kr
5	Rb	Sr	Y	Zr	Nb	Mo	Tc	Ru	Rh	Pd	Ag	Cd	In	Sn	Sb	Te	I	Xe
6	Cs	Ba	La	Hf	Ta	W	Re	Os	Ir	Pt	Au	Hg	Tl	Pb	Bi	Po	At	Rn
7	Fr	Ra	Ac															

KEY: metals | non-metals | noble gases

FIGURE 8.4 The Periodic Table

Ionic bonding

The main features of ionic bonding are:

1 Ionic bonds are formed between metals and non-metals.
2 Electron(s) transfer from the outer energy level (shell) of the metal atoms to the outer energy level (shell) of the non-metal atoms.
3 Once the electrons have transferred, the atoms have changed into positively charged metal ions and negatively charged non-metal ions usually with noble gas structures.
4 The oppositely charged ions are strongly attracted together by electrostatic forces of attraction and an ionic bond is made.

Electrons TRANSFER in ionic bonding.

Here is an example: sodium ($_{11}Na$) joining with chlorine ($_{17}Cl$) to make sodium chloride (NaCl).

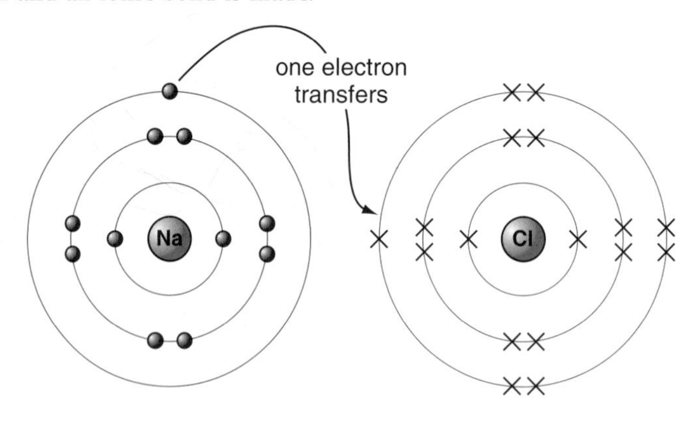

Sodium has one electron in its outer energy level.
If it loses it, the electron structure will be the same as neon.

Chlorine is short of one electron in its outer energy level.
If it gains one, the electron structure will be the same as argon.

One electron transfers from sodium (Na) to chlorine (Cl) making Na^+ and Cl^- ions.

The Na^+ ion has a single positive charge because it has lost a negatively charged electron.

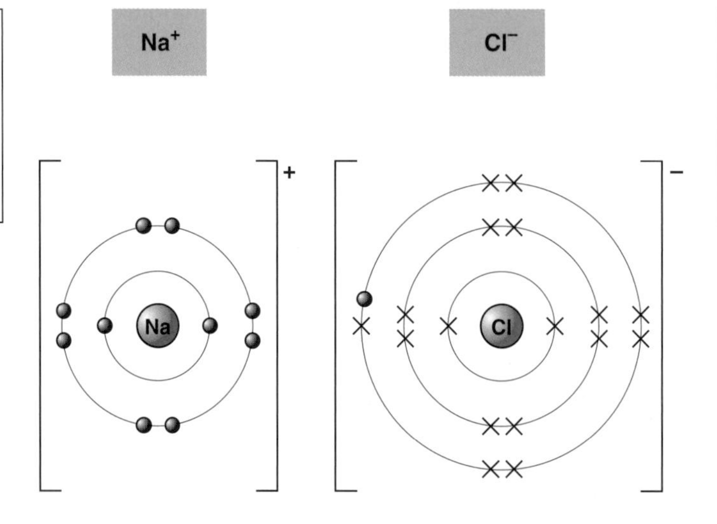

The Cl^- ion has a single negative charge because it has gained a negatively charged electron.

The two oppositely charged ions are electrostatically attracted and the compound sodium chloride (NaCl), containing an ionic bond, is made.

FIGURE 8.5 Ionic bonding in sodium chloride

Sometimes more than one electron is transferred from the metal atom to the non-metal atom forming ions that have more than one positive or negative charge.

Sometimes more than one atom of metal or non-metal is needed.

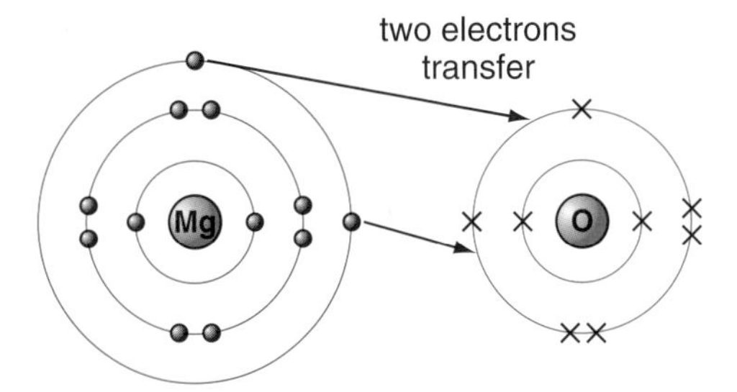

This makes Mg^{2+} and O^{2-} ions which attract to make magnesium oxide (MgO).

REMEMBER – In ionic compounds the charges on the ions must cancel out.

FIGURE 8.6 Ionic bonding in magnesium oxide

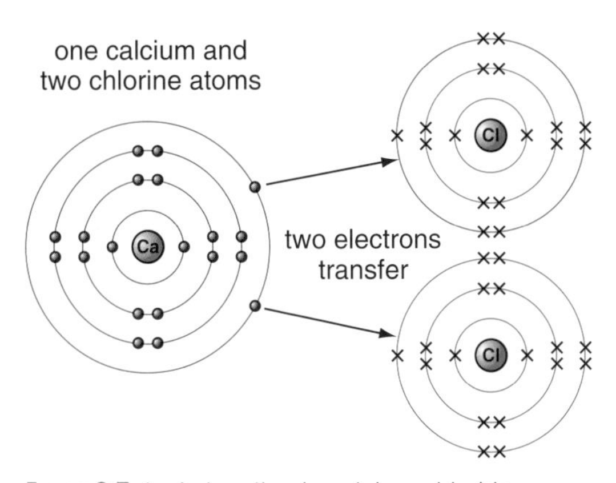

This makes one Ca^{2+} and two Cl^- ions which attract to make calcium chloride ($CaCl_2$).

FIGURE 8.7 Ionic bonding in calcium chloride

Extra information:

1 Metals have one, two or three electrons in their outer energy level (shell) and they always transfer all of them when making ionic bonds.

2 Non-metals are short of electrons in their outer energy level (shell) and they gain as many electrons as are needed to fill the outer energy level.

3 The direction of electron transfer is always from metal to non-metal.

4 Metals always form positive ions, non-metals always form negative ions.

5 The strong electrostatic forces of attraction between lots of ions holds the ions tightly together so ionic compounds are solids with high melting points and high boiling points.

6 The nucleus containing protons and neutrons does not change as the bond is made.

7 Solid ionic compounds do not conduct electricity because the ions are not free to move and carry the current. Melting the solid or dissolving it in water allows the ions to move and conduct electricity. This is called electrolysis (see page 50).

CHECK YOUR UNDERSTANDING

❶ Write down the three main stages in the formation of an ionic bond.

❷ Draw 'dot and cross' diagrams to show how lithium ($_3Li$) and oxygen ($_8O$) could form the ionic compound lithium oxide (Li_2O). Include the charges on the ions formed.

❸ Why does solid sodium chloride NOT conduct electricity when molten sodium chloride does?

Covalent bonding

The main features of covalent bonding are:

1 Covalent bonds are formed between non-metal atoms.

2 Electrons are shared in pairs between the atoms, each atom donating one electron to each shared pair.

3 Each atom shares as many of its electrons as are needed to allow its outer energy level to become full.

4 Once the electrons have been shared, the particles formed are usually small separate molecules.

5 The forces holding the atoms together in each molecule are strong but often the forces between adjacent molecules are quite weak so covalent substances are either gases, low boiling-point liquids or low melting-point solids.

6 Covalent compounds do not conduct electricity because they do not carry an overall electrical charge.

Electrons are SHARED IN PAIRS in covalent bonding.

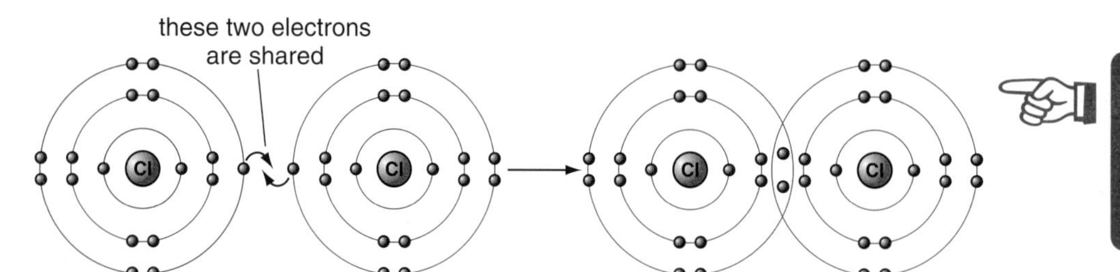

FIGURE 8.8 Covalent bonding in a chlorine molecule

You will often be asked just to show the outer shell electrons.

In Figure 8.8, two chlorine atoms (Cl) have donated one electron each to a shared pair of electrons. Note how the two outer energy levels are overlapped to show sharing.

Sometimes an atom of one element has to share its electrons with more than one atom of a different element. This can be seen in water (H_2O), ammonia (NH_3) and methane (CH_4).

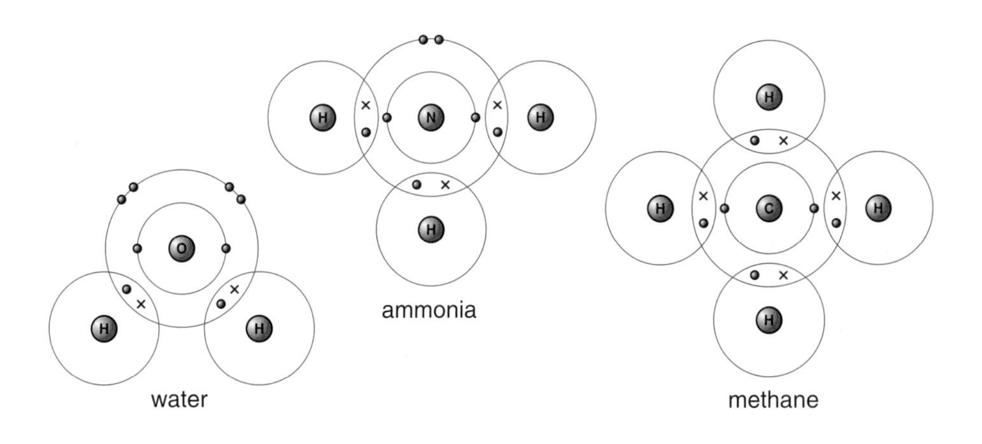

In water (H_2O), two separate covalent bonds are formed with two separate hydrogen atoms.

In ammonia (NH_3), three separate covalent bonds are formed with three separate hydrogen atoms.

In methane (CH_4), four covalent bonds are formed.

FIGURE 8.9 More examples of covalent bonding

Note that every atom in the structures in Figure 8.9 now has a noble gas structure with all energy levels full.

Sometimes atoms can form double covalent bonds with each other. For example in oxygen gas (O_2):

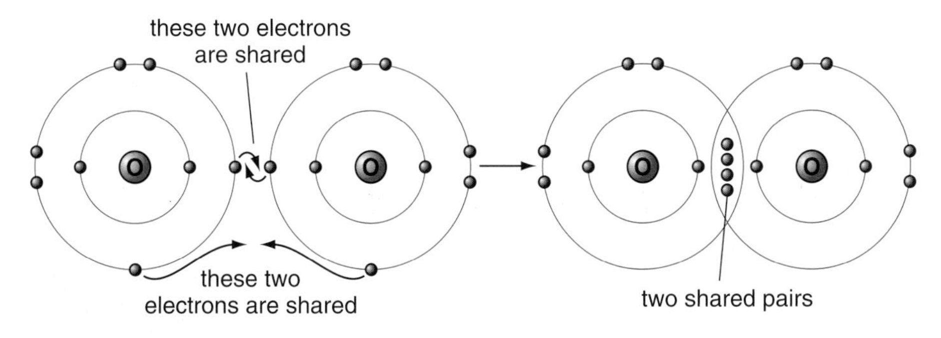

FIGURE 8.10 Covalent bonding in an oxygen molecule

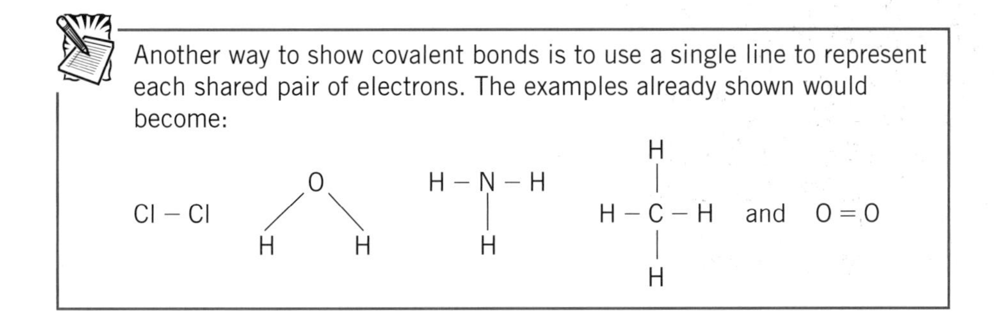
Another way to show covalent bonds is to use a single line to represent each shared pair of electrons. The examples already shown would become:

Diamond and graphite

These are different forms of the same element, carbon. They have the same chemical properties, but different physical properties. The differences in their physical properties are due to the way in which the atoms are arranged in each form. In diamond, each carbon atom is covalently bonded to four other carbon atoms in a giant covalent structure. The repeating unit is a tetrahedron and all the available electrons are used in forming the chemical bonds – there are no free electrons to carry an electric current.

In graphite, each carbon atom is covalently bonded to three other carbon atoms in a layer structure in which the layers are free to slide over each other. The repeating unit is a flat hexagon. Since only three electrons are used in bonding, graphite can use its fourth electron to conduct electricity.

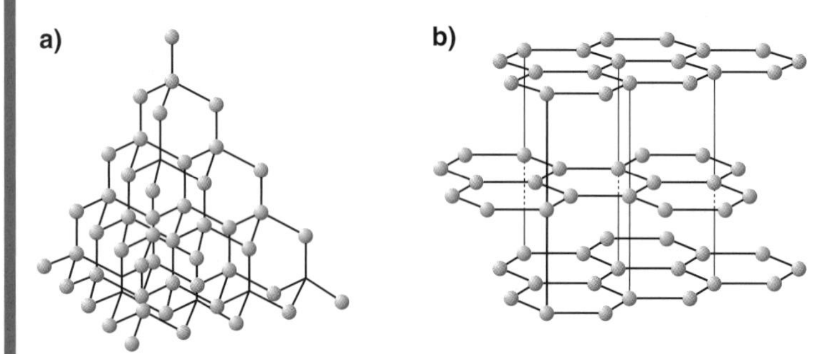

FIGURE 8.11 The arrangement of atoms in a) diamond and b) graphite

Metallic bonding

The main features of metallic bonding are:

1 Metallic bonds only involve metal elements.

2 Metal elements have one, two or three electrons in their outer shell and when metal atoms form a piece of metal, these outer electrons are pooled to form a sea of negative charge which holds together the rest of each atom (the nucleus and the full inner energy levels).

Outer electrons are POOLED in metallic bonding.

3 These pooled electrons are free to move through the metallic structure and allow the atoms to slide over each other (so they can be bent) and also allow them to conduct electricity and heat very quickly.

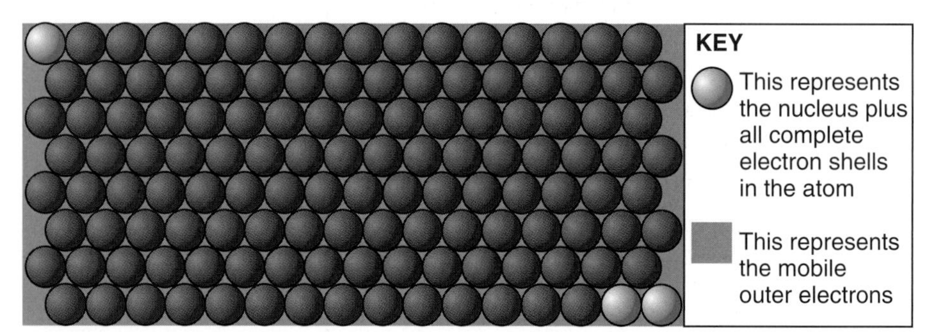

FIGURE 8.12 The arrangement of atoms and outer electrons in a metal

CHECK YOUR UNDERSTANDING

❶ Draw diagrams to show how covalent bonds could be formed between
a) two hydrogen atoms, to make hydrogen gas (H_2)
b) hydrogen and chlorine to make hydrogen chloride (HCl).

❷ Give the name of the type of chemical bond formed between the following pairs of elements:
a) sulphur and oxygen, b) copper and chlorine, c) silicon and hydrogen.

❸ What would you expect the physical states of the compounds in Q2 to be (solid, liquid or gas)?

❹ Why don't covalent substances conduct electricity?

Variations and similarities within groups

Group 1 – The alkali metals (lithium, sodium and potassium)

What they have in common	Trends down the group
They all have one outer electron which they can lose to form a 1+ ion e.g. Na^+.	The size of the atoms increases because more energy levels (shells) have been added.
They all float on the surface of water and react very vigorously with cold water producing hydrogen and an alkali e.g. sodium hydroxide (NaOH).	The outer electron is further away from the attraction of the nucleus and becomes easier to remove. This means K^+ ions will be more easily formed than Li^+ ions.
They are fairly soft, low density metals and are easily cut.	Reactivity with water and other substances increases.
They are good conductors of heat and electricity.	Melting and boiling points decrease.

Group 7 – The halogens (chlorine, bromine and iodine)

What they have in common	Trends down the group
They all have seven outer electrons and gain one more to form a 1- ion (e.g. Cl^-, Br^-, I^-).	The size of the atoms increases because more energy levels (shells) have been added.
They exist as diatomic molecules i.e. molecules composed of two atoms (e.g. Cl_2, Br_2, I_2).	Reactivity decreases because an incoming electron cannot get so close to the nucleus.
They all have coloured vapours (Cl_2 is green, Br_2 is red/brown, I_2 is purple).	Melting and boiling points increase down the Group.
They form ionic solids when reacted with metals.	There is a change from gas (Cl_2) to liquid (Br_2) to solid (I_2).
They form molecular compounds when reacted with non-metals.	A more reactive halogen (e.g. Cl_2) can displace a less reactive halogen (e.g. Br_2 or I_2) from a solution of its salt (e.g. KBr or KI).

Group 0 – The noble gases (helium, neon, argon)

What they have in common	Trends down the group
They all have full outer energy levels so they have no tendency to gain, to lose or to share electrons.	The size of the atoms increases because more energy levels (shells) have been added.
They are chemically unreactive.	
They exist as individual atoms rather than diatomic molecules like other gases.	
They are used as inert gases in light bulbs and discharge tubes.	

An important use for salt

Common salt is sodium chloride (NaCl). A solution of salt is called brine and this solution can be decomposed using electricity in a process called electrolysis (see page 50).

Sodium chloride solution contains four ions: Na^+; H^+; OH^- and Cl^-.

The positively charged anode attracts the OH^- and Cl^- ions.
The Cl^- ions lose electrons to the anode and become chlorine atoms (Cl).

$$Cl^- - 1e^- \rightarrow Cl$$

These chlorine atoms join together to make chlorine molecules (Cl_2).

$$2Cl \rightarrow Cl_2$$

Chlorine gas is made at the anode.

$$2Cl^- - 2e^- \rightarrow Cl_2$$

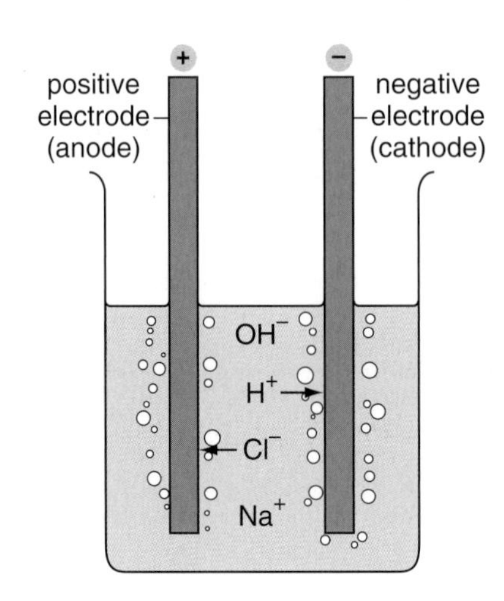

The negatively charged cathode attracts the Na^+ and H^+ ions.
The H^+ ions gain electrons from the cathode and become hydrogen atoms (H).

$$H^+ + 1e^- \rightarrow H$$

These hydrogen atoms join together to make hydrogen molecules (H_2).

$$2H \rightarrow H_2$$

Hydrogen gas is made at the cathode.

$$2H^+ + 2e^- \rightarrow H_2$$

A test for chlorine gas is that it bleaches damp litmus paper.

The Na^+ and OH^- ions stay in solution forming the alkali sodium hydroxide (NaOH).

A test for hydrogen gas is that it burns with a squeaky explosion.

Figure 8.13 The electrolysis of sodium chloride solution

Uses for the substances made from salt

Substance	Uses
chlorine	Killing bacteria in drinking water and swimming baths. Manufacturing hydrochloric acid, disinfectants, bleach and the plastic PVC.
hydrogen	Manufacturing ammonia and margarine.
sodium hydroxide	Manufacturing soap, paper and ceramics.

Silver halides and hydrogen halides

Silver chloride (AgCl), silver bromide (AgBr) and silver iodide (AgI) are silver halides which can be reduced to silver (Ag) by the action of light, X-rays and the radiation from radioactive substances.

e.g. $2AgBr \rightarrow 2Ag + Br_2$

They are used to make photographic film and photographic paper.

Hydrogen chloride (HCl), hydrogen bromide (HBr) and hydrogen iodide (HI) are hydrogen halides.

They are gases that dissolve in water to make acidic solutions, e.g. hydrochloric acid.

Word equations

These show the names of the starting materials (reactants) and new materials formed (products) in a chemical reaction. Some important ones to know are:

- acid + metal → a salt + hydrogen
- acid + metal oxide → a salt + water (metal oxides are known as bases)
- acid + alkali → a salt + water (an alkali is a soluble base)
- acid + metal carbonate → a salt + water + carbon dioxide

Chemical symbols for elements and ions

Each element is given a different symbol. For example carbon is C; sodium is Na.

Use a Data Sheet to find the symbols.

Each ion is also given a symbol. For example the sodium ion is Na^+; the carbonate ion is CO_3^{2-}.

Chemical formulae of substances

Each substance is given a chemical formula which shows the number of each type of atom present in the substance.

For example carbon dioxide (CO_2) has one carbon atom (C) and two oxygen atoms (O_2).

Sulphuric acid (H_2SO_4) has two hydrogen atoms (H_2), one sulphur atom (S) and four oxygen atoms (O_4).

Here are some important formulae:

Elements		Compounds	
hydrogen	H_2	hydrochloric acid	HCl
nitrogen	N_2	sulphuric acid	H_2SO_4
oxygen	O_2	nitric acid	HNO_3
chlorine	Cl_2	water	H_2O
bromine	Br_2	ammonia	NH_3
ozone	O_3	methane	CH_4
helium	He	sulphur dioxide	SO_2
argon	Ar	carbon dioxide	CO_2

LEARN these important formulae.

The formulae of ionic compounds can be worked out by using the symbols for the ions shown on the Data Sheet. (All you do is use enough of each ion to cancel out the electrical charges.)

e.g. sodium chloride is NaCl (i.e. $Na^+ + Cl^-$)
copper sulphate is $CuSO_4$ (i.e. $Cu^{2+} + SO_4^{2-}$)
potassium carbonate is K_2CO_3 (i.e. $2 \times K^+ + CO_3^{2-}$)

Writing balanced chemical equations

Each equation must have the same number of each type of atom on each side.

The physical state of each substance can also be shown. For example:

$$MgCO_3(s) + 2HCl(aq) \rightarrow MgCl_2(aq) + H_2O(l) + CO_2(g)$$

Note here that two HCl are needed to balance the equation.

(s) = solid
(l) = liquid
(g) = gas
(aq) = aqueous solution – a solution in water

Topic Test

1 How does a sodium atom change into a sodium (Na^+) ion? (1 mark)

2 How does an oxygen atom change into an oxide (O^{2-}) ion? (1 mark)

3 Copy the following table and fill in the blanks.

Particle	Number of			Atomic number	Mass number
	protons	neutrons	electrons		
N atom	7				14
B atom		6		5	
Al atom		14	13		
Ca^{2+} ion	20				40
F^- ion		10		9	

(15 marks)

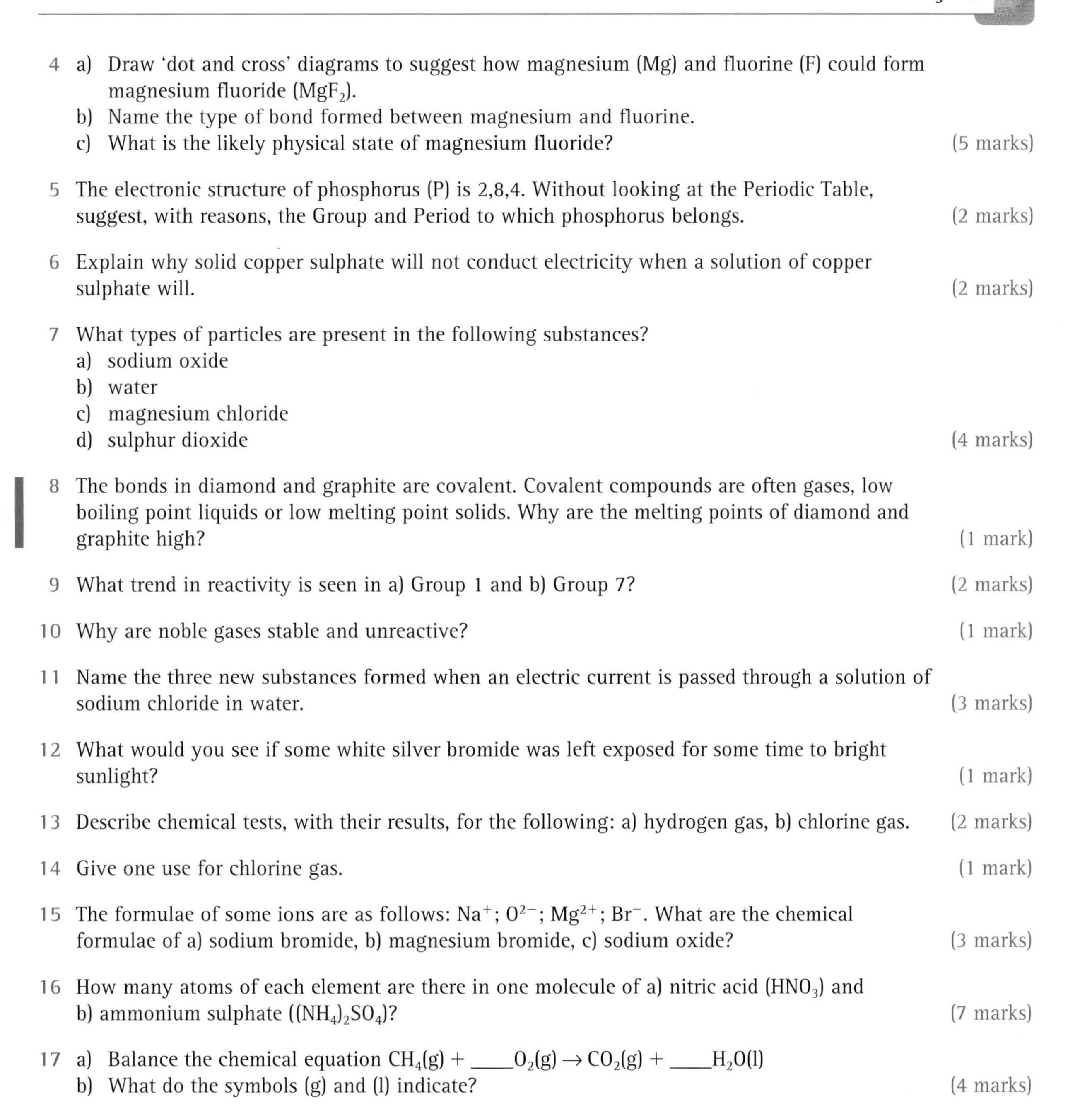

4 a) Draw 'dot and cross' diagrams to suggest how magnesium (Mg) and fluorine (F) could form magnesium fluoride (MgF_2).
b) Name the type of bond formed between magnesium and fluorine.
c) What is the likely physical state of magnesium fluoride? (5 marks)

5 The electronic structure of phosphorus (P) is 2,8,4. Without looking at the Periodic Table, suggest, with reasons, the Group and Period to which phosphorus belongs. (2 marks)

6 Explain why solid copper sulphate will not conduct electricity when a solution of copper sulphate will. (2 marks)

7 What types of particles are present in the following substances?
a) sodium oxide
b) water
c) magnesium chloride
d) sulphur dioxide (4 marks)

8 The bonds in diamond and graphite are covalent. Covalent compounds are often gases, low boiling point liquids or low melting point solids. Why are the melting points of diamond and graphite high? (1 mark)

9 What trend in reactivity is seen in a) Group 1 and b) Group 7? (2 marks)

10 Why are noble gases stable and unreactive? (1 mark)

11 Name the three new substances formed when an electric current is passed through a solution of sodium chloride in water. (3 marks)

12 What would you see if some white silver bromide was left exposed for some time to bright sunlight? (1 mark)

13 Describe chemical tests, with their results, for the following: a) hydrogen gas, b) chlorine gas. (2 marks)

14 Give one use for chlorine gas. (1 mark)

15 The formulae of some ions are as follows: Na^+; O^{2-}; Mg^{2+}; Br^-. What are the chemical formulae of a) sodium bromide, b) magnesium bromide, c) sodium oxide? (3 marks)

16 How many atoms of each element are there in one molecule of a) nitric acid (HNO_3) and b) ammonium sulphate ($(NH_4)_2SO_4$)? (7 marks)

17 a) Balance the chemical equation $CH_4(g) + \_\_\_\_ O_2(g) \rightarrow CO_2(g) + \_\_\_\_ H_2O(l)$
b) What do the symbols (g) and (l) indicate? (4 marks)

Total: 55 marks

Chemistry examination questions and model answers

1 The following equation represents the formation of ammonia from nitrogren and hydrogen in the Haber Process.

$$N{\equiv}N + 3(H{-}H) \rightleftharpoons 2\left[\begin{array}{c} H{-}N{-}H \\ | \\ H \end{array}\right]$$

a) Use the following information about bond energies to calculate the overall energy change for this reaction.

Bond	Bond energy in kJ
N≡N	945
H−H	436
N−H	390

(3 marks)

Energy needed to break bonds
1 × N≡N = 1 × 945 = 945
3 × H−H = 3 × 436 = 1308
Total amount of energy put in = 2253 kJ
Energy released when new bonds form
6 × N−H = 6 × 390 = 2340 kJ
Energy change for the reaction = 2253 − 2340 = −87 kJ
Energy change = −87 kJ

The examiner has given you a full structural formula for each reactant and product so that you can see the bonds present in each. The bonds in the reactants have to be broken (energy has to be put in to do this) and new bonds have to be made in the products (energy is released when this happens).

The calculation is in three parts.

(i) You need to calculate the amount of energy needed to break the triple bond in a nitrogen molecule (N≡N), and the single bonds in each of three hydrogen molecules, (H−H).

(ii) You then need to calculate the amount of energy released when the N−H bonds are formed in each of the two molecules of ammonia formed. There are six N−H bonds in two NH_3 molecules.

(iii) The total amount of energy put in has then to be compared with the total amount of energy given out to see if the reaction is exothermic or endothermic. This is done by subtracting the energy given out from the energy put in.

As you can see, in this case, more energy is given out than is taken in. The energy change has a negative value showing that the reaction is **exothermic**.

Don't forget to check your arithmetic! In any calculation it is important to **show your working**. If you make an error with your arithmetic you can still gain marks if your method of calculation is correct.

b) The reaction is heated in a closed system. What effect would this have on the amount of ammonia formed?
Explain how you decide on your answer. *(2 marks)*

The amount of ammonia formed will be reduced because the forward reaction is exothermic. The higher temperature makes some of the ammonia decompose and change back to nitrogen and hydrogen.

Remember that in **endothermic** reactions, increasing the temperature *increases* the yield of product, but in **exothermic** reactions, increasing the temperature *decreases* the yield. Note also that this is a question about the **amount** of ammonia formed, not the rate of reaction.

2 The diagram shows the energy profiles of a reaction both with and without a catalyst present.

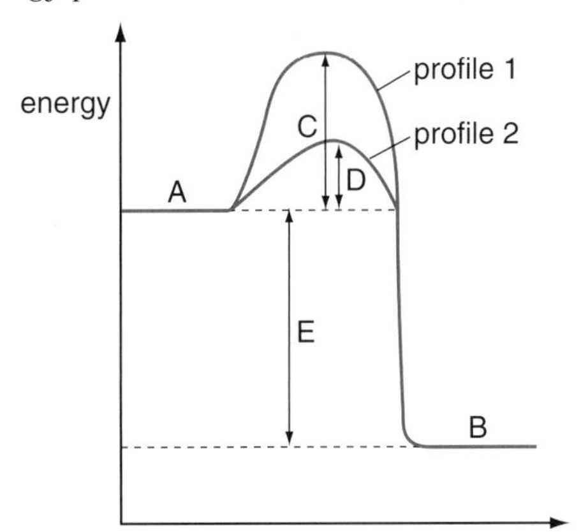

To gain full marks in this question you should write your ideas in good English. Put them into a sensible order and use the correct scientific words.

Explain, as fully as possible, what the energy diagram is showing about the two reactions. *(5 marks)*

The diagram shows the energy changes taking place as the reactants (A) are changed to the products (B). This is an exothermic process because the energy of the products is lower than the energy of the reactants. The amount of energy given out in the reaction is represented by E in the diagram.
Profile 1 is for the reaction without a catalyst and shows that the energy of activation – the energy needed to start the reaction (C) – for this reaction is quite large. Profile 2 is for the catalysed reaction and shows that the energy of activation (D) is smaller when a catalyst is present so the reaction takes place faster.

There are 5 marks for this question so the examiner will be looking for five scoring points.

The diagram has lots of labels on it, so it is advisable to refer to these in your written answer. In the specimen answer all of the letters (A to E) and the two other labels have been used.

It is also possible to present your explanation using bullet points, e.g.

- A represents the reactants and B represents the products.
- The reactions both with and without a catalyst are exothermic.
- E is the amount of energy given out during the reactions.
- Profile 1 shows that the energy of activation for the reaction without a catalyst (C) is quite large.
- Profile 2 shows that the energy of activation for the reaction with a catalyst (D) is smaller so this reaction goes faster.

If your answer has all five scoring points in it but is written in a confusing way, then one mark will be deducted for poor quality of written communication. So it is worth planning your answer before you write it down. (You could use one of the blank pages in the question paper for this.)

MODULE 9

ENERGY

Transferring heat (thermal) energy

Heat (thermal) energy is transferred from a place at higher temperature to a place at lower temperature by three methods: conduction, convection and radiation.

Conduction

In conduction vibrating particles transfer their movement energy to neighbouring particles. The hotter the material, the more kinetic energy the vibrating particles have. Conduction occurs most easily in metals where the free electrons collide with the vibrating ions. The electrons diffuse throughout the metal and transfer the kinetic energy in further collisions with the ions and other electrons in the metal.

Convection

Convection only occurs in fluids (liquids and gases). Faster moving particles are further apart, causing the hotter fluid to expand. This less dense fluid is pushed upwards by the more dense colder fluid falling. Convection currents occur as the colder fluid is heated, and is in turn pushed upwards.

Radiation

Radiation involves the transfer of energy by electromagnetic waves.

Only radiation allows the transfer of energy through a vacuum. This method does not involve particles of matter.

Emitting radiation

Hot objects give out mainly infrared radiation. The hotter the object, the more energy it radiates.

Dark, matt surfaces give out more radiation than light, shiny surfaces at the same temperature.

The dark coloured tin radiates heat energy faster than the shiny tin.

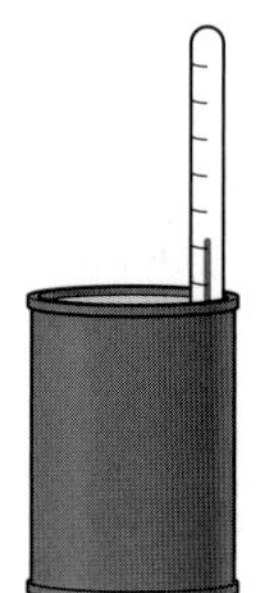

FIGURE 9.1 Dark surfaces emit more radiation than light, shiny surfaces

Absorbing radiation

Dark surfaces are good absorbers of radiation. Very little of the radiation falling on the surface is reflected.

Light, shiny surfaces are good reflectors of radiation, as they absorb little of the radiation.

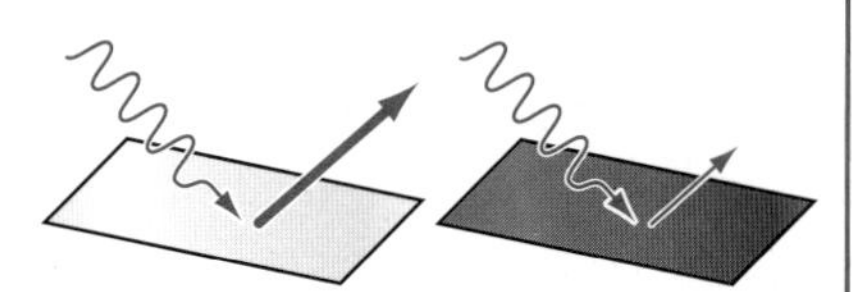

FIGURE 9.2 Dark surfaces absorb more radiation than light, shiny surfaces

How buildings lose heat energy

Heat energy from the warm inside of the house is lost to the cool outside by:

- conduction through the solid surfaces, such as walls, window panes, roof tiles, floors
- convection moving the warm air inside rooms, cavity walls or the roof space, to cooler regions
- radiation from all the exterior surfaces of the house.

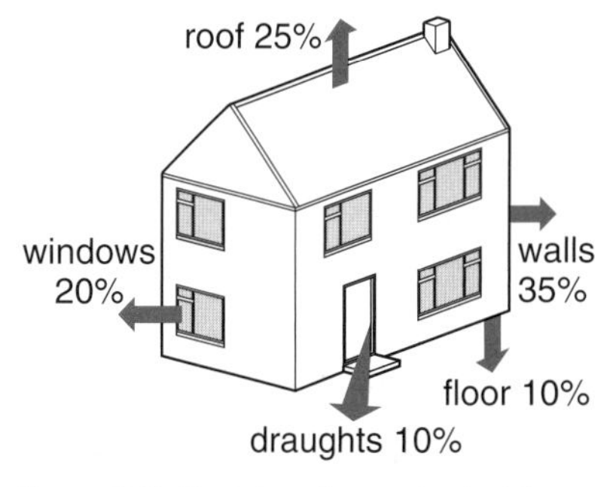

FIGURE 9.3 Heat loss from a typical house

Reducing the rate of heat loss from buildings

The heat energy is lost less quickly from a warm building by:

- conduction when the solid surface is thicker, or is made from a poor conductor or is in contact with a very bad conductor such as air
- convection when the movement of air is restricted
- radiation when the outer surface is light coloured and shiny.

Insulating buildings

The house in Figure 9.3 will lose heat energy less quickly if it is insulated as shown in the table.

Type of insulation	Cost to install insulation	Energy lost/ second in watts before insulating	Energy lost/ second in watts after insulating
Double glazing Air between the glass panes cannot move, so reducing heat loss by convection. Also air is a poor conductor/good insulator.	£4000	1400	840
Cavity wall insulation Foam fills the space between the two walls. The air pockets in the foam reduce convection and conduction.	£600	2450	1250
Loft insulation Mineral wool fibres trap air, reducing convection and conduction.	£240	1750	950
Floor insulation Thick carpets have air pockets which reduce convection and conduction.	£700	700	420
Draught-proofing Thick curtains stop air moving. The air layer between window and curtain acts as an insulator. Draught excluders stop warm air escaping by convection.	£150	700	350

In this example, cavity wall insulation has the greatest effect, conserving 1200 W.

If the house owner saves £200 on heating bills in one year when cavity wall insulation is installed, it will take three years to pay back this outlay.

$$\text{Pay-back time (years)} = \frac{\text{total cost}}{\text{saving in 1 year}} = \frac{£600}{£200} = 3$$

CHECK YOUR UNDERSTANDING

❶ Which method of heat transfer uses the wholesale movement of matter? Why does this not occur in solids?

❷ Explain why
a) the bonnets of racing cars are often painted black
b) houses in hot countries are often painted white.

❸ What are the ways of reducing heat loss from the windows of a house?

❹ The house owner installs floor insulation, giving a reduction of £50 in their heating bill. How long will it take to pay back this new installation?

Transferring electrical energy

Electrical energy is easily transferred as other forms of energy by different devices. Some examples are shown in the table.

Energy input to device	Device	Energy output from device
electrical	heater, immersion heater, cooker, hairdryer	heat (thermal) energy
electrical	filament lamp, TV screen	light energy
electrical	loudspeaker, bell	sound energy
electrical	electric motors, e.g. in a vacuum cleaner, CD driver	movement (kinetic) energy

REMEMBER – All forms of energy are measured in joules (J).

Many devices are designed to transfer electrical energy as more than one form of energy.

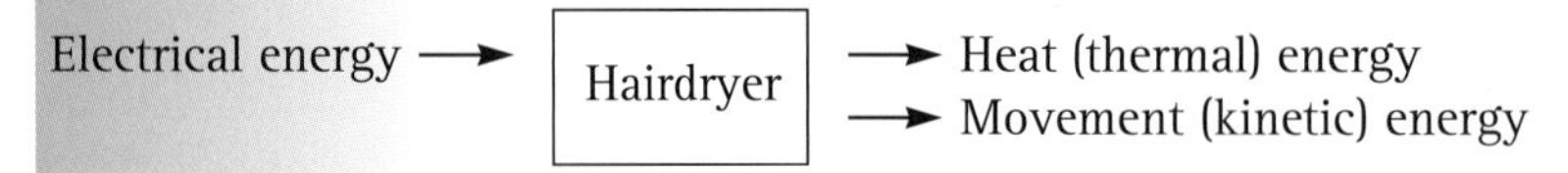

The energy needed to lift an object against the force of gravity is transferred as gravitational potential energy.
e.g. an electric lift transfers

electric energy ⟶ gravitational potential energy

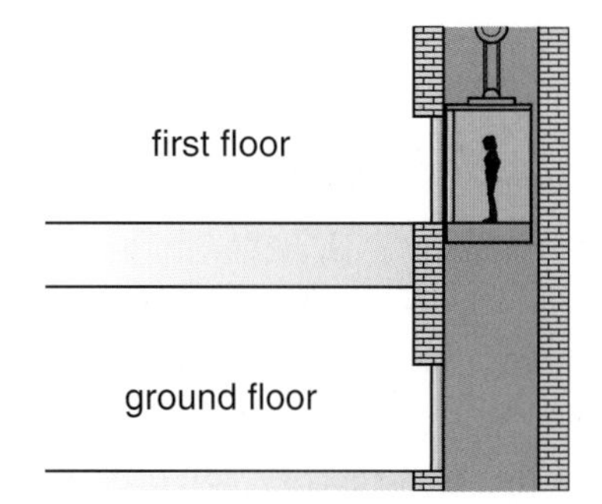

Figure 9.4 A person in a lift on the first floor has increased gravitational potential energy

Gravitational potential energy is the energy an object has due to its height above the Earth's surface.

Measuring amounts of energy

change in gravitational potential energy = weight × change in vertical height
(joules, J) (newtons, N) (metres, m)

Example: The total weight of a man and a lift is 2800 N. What is the gain in gravitational potential energy when the lift moves 5 metres?

change in GPE = weight × change in vertical height
= 2800 × 5
= 14 000 J (or 14 kJ, where 1 kJ = 1000 J)

LEARN this equation and the units.

How much electrical energy a device transfers depends on:

- the power of the device (how fast the device transfers energy)
- how long the device is switched on for.

$$\text{power} = \frac{\text{energy transferred}}{\text{time taken}}$$

power in watts (W)
energy transferred in joules (J)
time taken in seconds (s)

This equation will be given in an examination question.

1 watt is the transfer of 1 joule of energy in 1 second.

1000 W = 1 kilowatt (kW)

The power of the lift in Figure 9.4 is 8000 W (8 kW). So the lift transfers 8000 J of electrical energy in 1 s.

The amount of energy transferred is calculated by rearranging the power equation.

energy transferred = power × time taken

Example: A lift of power 8000 W takes 4 s to move between the first and second floor of a building. How much electrical energy is transferred in this time?

energy transferred = power × time taken
= 8000 × 4
= 32 000 J

Paying for electrical energy

When dealing with large amounts of electrical energy, another unit for energy is used. This is the kilowatt-hour (kWh).

Example: Calculate the energy transferred in kWh, by a 2000 W heater connected to the mains electrical supply for 3 hours.

energy transferred = power × time
(kilowatt-hours, kWh) (kilowatts, kW) (hours, h)
= 2 × 3
= 6 kWh

This equation will be given in an examination question.

Electricity companies calculate the cost of providing electrical energy using the kilowatt-hour as the unit. If the price for 1 unit is 8p, what is the total cost of using the heater?

total cost = number of units (kWh) × cost per unit

$= 6 \times 8$
$= 48\text{p}$

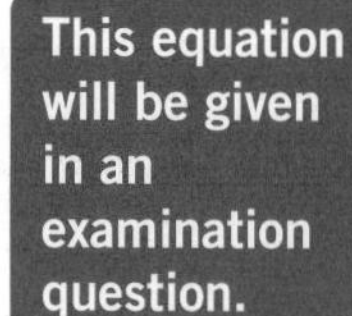

Example:

	New meter reading on 1 March	Old meter reading on 1 December
LOW	42649 kWh	40526 kWh
NORMAL	39736	39139

What is the cost of the electricity supplied at the low night rate of 2p/unit during these 3 months?

number of units = 42649 − 40526 = 2123 units (kWh)
total cost = 2123 × 2 = 4246 p = £42.46

CHECK YOUR UNDERSTANDING

1. Name a device that is designed to transfer electrical energy as a) sound energy, b) kinetic energy, c) gravitational potential energy.
2. What is the gravitational potential energy gained by a 600 N load lifted 10 m by a crane?
3. What are the two units used to measure electrical energy?
4. A 500 W drill is used for 5 minutes. How much electrical energy is transferred?
5. Use the two normal meter readings above to calculate the cost of the electricity supplied at the normal rate of 8p per unit.

Efficiency

As energy is transferred, only part of it ends up in the form for which the device was designed. This is the useful energy. The rest of the energy is wasted, usually as heat. The wasted energy spreads out to the surroundings, which become warmer. The wasted energy cannot be saved for further useful energy transfers.

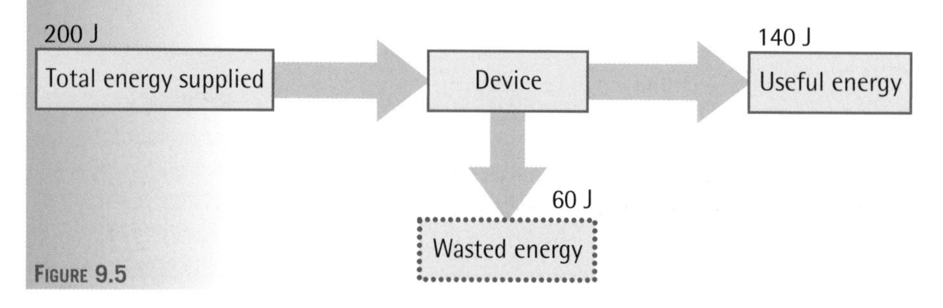

FIGURE 9.5

The more useful energy that the device transfers, the more efficient the device.

$$\text{efficiency} = \frac{\text{useful energy transferred by the device}}{\text{total energy supplied to the device}}$$

This equation will be given in an examination question.

Example: An electric motor has a power rating of 600 W. In 10 seconds it transfers electric energy as 4500 J of useful kinetic energy.

(i) What is the electrical energy supplied to the motor?
(ii) What is the efficiency of this device?
(iii) How much energy has been wasted?
(iv) What has happened to the wasted energy?

(i) Electrical energy supplied $= 600 \times 10 = 6000$ J

(ii) Efficiency $= \frac{\text{useful energy transferred by the device}}{\text{total energy supplied to the device}}$

$= \frac{4500}{6000}$

$= 0.75$ (as a percentage, this efficiency $= 0.75 \times 100\% = 75\%$)

(iii) The wasted energy = total energy − useful energy = 6000 − 4500 = 1500 J

(iv) The wasted energy transfers as heat energy to the motor and to the surrounding air.

CHECK YOUR UNDERSTANDING

Lamp	Light energy output in 1 second	Electric energy input in 1 second
A	0.3 J	15 J
B	1.3 J	20 J

❶ The table compares two lamps.
a) Which lamp is more efficient?
b) What is lamp A's efficiency?
c) How much energy does lamp B waste in 5 seconds?

❷ A heating system uses electric energy at the rate of 5000 W. It is 80% efficient.
a) What is the electric energy supplied in 1 hour? (*Hint*: 1 hour = 3600 seconds)
b) What is the useful energy transfer in this time?

Environmental effects of using fossil and nuclear fuels

Greenhouse effect

Radiation from the Sun passes through the atmosphere to the Earth's surface. The long wavelength infrared radiation reflected from the surface of the Earth cannot pass through the atmosphere, back into space. This energy is absorbed by carbon dioxide (CO_2) gas in the atmosphere, heating the atmosphere.

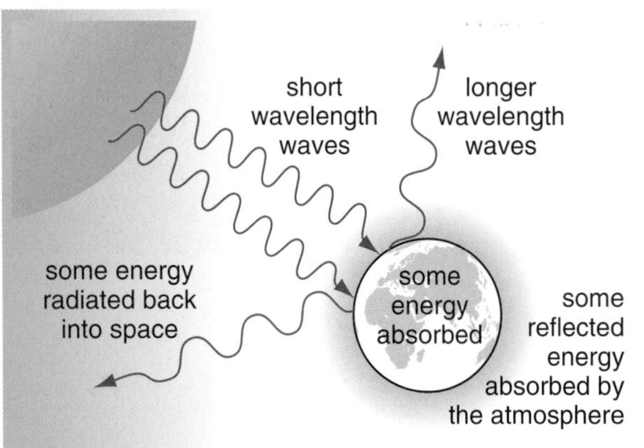

FIGURE 9.6 Some of the Sun's energy is reflected back into space

When fossil fuels are burned, the amount of carbon dioxide in the atmosphere increases.

This increases the greenhouse effect, causing increased global warming.

Acid rain

When coal and oil are burned, they produce sulphur dioxide (SO_2) gas. This gas can be removed before the waste gases from a power station are released into the atmosphere, or the sulphur can be removed before burning the fuels. However, this increases the cost of producing electricity. Sulphur dioxide dissolves in rain water to form acid rain. Acid rain is harmful to plants and animals.

Nuclear fuels

Nuclear fuels do not produce waste gases that cause acid rain or increase the greenhouse effect. But the waste products from a nuclear power station can be radioactive for a very long time. These wastes are stored in strong containers so that they do not contaminate the environment.

Normally, very little radiation or radioactive material is released by a working nuclear power station or the stored waste. If an accident happened, however, radioactive material could spread over a very large area and affect it for a long time.

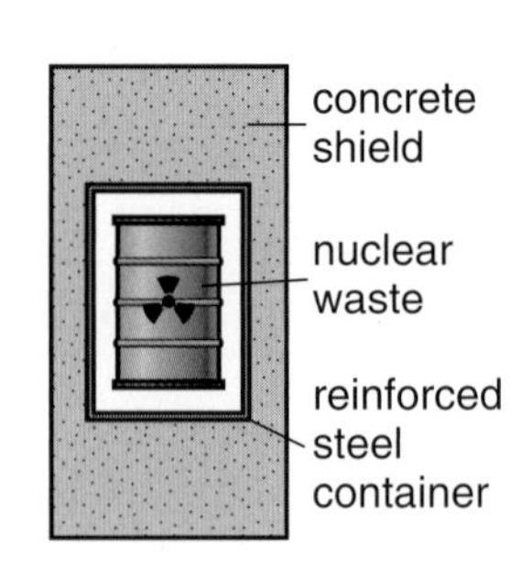

FIGURE 9.7 Storing nuclear waste

CHECK YOUR UNDERSTANDING

1. Which gases cause:
   a) the greenhouse effect, and b) acid rain?
2. Why must the waste from nuclear fuels be stored safely in strong containers?
3. Give one reason why sulphur dioxide gas is not removed from the waste gases produced by a coal- or oil-fired power station.
4. What is the environmental advantage in using nuclear fuels in preference to coal?

Generating electricity

Power stations

Most power stations in Britain use the energy from a non-renewable fuel to heat water. Figure 9.8 shows the stages in generating electricity.

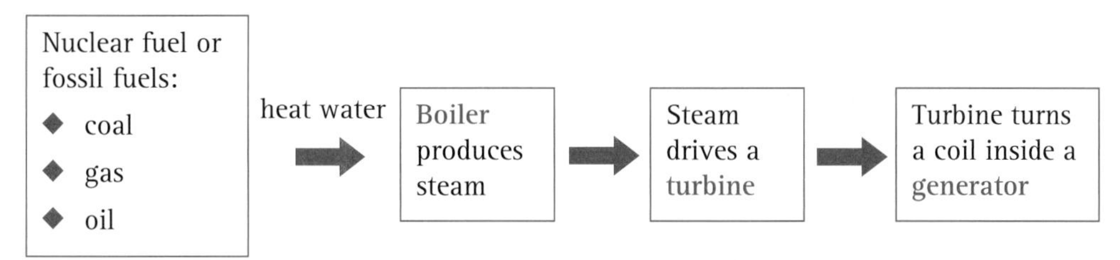

FIGURE 9.8 Generating electricity

Some smaller gas power stations can drive their turbines with hot air.

The time it takes to start up a power station so that it begins to generate electricity depends on the type of power station:

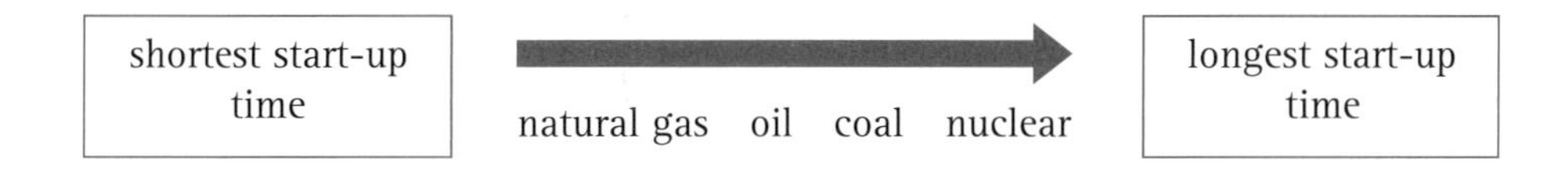

A geothermal power station uses the hot water in the rocks from certain areas just under the Earth's surface. This water rises to the surface as steam, and is used directly to drive turbines. Sometimes this renewable resource is only used to provide local heating.

Most other renewable energy resources provide movement (kinetic energy) to turn the turbines. See Figure 9.9.

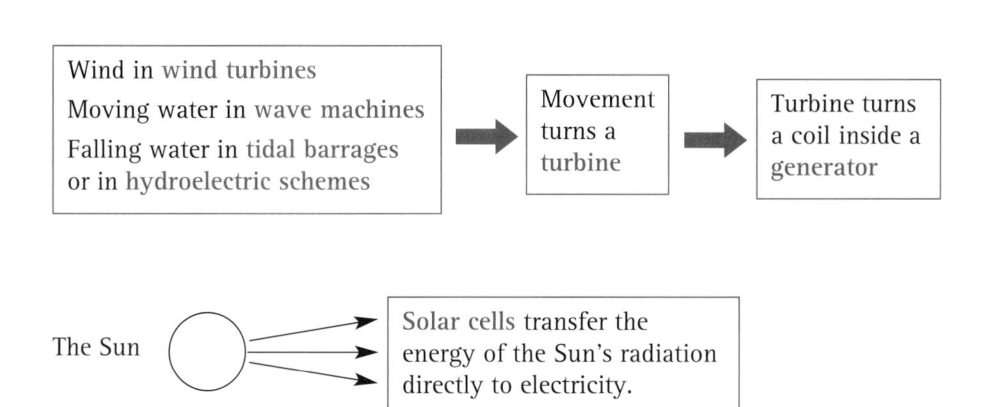

FIGURE 9.9 How renewable sources generate electricity

The table below compares the advantages and disadvantages for each resource used in the large-scale production of electric power.

Resource	Advantages	Disadvantages	Financial costs
Nuclear Fuel	No polluting gases produced. A small amount of fuel gives a large amount of energy.	Non-renewable energy resource. Some radioactive waste must be stored for thousands of years. Serious accidents may release radiation over a large area.	Building and decommissioning costs very high.
Fossil fuels – coal, oil, natural gas	Produce electricity when it is needed, they do not depend on the weather. Gas-burning power stations can be switched on and off quickly.	Non-renewable energy resource. Burning coal, oil and natural gas adds carbon dioxide, a greenhouse gas, to the atmosphere. Burning coal and oil adds sulphur dioxide to the atmosphere causing acid rain.	
Wind	Renewable energy resource. Low running costs. No polluting gases produced.	Wind generators can spoil the landscape and cause unwanted noise. Unreliable – electricity is only generated when there is a strong enough wind.	High installation costs for large construction as energy is dilute (a little energy is spread out over large mass of air).
Tides	Renewable energy resource. Low running costs. No polluting gases produced.	Very expensive to build. Destroys the habitat of wading birds. Electricity is only generated at certain times of the day.	Very high installation costs as energy is dilute.
Waves	Renewable energy resource. Low running costs. No polluting gases produced.	Difficult to build a power station strong enough to stand up to the power of rough seas.	High installation costs as energy is dilute.
Hydroelectric	Renewable energy resource. Can be switched on and off quickly. Can be used to store energy. No polluting gases produced.	Large areas of land may be flooded.	High installation costs.
Solar	Renewable energy resource. Ideal for remote places. Ideal when only a small amount of electricity is needed. No polluting gases produced.	Expensive to set up in large numbers. The amount of electricity produced depends on the brightness of the light.	
Geothermal	Massive amounts of energy are available.	Unless there are natural geysers it can be expensive and inefficient to generate electricity.	

CHECK YOUR UNDERSTANDING

❶ Which energy resource:
   a) reduces land space for forestry or farming?
   b) depends on a monthly and yearly cycle?
   c) allows a fossil fuel power station to start up most quickly?

❷ Which power stations are used to supply electricity at peak demands?

❸ Give an example of where a solar panel is used even though it is at high cost.

❹ The table compares the costs of two ways of providing electricity at an average 500 kWh/year.

	Installation cost	Fuel cost per kWh	Maintenance cost per kWh
Solar panel	£1000	0p	0p
Petrol generator	£250	20p	10p

   a) What is the cost of running the petrol generator for one year?
   b) In how many years will the total cost be the same for each installation?

Topic Test

1 a) Copy and complete these sentences explaining why an attic room feels cold in the winter and hot in the summer.

In winter, the heat energy is ______ from the room to the ______ outside mainly by ______ and ______ from the roof. The rate of energy entering the attic is ______ than the rate of energy transfer out of the attic, so the temperature ______. In summer, the roof ______ energy from the Sun at a ______ rate than energy going out, so the attic becomes ______. (9 marks)

b) A house has an insulating lining fitted to the inside of the roof. This costs £300. In one year, there is a saving of £60 to the heating bill for the attic room. How long will it take to pay back the initial cost? (2 marks)

2 a) What are the energy transfers for a hydroelectric scheme?

b) One such scheme, generating 200 kW, is 40% efficient.
   i) What is the electrical energy generated each second?
   ii) What is the total energy available each second?
   iii) How much power is wasted? (5 marks)

energy transferred = power × time

$$\text{efficiency} = \frac{\text{useful energy transferred by device}}{\text{total energy supplied to device}}$$

3 A housing estate is provided with hot water and heating from a central supply. This is attached to an oil-fired power station.

a) How does this increase the efficiency of the power station?

b) What is the environmental advantage in using such a scheme?

c) What problems will there be in transferring hot water to the houses?

d) Describe how these problems could be solved. (4 marks)

4 The cost of using electricity is 7p for 1 unit. From these readings find a) the amount of units used, b) the total cost.

total cost = number of units × cost per unit

New meter reading

6	8	9	5	7

kWh

Old meter reading

6	7	4	3	2

kWh

(2 marks)

5 The bar graph shows the cost of producing electricity from different fuels.

a) How much more expensive, in pence/unit, is the cost of electricity from nuclear fuel, than from coal?

b) Nuclear fuel is cheaper than coal. Give two reasons why the electricity production cost is much greater for nuclear fuel than it is for coal.

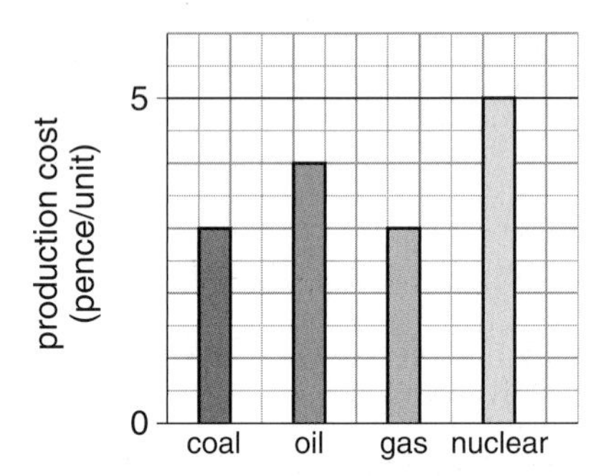

FIGURE 9.10

(3 marks)

6 A wind driven pump lifts water from a deep well. The power obtained from the wind for this device is 200 W. In 24 seconds, 5 kg of water is raised to the top.

a) What is the gravitational potential energy gained by 5 kg of water?

b) What is the rate at which this energy was transferred?

c) What is the efficiency of the device?

d) If the device continues to work at the same rate how long will it take to lift 25 kg of water?

On Earth, 5 kg of water weighs 50 N.

$$\text{power} = \frac{\text{energy transferred}}{\text{time taken}}$$

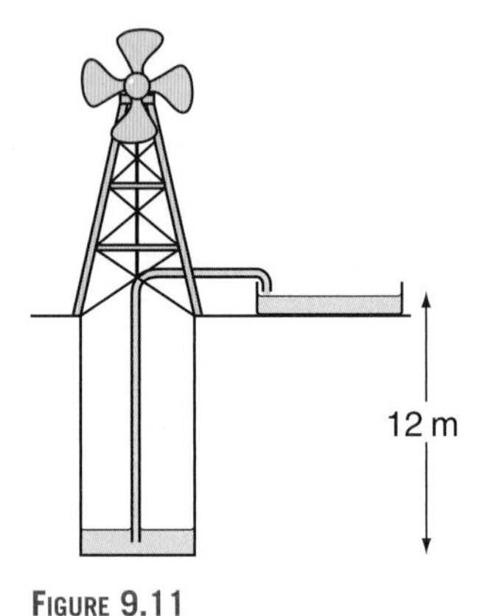

FIGURE 9.11

(5 marks)

Total: 30 marks

MODULE 10

ELECTRICITY

Circuits

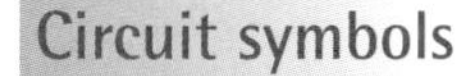

Circuit symbols

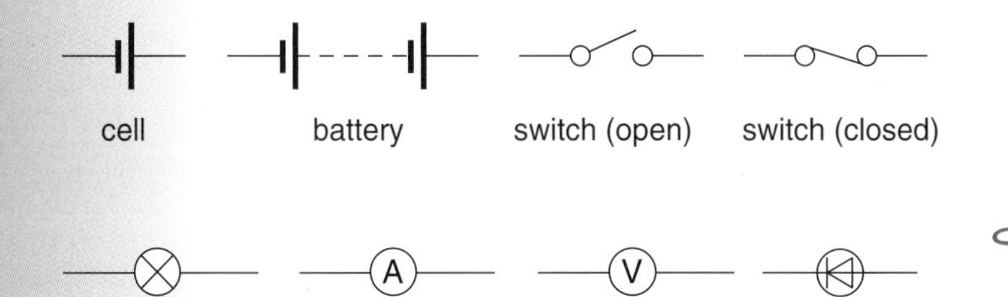

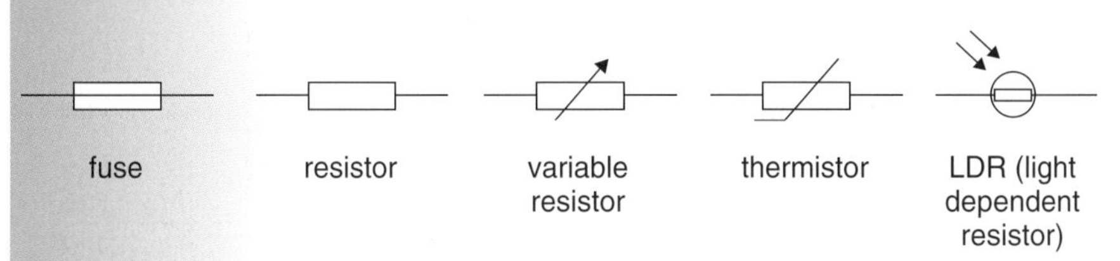

FIGURE 10.1 Electrical components and their symbols

LEARN these circuit symbols. You may be asked to draw and/or interpret circuit diagrams using them.

REMEMBER – A battery is two or more cells joined together.

Series circuits

The current in a series circuit has only one path it can take. So the same current (I) must flow through each component and wire in the circuit. Adding more components to the circuit will increase the resistance of the circuit and decrease the current.

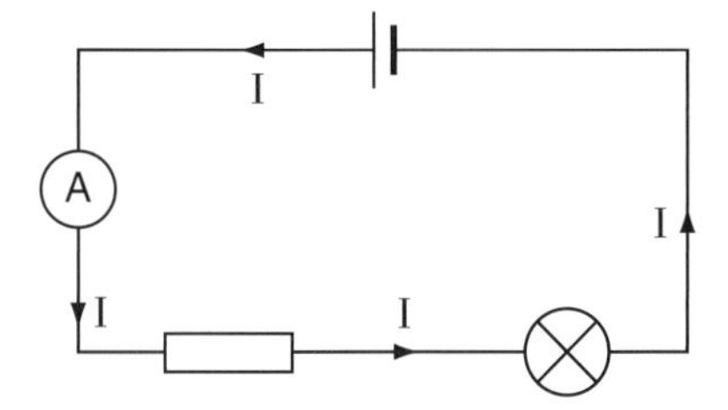

FIGURE 10.2 A series circuit

The total resistance of a series circuit is worked out by adding together the resistances of all the individual components.

When components are joined in series, the potential difference (p.d.) of the power supply is shared between the components in the circuit.

REMEMBER – Potential difference (p.d.) is the same as voltage.

total p.d. across all components = p.d. of the power supply

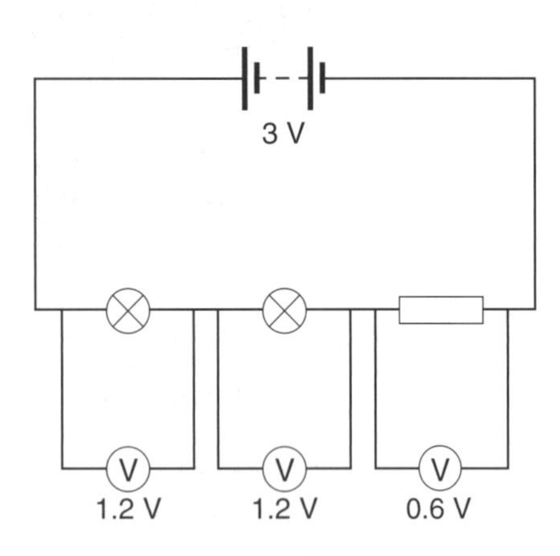

FIGURE 10.3 Measuring the p.d. across components in a series circuit

When cells are joined in series, the total potential difference is the sum of the individual potential differences. Remember, this only works if the cells are joined correctly, positive (+) to negative (−).

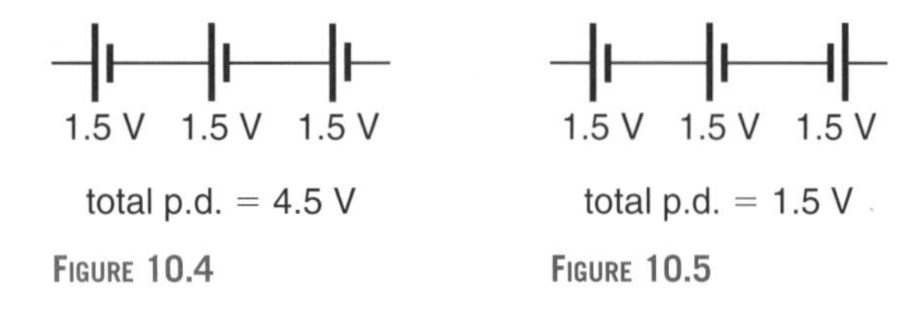

FIGURE 10.4 **FIGURE 10.5**

Parallel circuits

For components joined in parallel:

- The potential difference across each component is the same.
- The bigger the resistance of a component, the smaller the current flowing flowing through it.
- The total current flowing in the whole circuit is the sum of the currents through the individual components.

e.g. $I = I_1 + I_2$

$0.4\text{ A} = 0.3\text{ A} + 0.1\text{ A}$

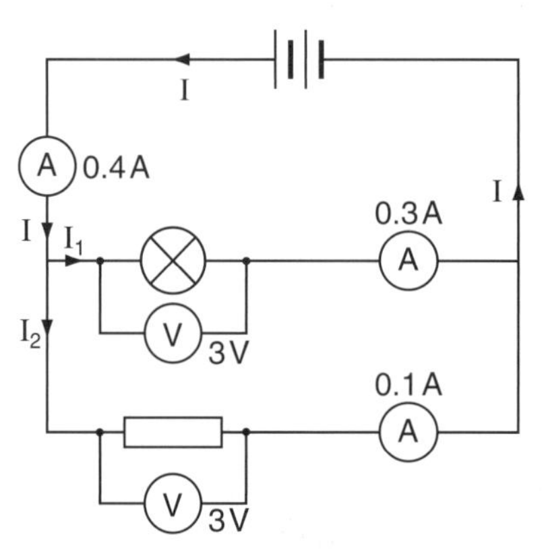

FIGURE 10.6 A parallel circuit

Resistance

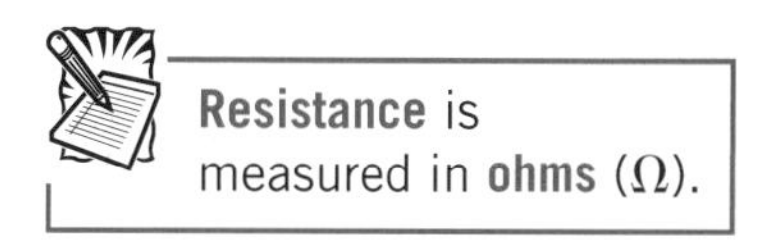

The current through a component depends on the potential difference across the component and the resistance of the component.

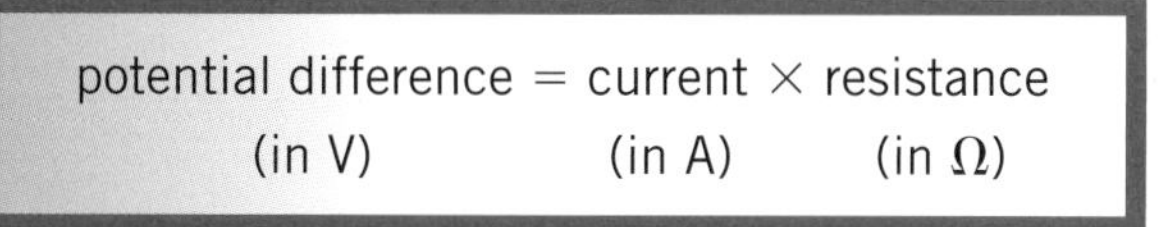

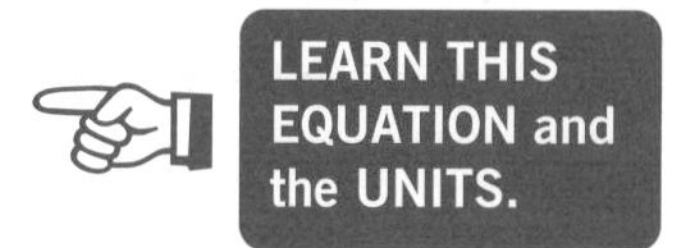

Light dependent resistor (LDR)

The resistance of a light dependent resistor goes down as the intensity of the light hitting it goes up (Figure 10.7).

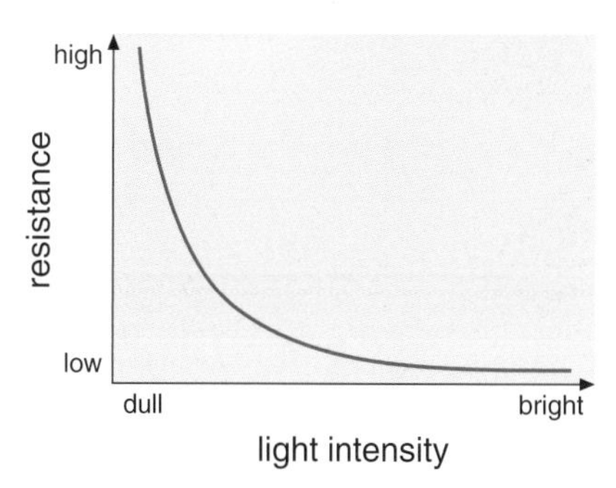

Figure 10.7 Variation of resistance with light intensity for an LDR

Thermistor

The resistance of a thermistor goes down as the temperature of the thermistor goes up (Figure 10.8).

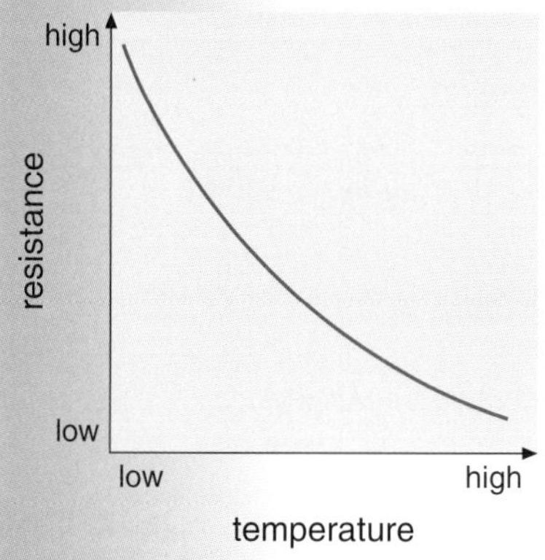

Figure 10.8 Variation of resistance with temperature for a thermistor

Current–voltage graphs

The circuit in Figure 10.9 can be used to investigate how the current through a component depends on the voltage (p.d.) across the component.

The circuit can also be used to measure the resistance of a component.

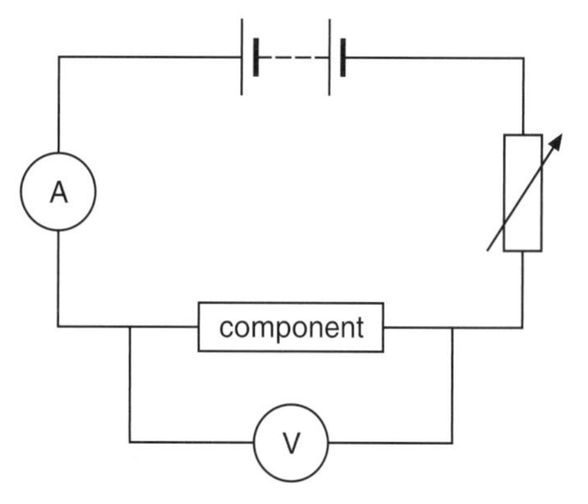

Figure 10.9

Resistor at constant temperature

The current through a resistor is directly proportional to the voltage across the resistor. (So the resistance is constant.)

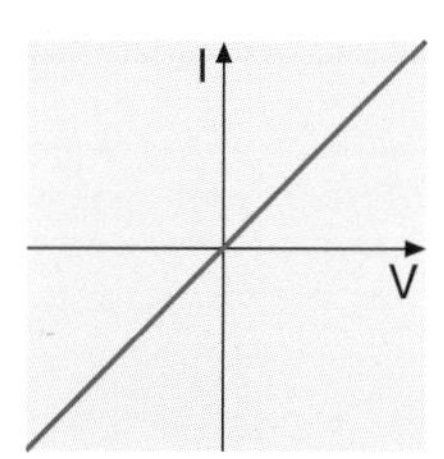

Figure 10.10 Current and potential difference for a resistor

Filament lamp

Increasing the voltage makes the filament in the lamp brighter and hotter. As the temperature of the filament goes up, the resistance of the lamp goes up.

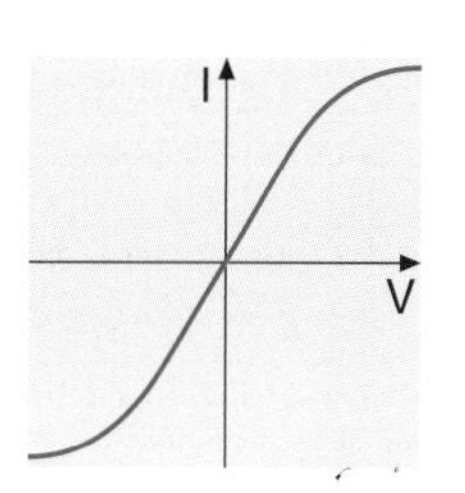

Figure 10.11 Current and potential difference for a filament lamp

Diode

Diodes only let current flow in one direction. In the reverse direction diodes have a very high resistance so no current flows.

You should be able to recognise and/or draw the graphs in Figures 10.10 to 10.12.

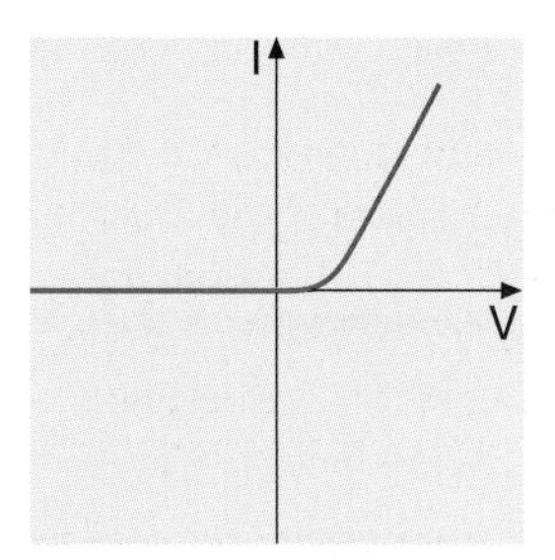

FIGURE 10.12 Current and potential difference for a diode

CHECK YOUR UNDERSTANDING

1. Why can a diode be used to stop current flowing the wrong way in a circuit?
2. The current through a thermistor at 40°C is 0.02 A. The resistance of the thermistor is 600 Ω.
   a) Calculate the voltage across the thermistor.
   b) What happens to the resistance of the thermistor as its temperature goes up?
3. Draw (without looking) the current–voltage graph for a) a filament lamp and b) a diode.
4. How does the current through an LDR change with light intensity?

Electricity and magnetism

When an electric current flows through a coil of wire, the coil becomes an electromagnet. Reversing the current reverses the north and south poles of the electromagnet.

The d.c. electric motor

When a current flows through the coil it becomes an electromagnet. This magnetic field interacts with the permanent magnetic field. Each side of the coil experiences a force, but in opposite directions. So one side goes up, the other side goes down and the coil turns. This is the basis of an electric motor.

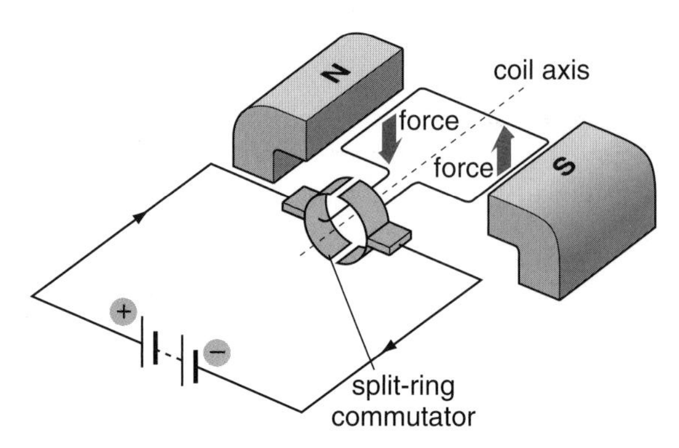

FIGURE 10.13 A d.c. electric motor

The circuit breaker

This is a switch that breaks a circuit when the current gets too high. The type of circuit breaker in Figure 10.14 uses an electromagnet. If a fault makes the current increase, the electromagnet becomes strong enough to pull across the iron catch. This opens the contacts, switching off the circuit. Once the fault is repaired, the contacts are closed by pressing the reset button.

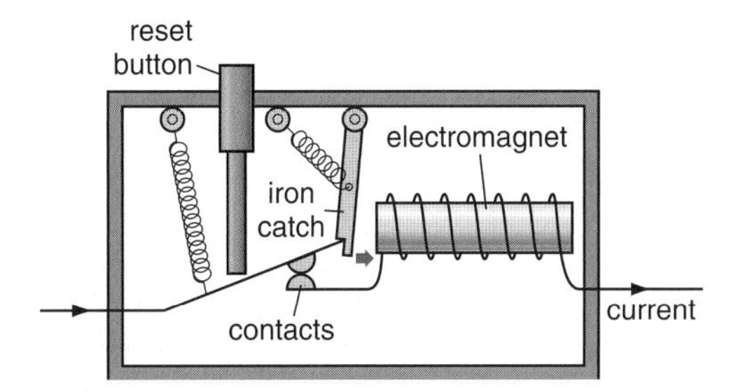

FIGURE 10.14 A circuit breaker

CHECK YOUR UNDERSTANDING

1. Explain why the coil in an electric motor turns when a current flows through it.
2. Suggest why it may be better to use a circuit breaker rather than a fuse in a mains circuit.

Static electricity

Rubbing different insulating materials together will usually make them become electrically charged. This is because electrons move off one material on to the other. The material that loses electrons becomes positively charged and the one gaining electrons negatively charged.

Charging a polythene rod

The rod gains electrons from the cloth. The rod becomes negative.

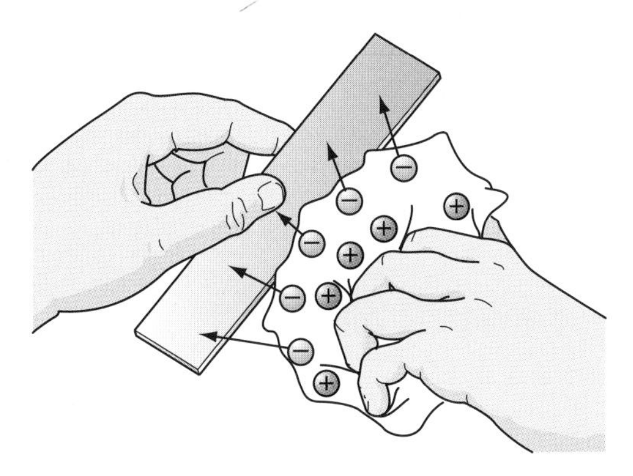

The cloth loses electrons. The cloth becomes positive.

FIGURE 10.15 Charging a polythene rod

Charging a Perspex rod

The rod loses electrons to the cloth. The rod becomes positive.

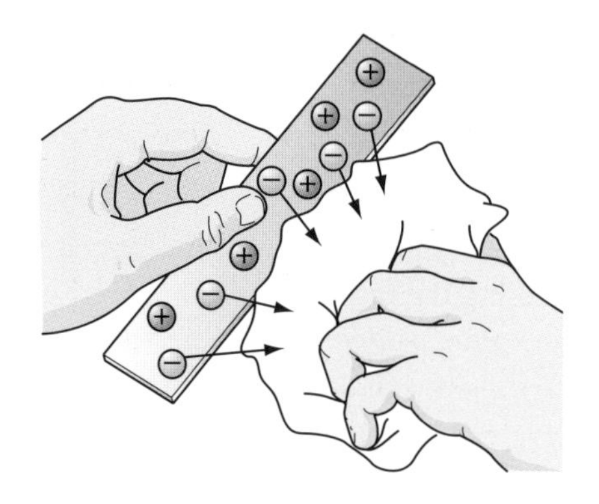

The cloth gains electrons. The cloth becomes negative.

FIGURE 10.16 Charging a Perspex rod

Charged objects exert forces on each other:

- Objects with the same charge repel (+ and + OR − and −).
- Objects with opposite charge attract (+ and −).

If the objects are close enough, the forces may make them move. Charged objects can also attract small uncharged objects that are nearby. For example, a charged nylon comb will attract dry hair.

Uses of static electricity

Electrostatic smoke precipitator

This is used to remove smoke from waste gases.

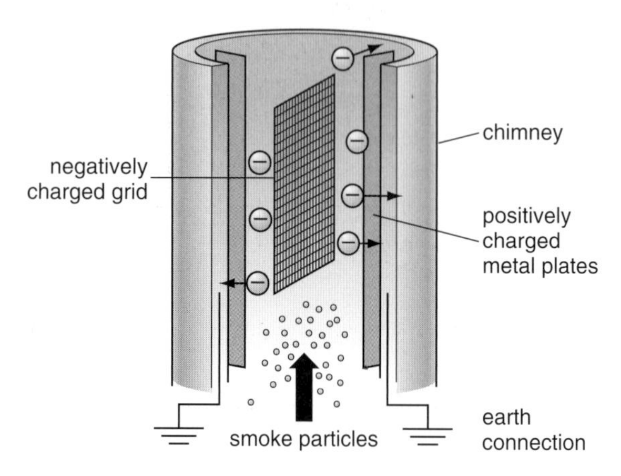

FIGURE 10.17 An electrostatic smoke precipitator

1 The gases and smoke pass a charged grid.

2 The smoke particles gain the same charge as the grid.

3 The smoke particles are repelled by the grid and attracted to the oppositely charged metal plates where they stick to the plates.

4 The metal plates are knocked so the smoke particles fall and can be collected.

Making a photocopy

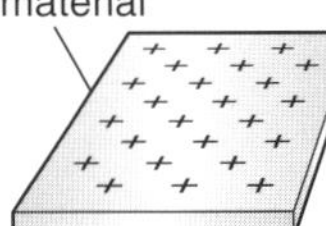

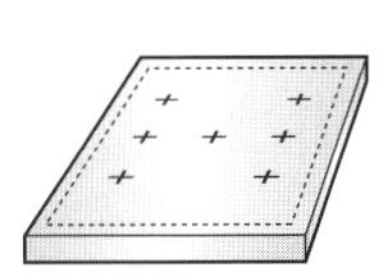

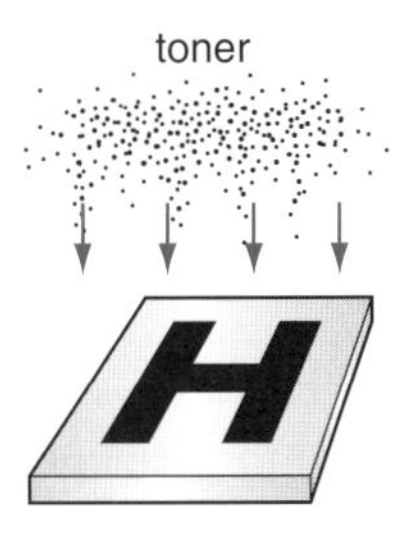

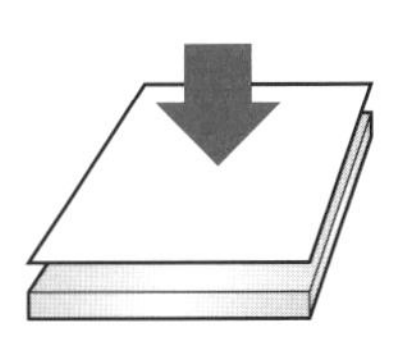

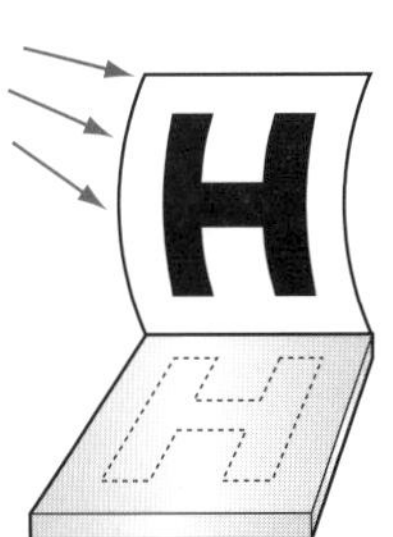

FIGURE 10.18 Making a photocopy

1 The light-sensitive (photoconductive) copying plate is given a charge.
2 The page to be copied is placed above the plate and lit with a strong light.
3 Where light hits the plate, the charge leaks away.
4 The pattern of the charge left on the plate is the same as the dark parts of the original page.
5 Black powder (toner) is attracted to the charge still on the plate.
6 The toner is transferred to a sheet of paper.
7 The paper is heated to make the toner stick.
8 The sheet of paper is a photocopy of the original.

Dangerous situations

If the charge on an object is allowed to build up, the voltage (potential difference) between the object and earth increases. When the voltage is high enough, a spark may jump from the object to a nearby earthed conductor. The spark could then cause an explosion.

Delivering fuel

Tankers deliver large amounts of fuel to garages and aircraft. As the fuel flows through the delivery pipe both the pipe and the fuel become charged. To stop the charge building up, the tanker is earthed (joined to the ground by a metal wire). The charge flows safely through the wire to earth.

Lightning

A tall building is usually protected by a lightning conductor. This is a thick strip of copper (a good conductor) that runs from the roof of the building into the ground. If lightning did strike, the charge would flow through the lightning conductor to earth without damaging the building.

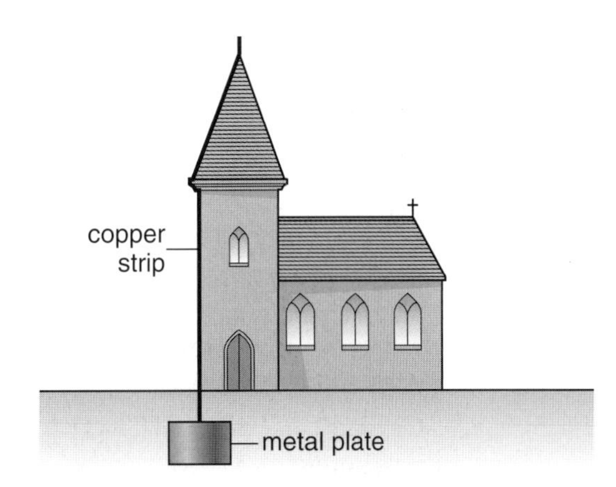

FIGURE 10.19 A lightning conductor

CHECK YOUR UNDERSTANDING

❶ Explain what is meant by something being 'earthed'.

❷ Will two charged ebonite rods placed close together attract or repel? Explain the reason for your answer.

❸ A charged balloon is placed close to some small pieces of paper. What happens?

Mains electricity

Many electrical appliances work by plugging them into the 230 volt mains electricity supply. The cable joining the appliance to the plug and the plug itself are designed to make the appliance safe to use.

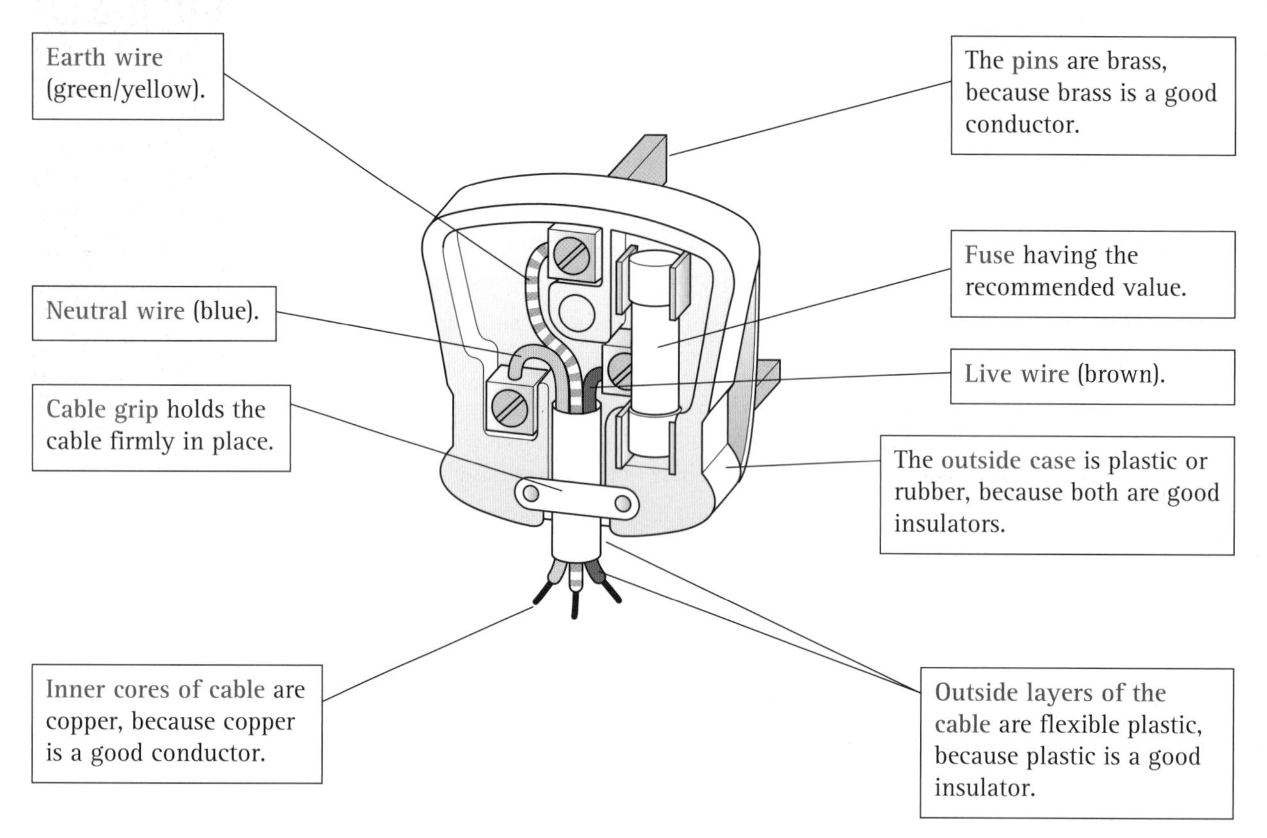

Figure 10.20 A correctly wired three-pin plug

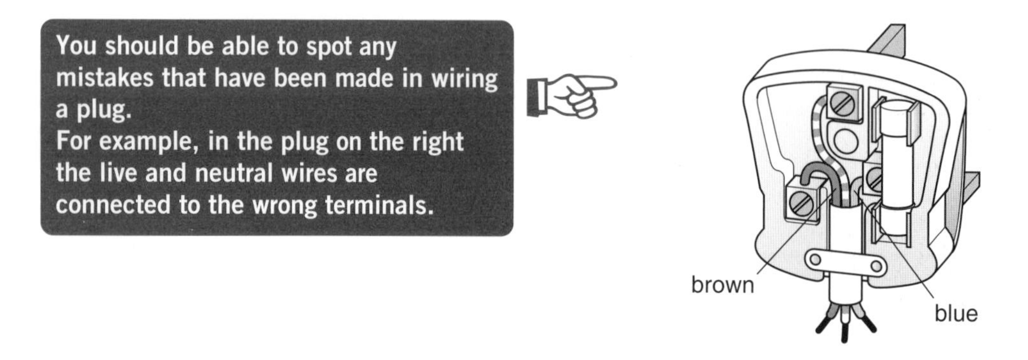

Figure 10.21 An incorrectly wired plug

Fuses

A fuse is a thin piece of wire that lets a current up to a certain value flow through it. Above this value the fuse will overheat and melt. This breaks the circuit and switches off the current. To protect an appliance, the fuse should have a value close to but higher than the normal working current of the appliance.

Earthing

All appliances with a metal case should be earthed. The earth wire (yellow/green) joins the earth pin of the plug to the metal case of the appliance.

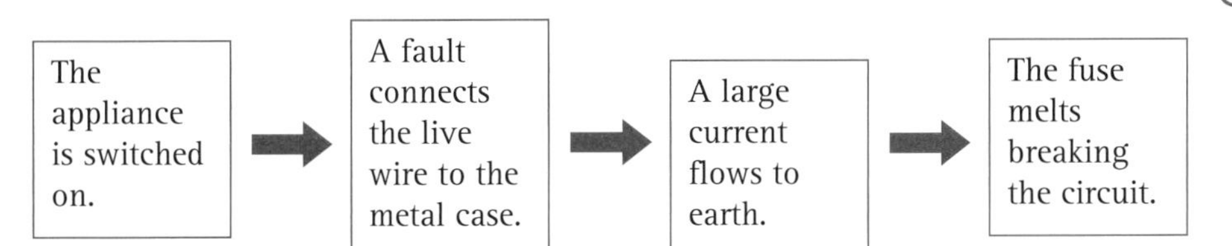

Mains electricity is dangerous; it is important it is used correctly. You should be able to recognise from diagrams situations that could be dangerous. For example, switching an appliance on or off with wet hands.

Alternating current (a.c.)

An alternating current (a.c.) in a circuit is constantly reversing direction. The number of times the current (or voltage) changes direction in one second gives the frequency of the supply.

Frequency of the UK mains supply = 50 hertz (Hz)

The live terminal of the a.c. mains supply alternates between a positive and negative voltage when compared with the neutral terminal. The neutral terminal stays at a voltage close to zero.

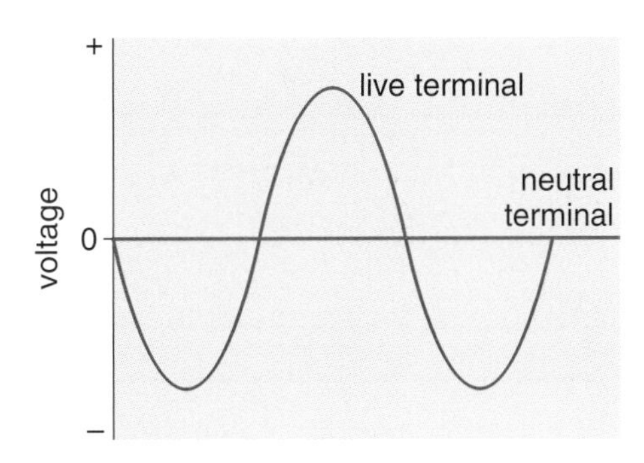

FIGURE 10.22

An oscilloscope (CRO) is used to compare the frequency and peak voltage (maximum) of a.c. supplies. (The controls on the CRO must stay the same.)

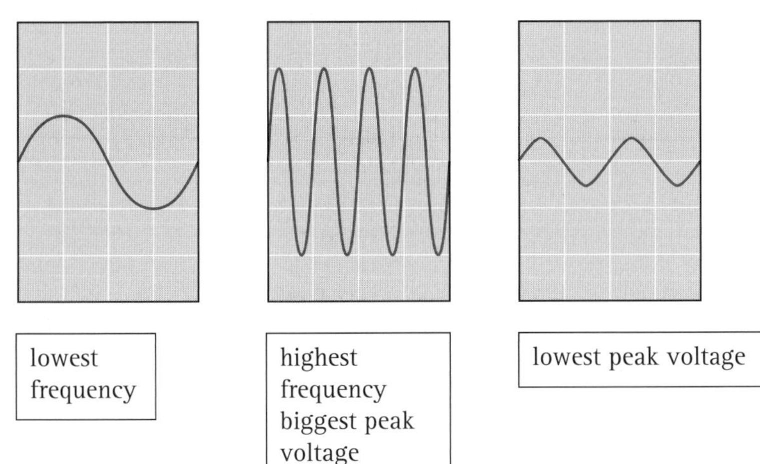

FIGURE 10.23 CRO traces for a.c. supplies

Direct current (d.c.)

A direct current (d.c.) always flows in the same direction. A cell or battery gives a steady direct current.

The oscilloscope (CRO) trace for a steady d.c. supply is a horizontal line. The bigger the voltage of the supply the further the line is from the centre of the screen.

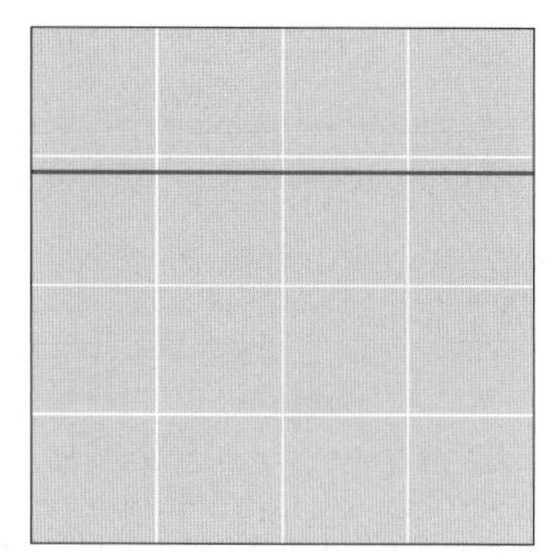

FIGURE 10.24 The wave trace on a CRO for a d.c. supply

CHECK YOUR UNDERSTANDING

1. What is the colour of the insulation on the neutral wire inside a cable?
2. Why is brass used to make the pins of a plug?
3. What material is used to make the case of a plug?
4. Draw the oscilloscope trace for an a.c. supply.
5. Explain how a fuse works.

Electrolysis

An **ion** is an atom that has lost or gained one or more electrons.

Some chemical compounds conduct electricity when they are melted or dissolved in water. The compounds conduct because they contain ions. The negatively charged ions move to the positive electrode, and the positively charged ions move to the negative electrode. When the ions reach the electrodes, simpler substances, either gases or solids, are released.

During the electrolysis of copper sulphate solution the substances released are:

- copper (solid) at the negative electrode.
- oxygen (gas) at the positive electrode.

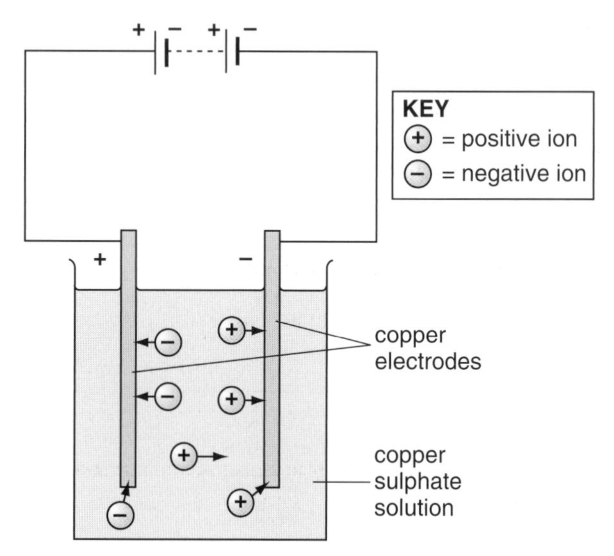

FIGURE 10.25 Electrolysis of copper sulphate

The quantity of substance released at each electrode is directly proportional to:

- the current flowing
- the time for which the current flows.

For example the table shows the quantity of copper released at the negative electrode from copper sulphate solution.

Current in amps	Time in seconds	Mass of copper deposited on the negative electrode in grams
2	300	0.2
4	300	0.4
2	600	0.4
4	600	0.8

CHECK YOUR UNDERSTANDING

1. A cheap metal spoon can be plated with a layer of silver using electrolysis. With a current of 3 amps flowing for 200 seconds, 0.7 g of silver are deposited on the spoon. How much silver would be deposited by a current of 1.5 amps flowing for 800 seconds?

Energy and power in a circuit

An electric current is a flow of charge (electrons or ions).

Metals have some electrons that are able to move freely through the metal structure (free electrons). This is why metals are good electrical conductors.

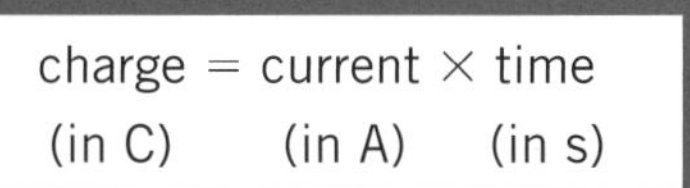

charge = current × time
(in C) (in A) (in s)

LEARN THIS EQUATION and the UNITS.

Charge is measured in **coulombs** (C)

The amount of energy transferred to the components in a circuit depends on:

- the potential difference (voltage) of the power supply
- the amount of charge flowing through the circuit.

energy transferred = potential difference × charge
(in J) (in V) (in C)

LEARN THIS EQUATION and the UNITS.

When charge flows through a resistor, electrical energy is transferred as heat.

The power of an appliance or component is the rate at which it transfers energy.

1 watt (W) of power is the transfer of 1 joule of energy in 1 second.

power (in W)	= potential difference (in V)	× current (in A)

LEARN THIS EQUATION and the UNITS.

Induced current

Pushing a magnet into a coil of wire will produce (induce) a current in the wire. For this to happen the coil must be part of a complete circuit (Figure 10.26).

Pulling the magnet out of the coil or pushing the other pole of the magnet into the coil reverses the direction of the induced current (Figure 10.27).

No current is induced when the magnet is not moving.

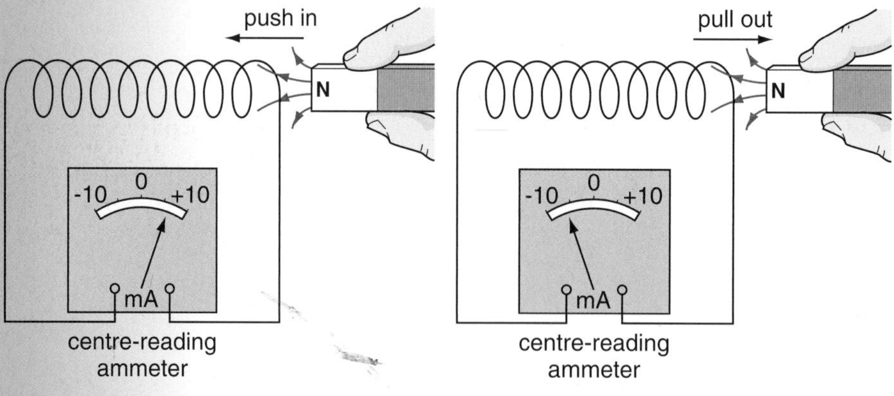

FIGURE 10.26

FIGURE 10.27

Generating electricity

Electricity is generated using the induction effect. This can be done in two ways.

- A coil of wire is rotated in a magnetic field.
- A magnet is rotated inside a coil of wire.

The coil rotating between the north and south poles of the magnet cuts through magnetic field lines. This induces a voltage in the coil which, if the coil is part of a complete circuit, causes a current to flow.

The induced voltage changes direction twice during each rotation of the coil. So the generator produces an alternating output.

The slip rings, which rotate with the coil, and the fixed contact brushes link the coil to the rest of the circuit.

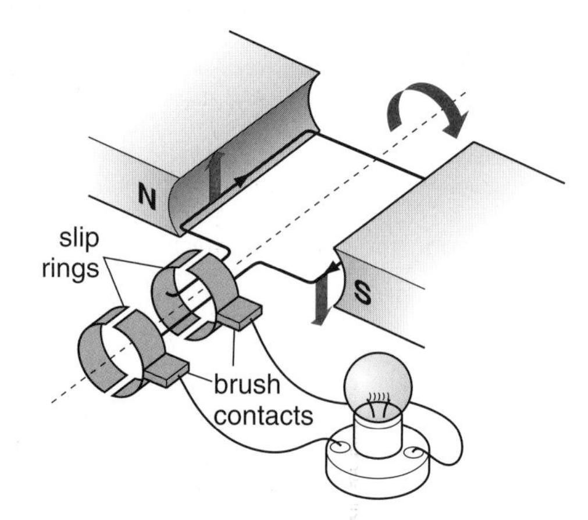

FIGURE 10.28 A simple generator

The size of the induced voltage (and current) can be increased by:

- rotating the coil faster
- using a stronger magnet
- having more turns on the coil
- increasing the area of the coil.

Transformers

A transformer is used to increase or decrease the voltage of an a.c. supply.

The alternating voltage applied across the primary coil creates a changing magnetic field in the iron core. This changing magnetic field links with the secondary coil. This causes a voltage to be induced in the secondary coil.

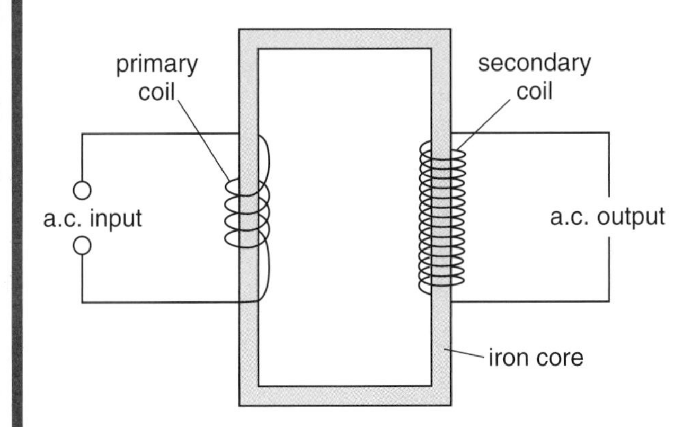

FIGURE 10.29 The principle of a transformer

LEARN THIS EQUATION and the UNITS.

$$\frac{\text{voltage across primary coil (in V)}}{\text{voltage across secondary coil (in V)}} = \frac{\text{number of turns on primary coil}}{\text{number of turns on secondary coil}}$$

Transformers are an essential part of the electricity distribution system. The network of power lines is called the National Grid.

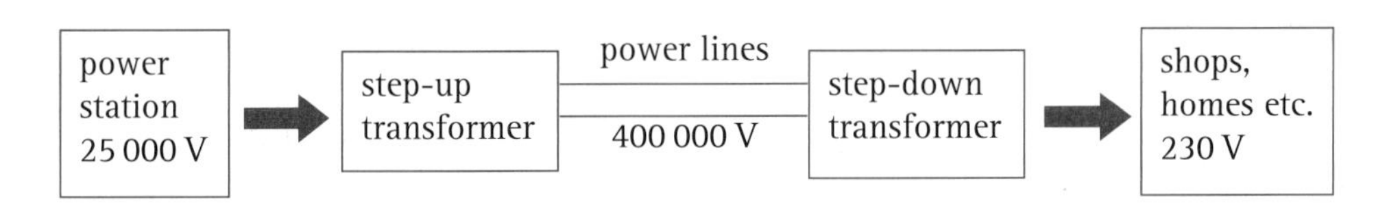

A step-up transformer increases the voltage across the power lines. Increasing the voltage decreases the current. The smaller the current the less energy that is wasted as heat in the power lines. This increases the efficiency of the system.

CHECK YOUR UNDERSTANDING

❶ A current is induced in a coil of wire as it rotates between the poles of a magnet. What changes can be made to increase the induced current?

❷ A transformer is designed to step-up 110 V to 230 V. There are 550 turns of wire on the primary coil. Calculate the number of turns on the secondary coil.

❸ A 6 V immersion heater transfers 7200 J of energy to a beaker of water in 5 minutes. Calculate the current flowing through the immersion heater during the 5 minutes.

❹ Calculate the current drawn from the 230 V mains supply by a 1.5 kW hairdryer.

Topic Test

1 Match each word in the box to one of the statements below.

conductor	electrodes	electrons	ions

a) These allow charged particles to flow through them.
b) During electrolysis simpler substances are released here.
c) These have a negative charge only.
d) These can have a positive or a negative charge.

(4 marks)

2 A 9 volt battery is connected across a lamp.
The resistance of the lamp is 36 ohms.

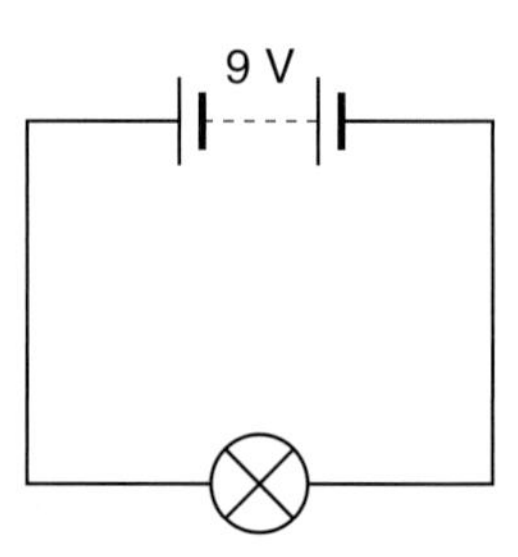

FIGURE 10.30

a) What is the current through the lamp?
A – 0.25 A B – 0.5 A C – 1 A D – 4 A

b) What charge flows through the lamp in 2 minutes?
A – 0.5 C B – 30 C C – 60 C D – 120 C

c) How much energy does the lamp transfer in 2 minutes?
A – 4.5 J B – 18 J C – 270 J D – 1080 J

d) What is the power of the lamp?
A – 0.4 W B – 1.2 W C – 2.25 W D – 5.0 W

(4 marks)

3 This question is about a hairdryer. Match each quantity in the box to the correct space in the sentences.

6 amps	50 hertz	230 volts	1380 watts

The hairdryer plugs into the mains supply of ____(a)___. The frequency of the mains supply is ____(b)____. The hairdryer has a power of ____(c)____ and draws a current of _____(d)______ from the supply. (4 marks)

4 For safety, an electric iron is fitted with an earth wire. Explain how the earth wire acts as a safety device. (3 marks)

5 An electric fire draws a current of 8 amps from the 230 volt power supply.

a) Calculate the power rating of the fire. (3 marks)

b) Calculate the resistance of the fire's heating element when it is working normally. (3 marks)

6 Explain how a smoke precipitator inside a power station chimney separates the soot and ash particles from waste gases. (3 marks)

7 During the electrolysis of molten aluminium oxide, aluminium is produced at the negative electrode.

a) What type of charge do aluminium ions have?

b) How does the mass of aluminium produced depend on the current flowing? (2 marks)

8 Explain the function of the slip rings and brushes in an a.c. generator. (1 mark)

9 The primary coil of a transformer is connected to the 230 volt mains supply. The primary coil has 1000 turns and the secondary coil has 100 turns. Calculate the voltage across the secondary coil. (3 marks)

Total: 30 marks

FORCES

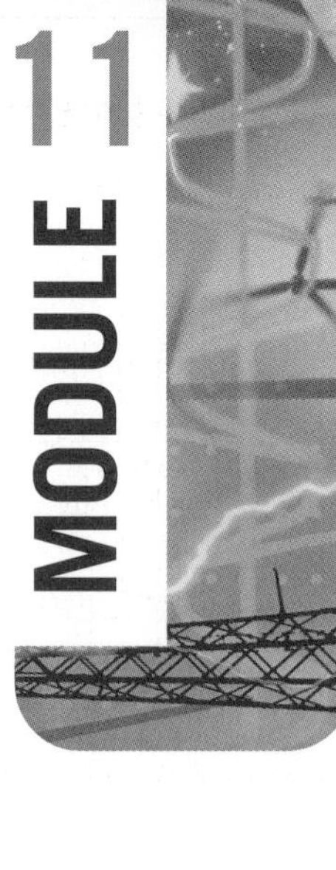

Measuring and representing motion

Velocity and acceleration

Velocity

Velocity is *not* the same as speed. To give velocity you must give both speed and direction. This is because the velocity of an object is its speed in a given direction. It is measured in metres/second (m/s).

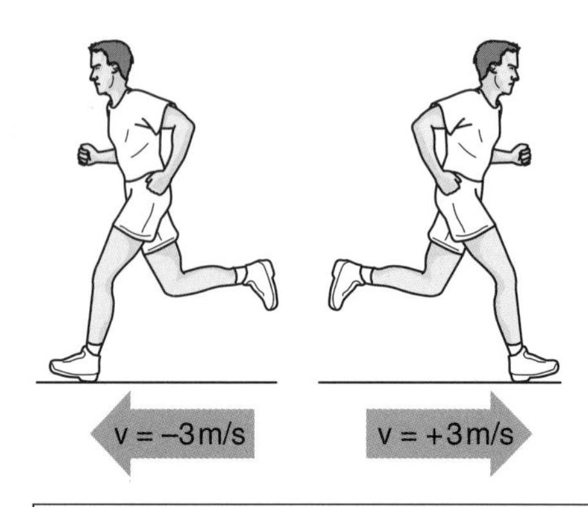

The two joggers are running at the same speed but in different directions. So they have different velocities.

FIGURE 11.1 These joggers have different velocities

Acceleration

An object is accelerating when its velocity is changing. The faster the velocity changes, the larger the acceleration. Slowing down is a negative acceleration.

$$\text{acceleration (in m/s}^2\text{)} = \frac{\text{change in velocity (in m/s)}}{\text{time taken (in s)}}$$

LEARN THIS EQUATION and the UNITS.

Example: At the start of a race, a cyclist accelerates in a straight line, to 15 m/s in 3 s. What is the acceleration of the cyclist?

$$\text{acceleration} = \frac{\text{change in velocity}}{\text{time taken}} = \frac{15 - 0}{3} = 5\text{ m/s}^2$$

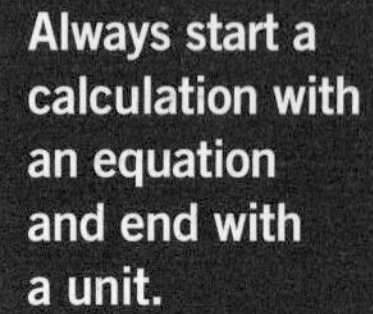

Distance–time graphs

A distance–time graph can be used to describe the speed of an object.

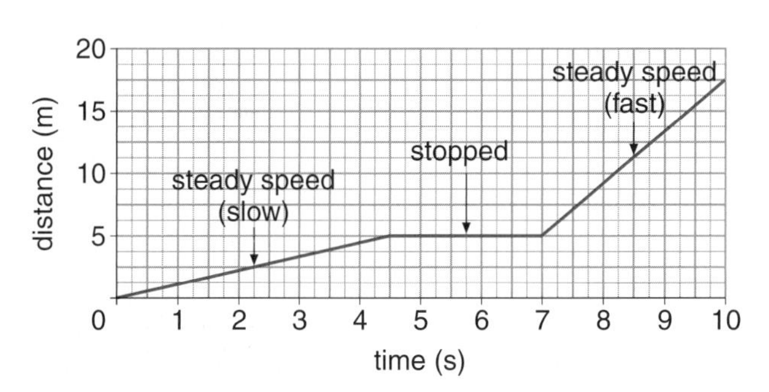

FIGURE 11.2 A distance–time graph

A horizontal line means the object is not moving.

A straight line going up means the object is moving with a steady speed.

The steeper the slope (gradient) of the line, the faster the speed of the object.

The gradient of a straight line graph is calculated as shown in Figure 11.3.

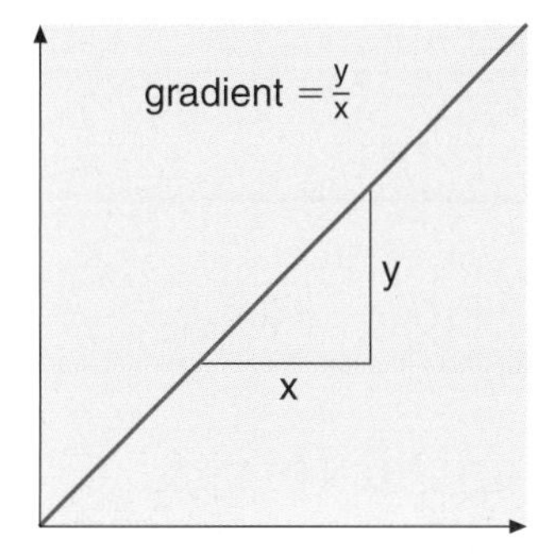

FIGURE 11.3

You should be able to calculate the gradient of a graph line.

Velocity–time graphs

A velocity–time graph can be used to describe velocity and acceleration.

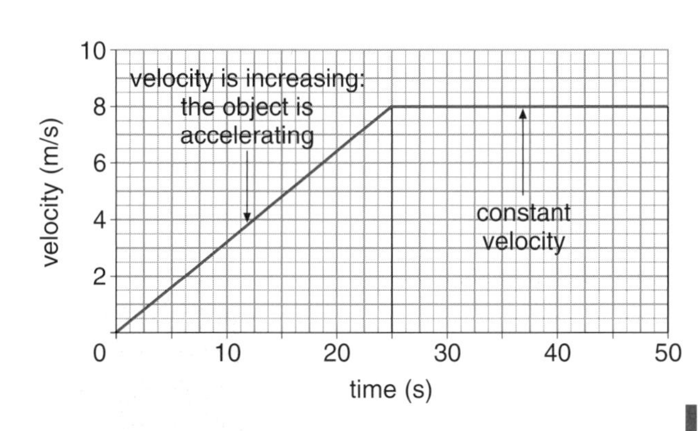

FIGURE 11.4 A velocity–time graph

The steeper the slope (gradient) of the line, the larger the acceleration.

A horizontal line (gradient = 0) means the object is not accelerating – it is moving with a constant velocity.

REMEMBER – Constant velocity means both speed and direction are not changing.

The value of the gradient of the graph gives the acceleration of the object.

The area under the graph gives the distance the object has travelled.

For the graph above: initial acceleration = gradient $= \frac{8}{25} = 0.32\ \text{m/s}^2$

total distance travelled $= \frac{1}{2} \times 25 \times 8 + 25 \times 8 = 100 + 200 = 300\ \text{m}$

CHECK YOUR UNDERSTANDING

1. How is velocity different from speed?
2. Draw a distance–time graph for a car moving at constant speed along a straight road.
3. During a crash test a car is driven into a wall at 12 m/s. The car takes 0.3 s to stop. Calculate the deceleration of the car.
4. The velocity–time graph shown is for a motorcyclist travelling along a straight road. Calculate:
   a) The initial acceleration of the motorcyclist.
   b) The total distance travelled by the motorcyclist.

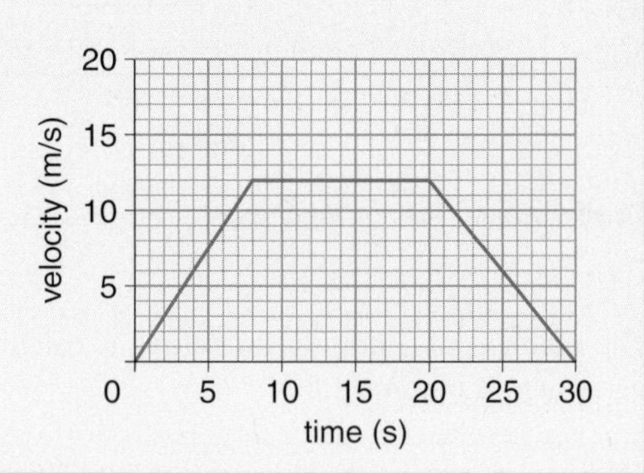

Balanced and unbalanced forces

Balanced forces

Balanced forces do not change the movement of an object.

If an object is stationary (not moving), it will remain stationary. So if the bag of shopping in the picture is not moving, the forces must be balanced.

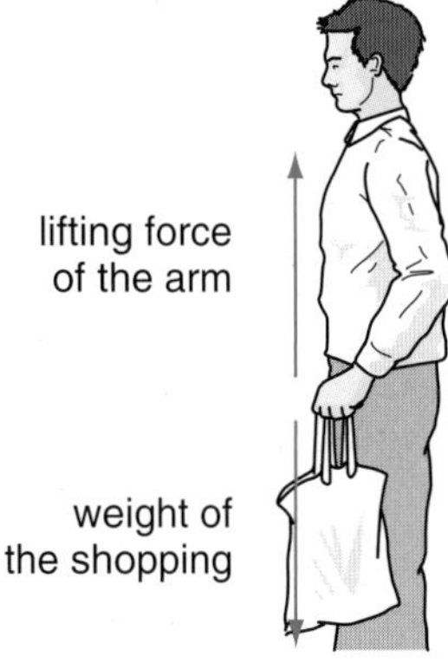

FIGURE 11.5

Lifting force upwards = Weight downwards

All forces are measured in newtons (N).

When the forces on a moving object are balanced, the object will keep moving at the same speed in the same direction.

Figure 11.6 shows the forces on a flying aircraft. When the force down balances the force up and the force forward balances the force backward, the aircraft will be flying at a constant height with a constant speed.

Air resistance (or drag), is a force of friction. The direction of air resistance is always opposite to the direction of the moving object.

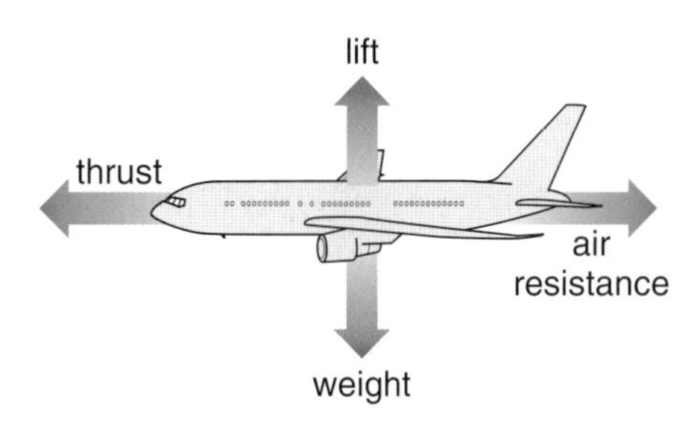

FIGURE 11.6 Forces on an aircraft

Unbalanced forces

Unbalanced forces change the movement of an object. An unbalanced force can make an object speed up or slow down.

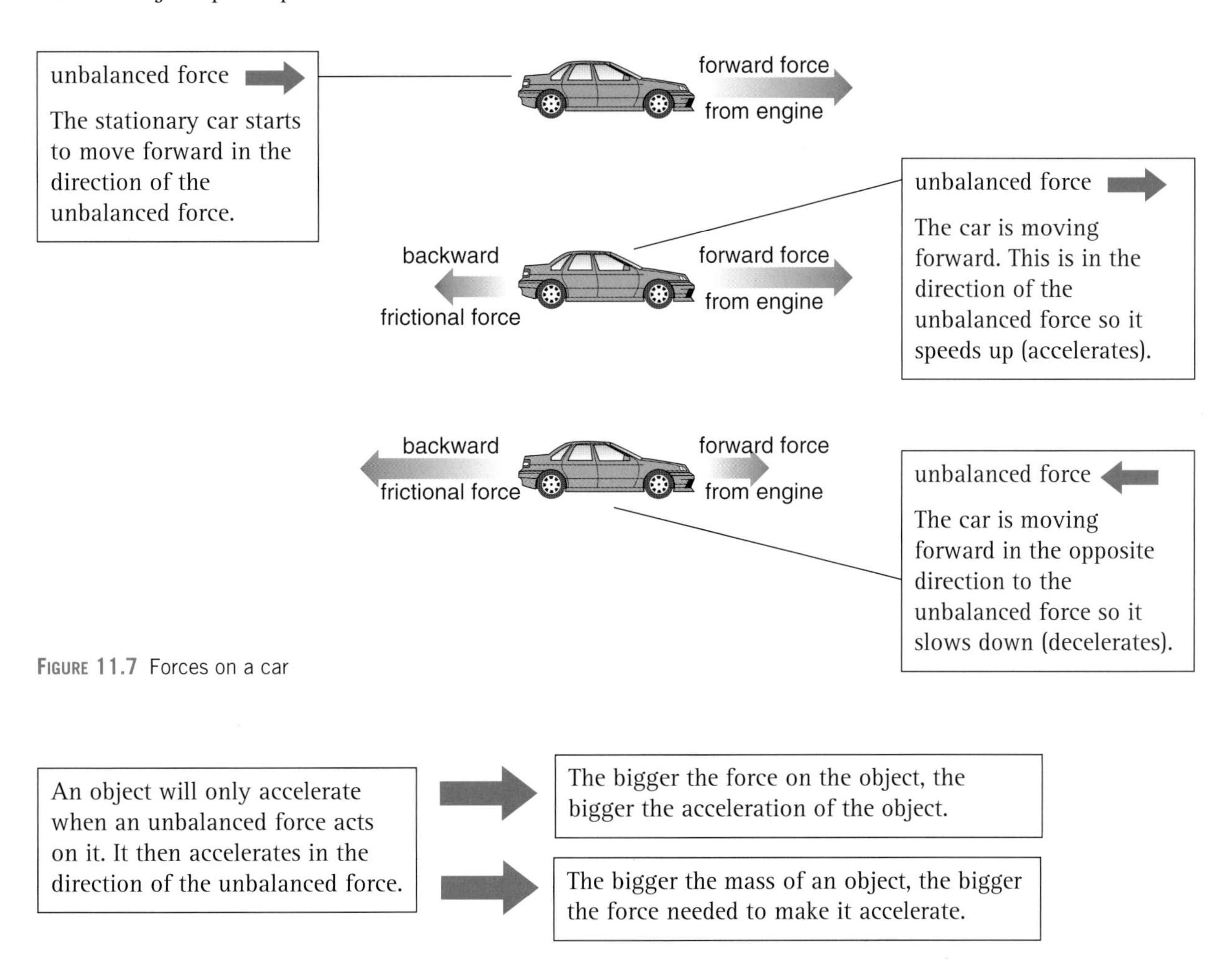

FIGURE 11.7 Forces on a car

An object will only accelerate when an unbalanced force acts on it. It then accelerates in the direction of the unbalanced force.

- The bigger the force on the object, the bigger the acceleration of the object.
- The bigger the mass of an object, the bigger the force needed to make it accelerate.

The three quantities, acceleration, force and mass are linked by the equation:

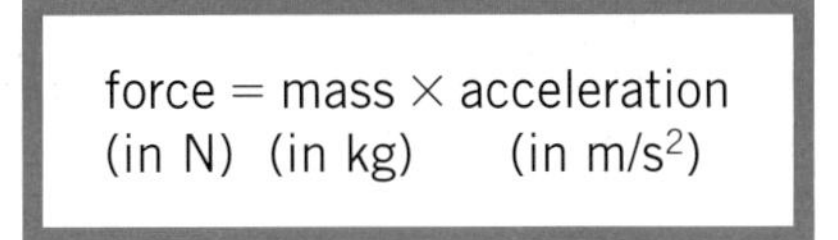

$$\text{force (in N)} = \text{mass (in kg)} \times \text{acceleration (in m/s}^2\text{)}$$

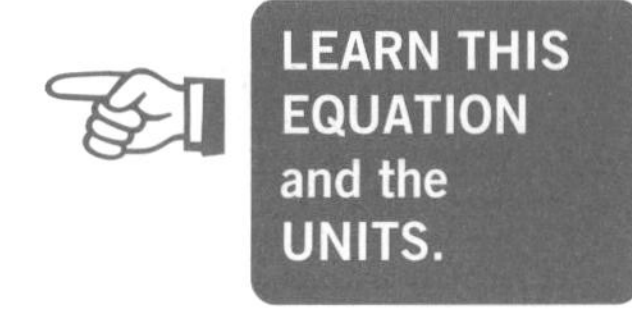

So a force of one newton will give a mass of one kilogram an acceleration of one metre per second squared.

Falling bodies

Gravity will cause a falling body to accelerate. Weight is the force due to gravity.

On Earth, gravity pulls on every one kilogram of mass with a force of about 10 newtons. This is called the gravitational field strength (g).

g = 10 N/kg

weight = mass × gravitional field strength
(in N) (in kg) (in N/kg)

LEARN THIS EQUATION and the UNITS.

Forces on a skydiver

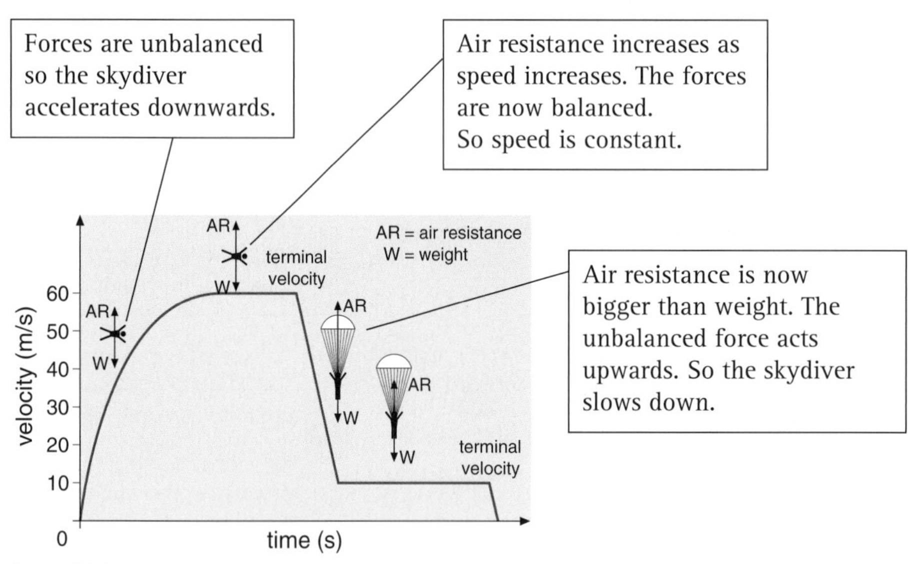

FIGURE 11.8 Graph showing the forces on a skydiver

The constant speed reached by a falling body is called its terminal velocity.

CHECK YOUR UNDERSTANDING

1. A book has a mass of 325 g. What does the book weigh?
2. Explain why a ball thrown up into the air slows down.
3. Explain why a lorry needs a more powerful brakes than a car.
4. An 800 kg car increases it speed from 5 m/s to 15 m/s in 20 s. Calculate the size of the unbalanced force needed to produce this acceleration.

Stopping safely

The total stopping distance of a vehicle is made up of two parts: thinking distance and braking distance.

stopping distance = thinking distance + braking distance

Thinking distance is how far a vehicle travels during the time it takes the driver to react to a hazard and apply the brakes.

Braking distance is how far a vehicle travels before stopping, after the brakes have been applied.

Speed changes the stopping distance. The faster the vehicle the longer the stopping distance. Figure 11.9 shows the average stopping distance for a family car at different speeds. The braking force is the same for each speed.

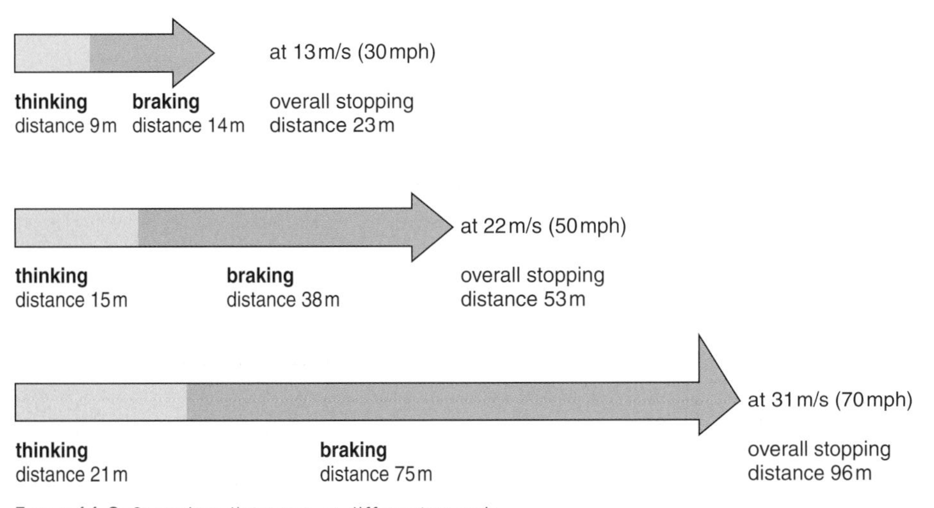

Figure 11.9 Stopping distances at different speeds

For a certain braking force, the faster the car, the greater the stopping distance.

The faster the car, the greater the braking force needed to stop the car quickly.

The stopping distance is also affected by:

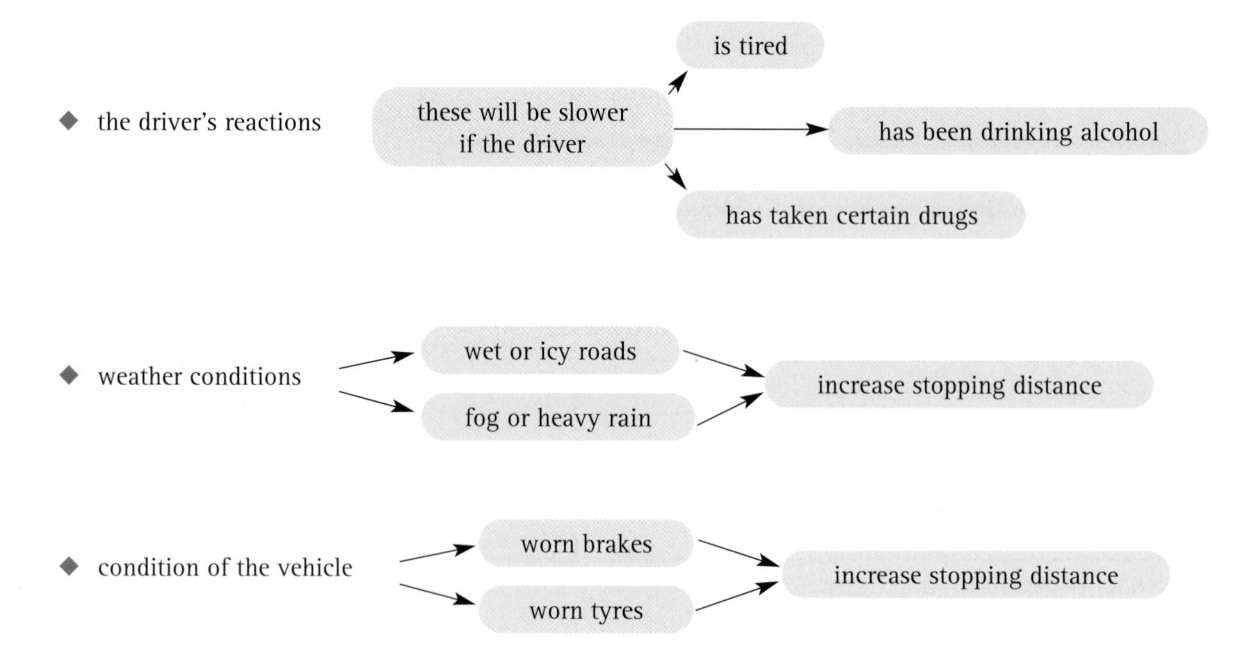

Work and energy

Forces that make something move are doing work. The amount of work done depends on:

- the size of the force
- the distance the force moves.

The bigger the force, and the further it moves, the more work is done.

work done = force × distance moved (in the direction of the force)
(in J)   (in N)   (in m)

LEARN THIS EQUATION and the UNITS.

Example: How much work is done by a high jumper lifting her own weight of 480 N a height of 1.2 m?

work done = force × distance moved
= 480 × 1.2 = 576 joules

REMEMBER – Start with the equation and finish with the unit.

Whenever a force moves an object, work is done and energy is transferred from one form into another.

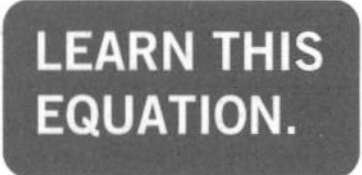

work done = energy transferred

Work and energy are measured in joules (J).

When work is done against frictional forces, most energy is transferred as heat. This is why rubbing your hands together makes them warm.

Elastic potential energy

An elastic object can be stretched, squashed, twisted or bent. But it goes back to the way it was when the force is taken away.

Elastic potential energy is the energy stored in an elastic object when a force does work to change the shape of the object.

Kinetic energy

Kinetic energy is the energy that an object has because it is moving.

$$\text{kinetic energy} = \tfrac{1}{2} \times \text{mass} \times \text{speed}^2$$

(in J) (in kg) (in $[\text{m/s}]^2$)

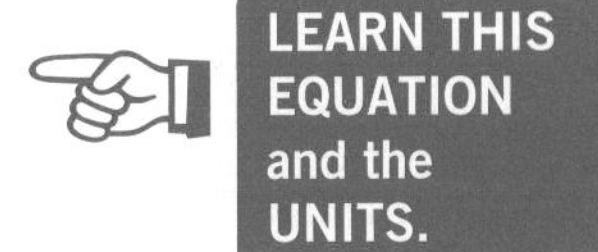

For a moving object, the bigger its mass and/or the faster its speed, the greater its kinetic energy.

Example: Calculate the kinetic energy of an elephant of mass 1800 kg moving at 6 m/s.

$$\text{kinetic energy} = \tfrac{1}{2} \times \text{mass} \times \text{speed}^2$$
$$= \tfrac{1}{2} \times 1800 \times 6 \times 6 = 32\,400 \text{ joules}$$

Example: A car of mass 800 kg accelerates from 10 m/s to 12 m/s. Calculate the increase in the kinetic energy of the car.

$$\text{kinetic energy (KE)} = \tfrac{1}{2} \times \text{mass} \times \text{speed}^2$$
$$\text{KE before acceleration} = \tfrac{1}{2} \times 800 \times 10 \times 10 = 40\,400 \text{ joules}$$
$$\text{KE after acceleration} = \tfrac{1}{2} \times 800 \times 12 \times 12 = 57\,600 \text{ joules}$$
$$\text{increase in KE} = 57\,600 - 40\,000 = 17\,600 \text{ joules}$$

CHECK YOUR UNDERSTANDING

1. A motorcyclist is travelling at 18 m/s. Write down three factors that could affect the stopping distance of the motorcyclist.
2. A shopper pushes a loaded trolley 20 m using a constant force of 50 N. How much work does the shopper do?
3. What type of energy does a stretched rubber band store?
4. Calculate the kinetic energy of a 1500 kg rhinoceros moving at 4 m/s.

The Earth and beyond

The Solar System

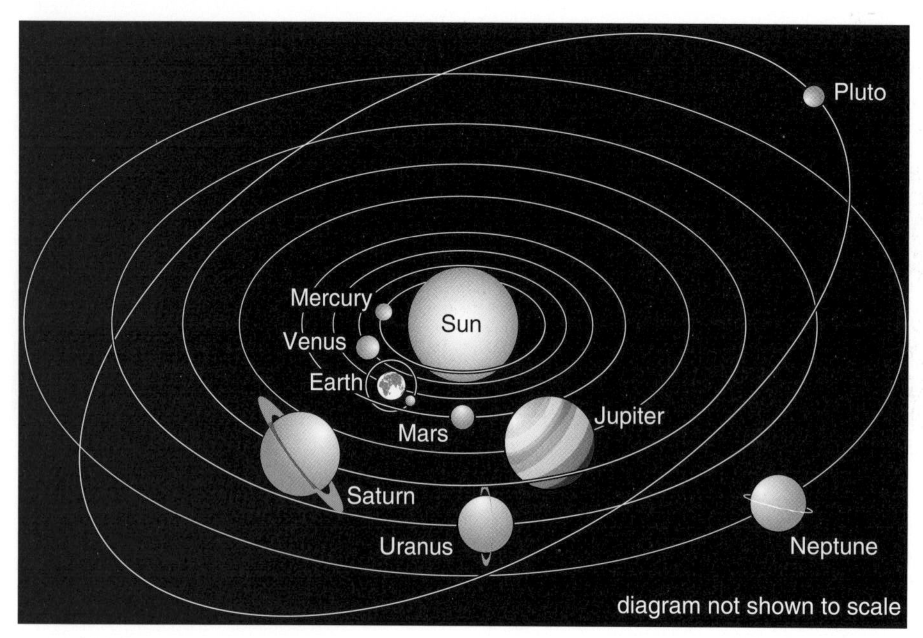

FIGURE 11.10 The Solar System

The orbits of the planets are elliptical. This means they are like a squashed circle with the Sun close to the centre.

The further a planet is away from the Sun, the longer it takes to complete one orbit.

An **orbit** is the path taken by one object going around another object. For example, the path taken by the Earth around the Sun.

Comets

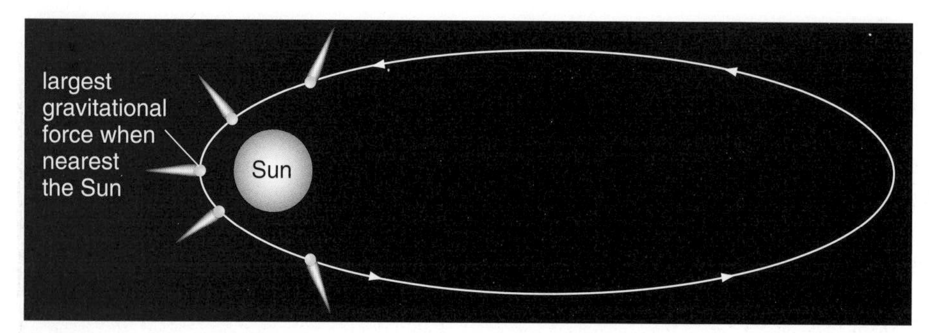

FIGURE 11.11 The path of a comet

A comet has a very elliptical orbit, so most of the time it will be a huge distance from the Sun. A comet is only seen when its orbit passes close to the Sun.

Gravity in space

The gravitational pull of the Sun affects all objects in the Solar System. The force of gravity between the Sun and a planet together with the high speed of the planet keeps the planet in its orbit.

As the distance between objects gets bigger, the gravitational pull between them gets smaller. For example, when the distance between a rocket and the Earth doubles, the force of gravity goes down by more than half.

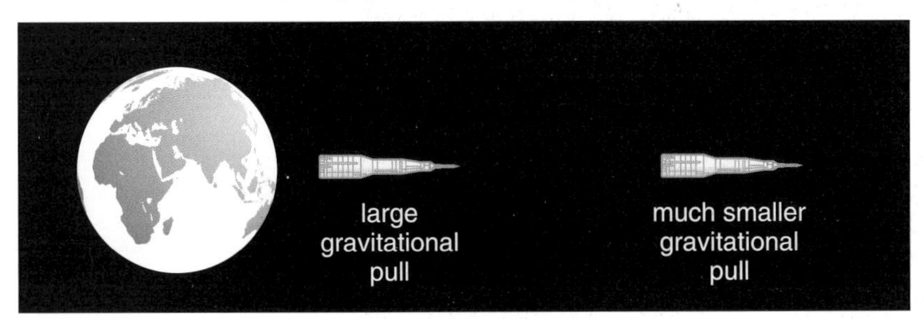

FIGURE 11.12

Satellites

A satellite is an object that orbits a planet. The further a satellite is from the Earth, the longer it takes to complete an orbit. To stay in a particular orbit a satellite must have the right speed.

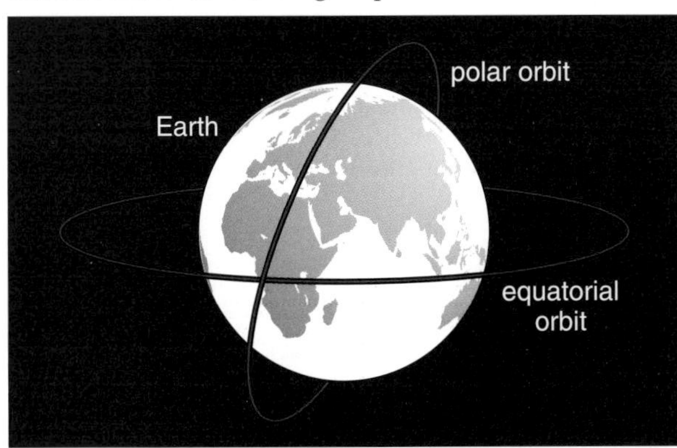

FIGURE 11.13 Satellite orbits

Satellites in low polar orbits are used to monitor the Earth's surface. Such things as forest fires and troop movements can be watched and monitored. Because the Earth spins, the whole of its surface can be scanned each day.

Satellites in high equatorial orbits are often used for communications. They are geostationary orbits. The satellite takes 24 hours to complete one orbit. This means that the satellite will always be above the same point on the Earth's surface.

CHECK YOUR UNDERSTANDING

1. What force keeps a planet in its orbit around the Sun?
2. Why are communications satellites put into geostationary orbits?
3. Why are spy satellites put into polar orbits?
4. Describe how the gravitational force between the Sun and a comet changes as the comet orbits the Sun.

Outside the Solar System

- The Sun is one of the 100 000 million stars in the Milky Way galaxy.
- The distance between stars in a galaxy is often millions of times bigger than the distance between the planets in the Solar System.
- The Universe is made up of at least a billion (a thousand million) galaxies.
- The distance between galaxies is often millions of times bigger than the distance between the stars in a galaxy.

Life on other planets

The search for any form of life in space has not been easy. Unmanned space probes have been sent to Mars and photographs taken of other planets. Experiments have been designed and clues looked for. Some important ones are noted below.

The presence of water

Recent photographs of Europa (one of Jupiter's moons) show that its surface could be an icy crust, possibly with water below. There is evidence that there was once water on Mars.

Changes to the atmosphere of a planet

Living things change the atmosphere of a planet. For example, without plants there would be much less oxygen in the Earth's atmosphere.

Fossils in rocks

A meteorite thought to have come from Mars seemed to show the presence of microscopic worm-like structures in the rock.

SETI (Search for Extra-Terrestrial Intelligence)

The search for intelligent radio signals from space has gone on for more than 40 years. So far the project has not found anything.

The life cycle of a star

The birth of a star

FIGURE 11.14

Masses too small to become stars join together to form planets and moons.

A star is formed when the temperature is high enough for the nuclei of lighter elements (mainly hydrogen) to fuse and form the nuclei of heavier elements. This process of nuclear fusion continues for the lifetime of the star. These nuclear fusion reactions release the energy that is radiated into space by the star.

Stable period of a star

Gravitational forces pulling inwards balance the outward forces caused by the star's high temperature. The Sun is in the stable part of its life cycle.

FIGURE 11.15

The death of a star

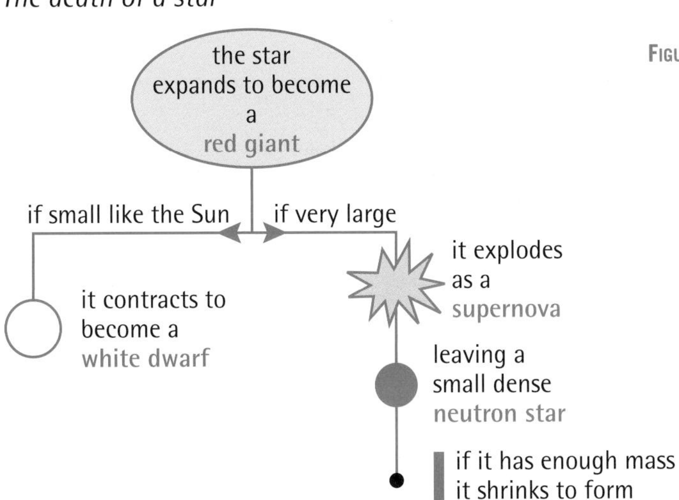

FIGURE 11.16 The death of a star

If a neutron star has enough mass it may shrink to form a black hole. The gravitational field of a black hole is so incredibly strong that not even light can escape from it. When the gases from a star spiral into a black hole, X-rays are emitted.

The Sun and the Solar System are thought to have been formed from the dust and gases produced when an earlier star exploded (a supernova). The evidence for this idea is in the presence of the nuclei of the heaviest elements in both the Sun and the inner planets.

The origin of the Universe

The Big Bang theory suggests that the Universe began about 15 billion years ago with a massive explosion. This created the dust and gases that formed stars and planets. Ever since the Big Bang, matter has been moving rapidly away from the explosion. So the Big Bang theory would suggest that the Universe is expanding. Evidence for the idea of an expanding Universe comes from the observation of red shift.

Red shift – The wavelength of light from other galaxies is longer than expected. The light has moved towards the red end of the spectrum.

Red shift can be explained if the other galaxies in the Universe are moving away from the Earth at great speed. It has also been observed that the further a galaxy is from the Earth, the bigger the red shift. This can be explained if the more distant a galaxy is from the Earth, the faster it is moving.

CHECK YOUR UNDERSTANDING

1. What clues are there that life may once have existed on Mars?
2. What will happen to the Sun when the stable period of its life ends?
3. Explain why red shift supports the idea of an expanding Universe.
4. Describe the process by which a star produces the energy that it radiates.
5. Why is the name black hole given to the remains of a neutron star?

Topic Test

1 The graph shows how the distance travelled by a person changes with time during a short journey.

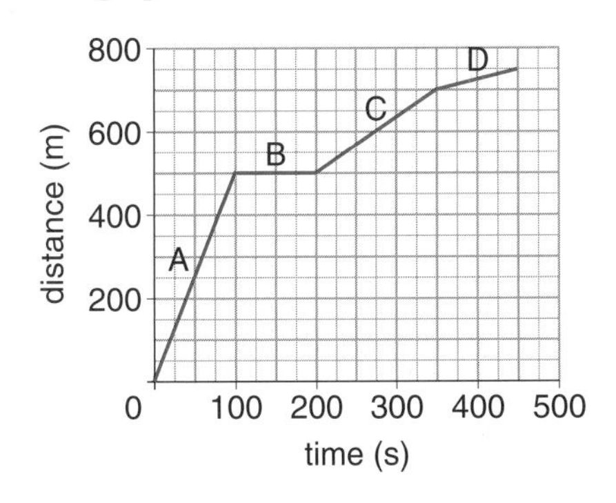

a) What distance was the journey?

b) How long did the journey take?

c) (i) Which part of the graph represents the fastest part of the journey?

(ii) Calculate the gradient of this part of the graph.

(5 marks)

2 Calculate the kinetic energy of a 400 kg horse galloping at 18 m/s. (3 marks)

3 Give three different uses for a satellite. (3 marks)

4 Describe what happens to a very large star after is has become a red giant. (3 marks)

5 How would an analysis of the atmosphere of a planet give evidence that life may exist or have existed at some time in the past on the planet? (2 marks)

6 Describe how the SETI project is trying to gain evidence for the existence of intelligent life on other planets. (2 marks)

7 The velocity–time graph for an athlete is shown.

a) Calculate the initial acceleration of the athlete.

b) What distance does the athlete run at constant velocity?

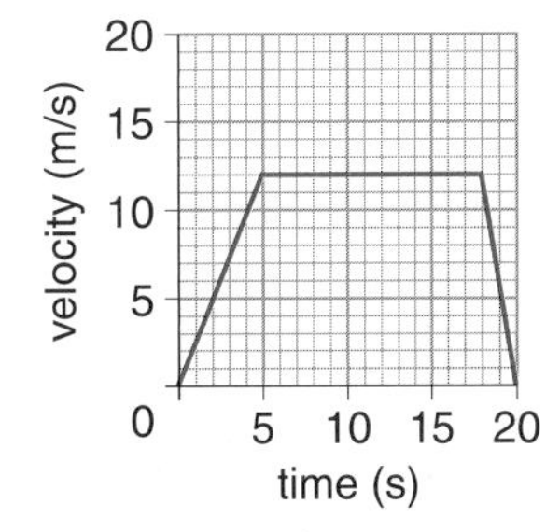

(6 marks)

8 Why do cyclists on a level road slow down when they stop pedalling? (2 marks)

9 State and explain the effect on the stopping distance of a car when the road is wet. (2 marks)

10 How much would a person of mass 70 kg weigh on the Moon? (Gravitational field strength on the Moon = 1.6 N/kg) (3 marks)

Total: 31 marks

WAVES AND RADIATION

Waves and waveforms

Energy can be transferred by waves. A stone falling on water causes ripples to move across the water surface. The water particles only move a small distance around their starting position, but the energy travels outwards to another place.

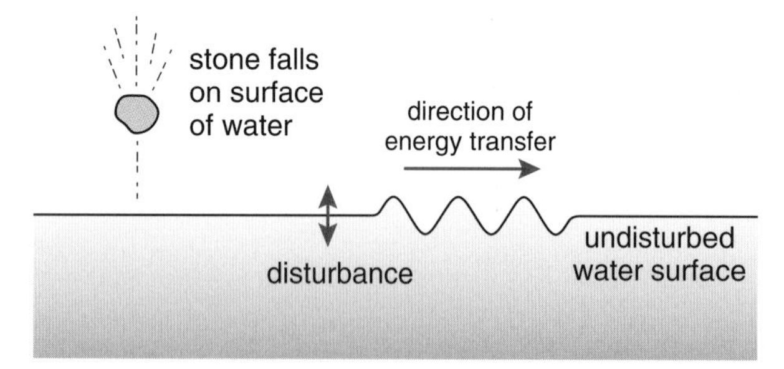

Figure 12.1 Ripples on a water surface

Waves can also be seen on a rope

Figure 12.2 Waves on a rope

or a spring.

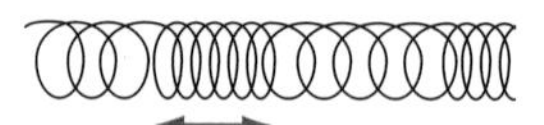

Figure 12.3 Waves in a 'slinky' spring

Sound waves can only travel through a solid, liquid or gas.

Light and radio waves can travel through a vacuum.

Types of wave

Transverse wave – the disturbance is at 90° to the direction the wave travels (direction of energy transfer).

Examples: Light waves and water waves.

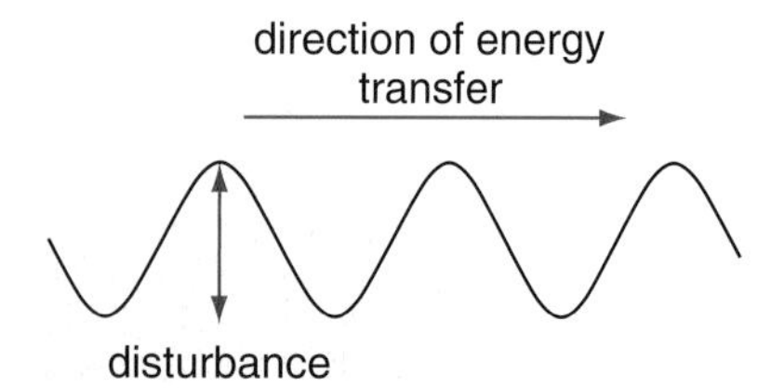

Figure 12.4 A transverse wave

Longitudinal wave – the disturbance is along (parallel to) the direction the wave travels (direction of energy transfer).

Examples: Waves along a slinky spring and sound waves in the air.

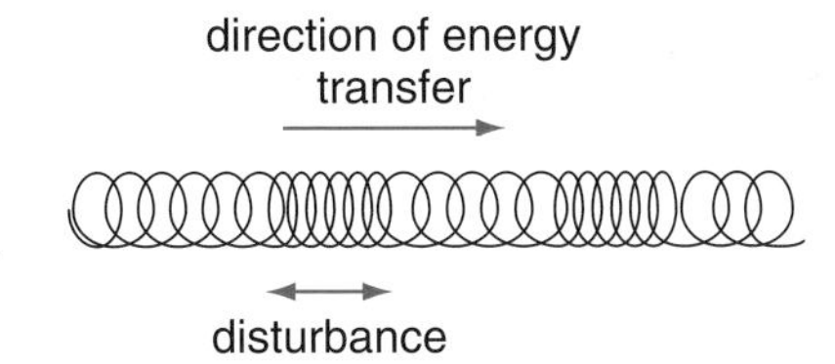

FIGURE 12.5 A longitudinal wave

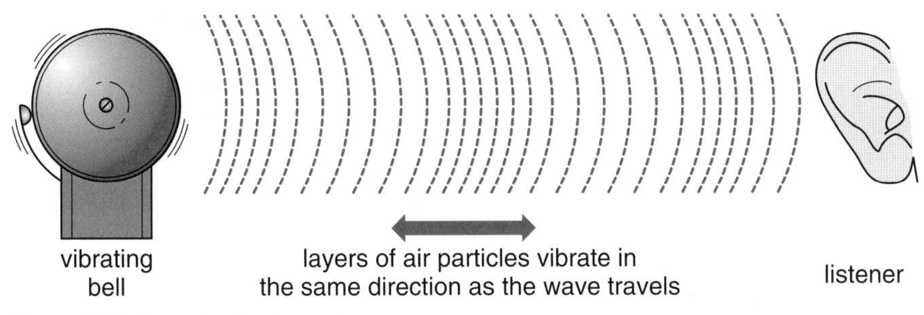

FIGURE 12.6 A longitudinal sound wave

Waveform features

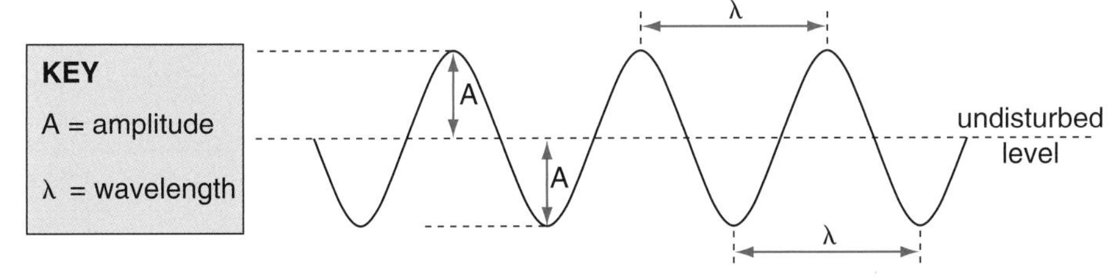

FIGURE 12.7 The features of a wave

Some wave definitions:

Frequency = the number of waves passing a particular point in 1 second, or the number of waves produced by a source in 1 second.

Wavelength = the distance from one point on a wave to the same point on the next wave.

Amplitude = the maximum disturbance of the wave.

Frequency is measured in **hertz** (Hz).

The wave equation relates the wave speed to the frequency and wavelength.

wave speed = frequency × wavelength
(in m/s) (in Hz) (in m)

LEARN THIS EQUATION and the UNITS.

Example: Calculate the speed of a water wave that has a wavelength of 3 m and a frequency of 20 Hz.

wave speed = frequency × wavelength
= 20 × 3 = 60 m/s

CHECK YOUR UNDERSTANDING

❶ What is the difference between a transverse and a longitudinal wave? Give one example for each type of wave.

❷ Which of the following waves can travel through a vacuum?

light radio sound

❸ A set of 30 regular water waves occupies a distance of 360 cm. The 30 waves take 5 s to pass a float.

a) What is the wavelength of the waves?

b) What is the frequency of the waves?

c) Use the wave equation to calculate the wave speed of the waves.

Behaviour of waves

Reflection

Water waves, like light and sound waves, can be reflected by a surface.

Waves on a rope or spring can also be reflected.

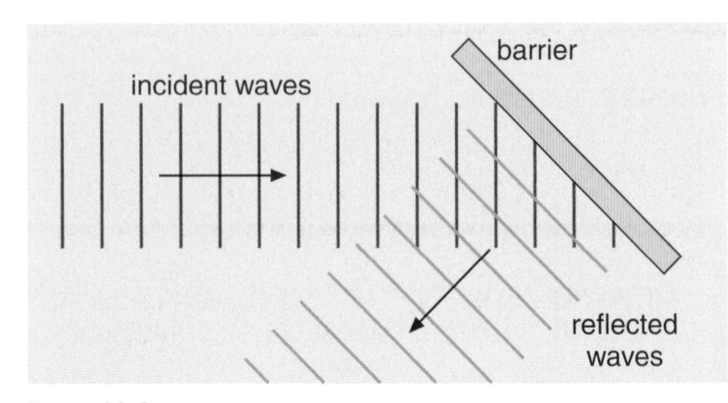

FIGURE 12.8 Reflection of water waves

Refraction

Water waves move faster across deep water than shallow water. So water waves moving across water of different depths change speed. This will usually make the waves change direction. When the waves change direction, they have been refracted.

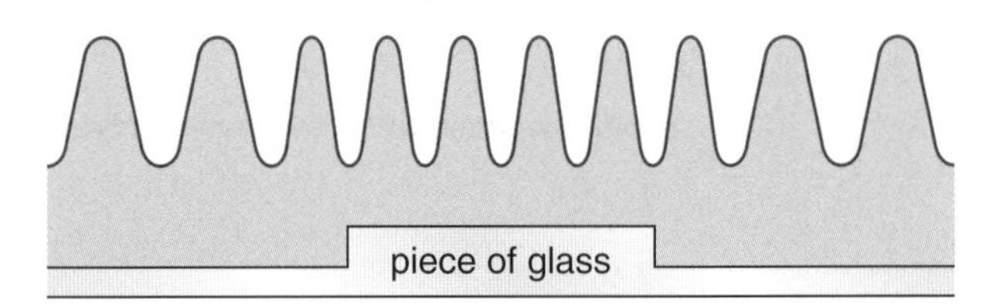

FIGURE 12.9 Change in speed of water waves

Waves are not refracted when the direction of travel of the waves is along a normal.

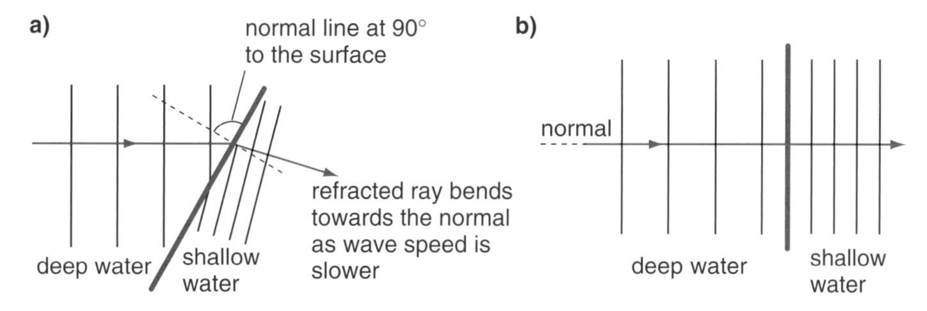

FIGURE 12.10

Sound and light waves change speed when they travel into a different medium. The change in speed causes a change in direction (refraction) provided the waves are not travelling along a normal.

CHECK YOUR UNDERSTANDING

1. Do water waves travel faster or slower when they reach deeper water?
2. What happens to the wavelength of water waves as they travel from shallow to deeper water?
3. A light wave travelling from air into glass does not refract. Why?

Total internal reflection

Light rays travel faster in air than in glass, Perspex or water. The light ray bends away from the normal when it enters the air.

The critical angle for glass = 42°.

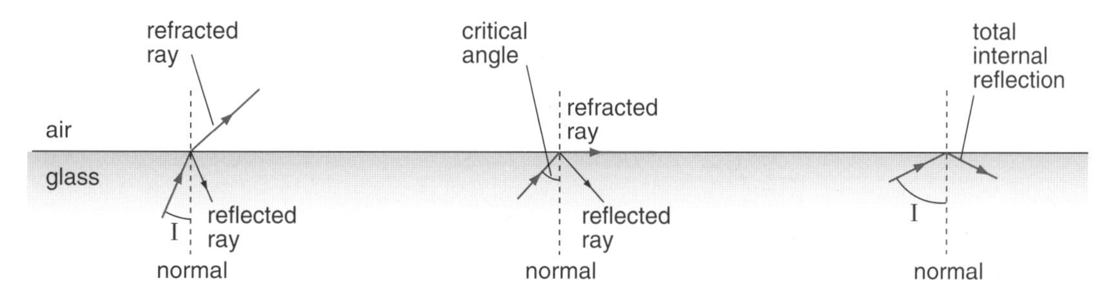

At small angles (I) most light is refracted into the air. There is a weak reflected ray.

When the angle I is equal to the critical angle the refracted light travels along the edge of the glass.

When the angle I is bigger than the critical angle, all the light is reflected back into the glass. This is called total internal reflection.

FIGURE 12.11 Total internal reflection

Optical fibres pass light into places that are difficult to reach. In an optical fibre, light can travel to, then back from, the object to be seen by the observer. This idea is used in an endoscope, an instrument used by doctors to see inside a patient's body.

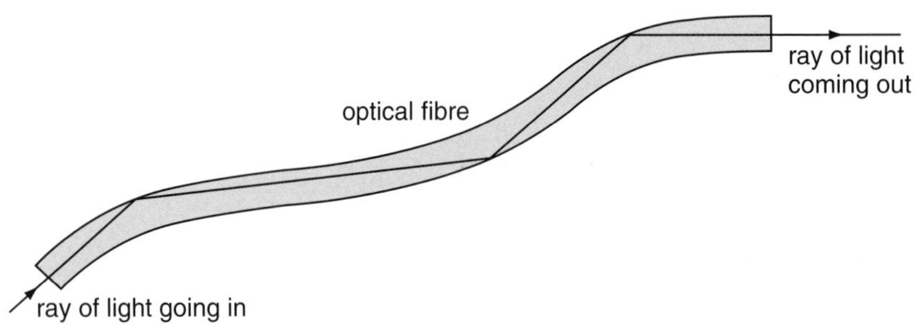

FIGURE 12.12 Passage of light through an optical fibre

Diffraction

All waves can diffract from the edge of an obstacle or through a gap. This spreading out of waves is easily seen in water waves, because the wavelength of the waves often matches the size of the gap.

Diffraction allows sound waves to spread out from doorways. Light waves are diffracted but not easily because their wavelengths are very small.

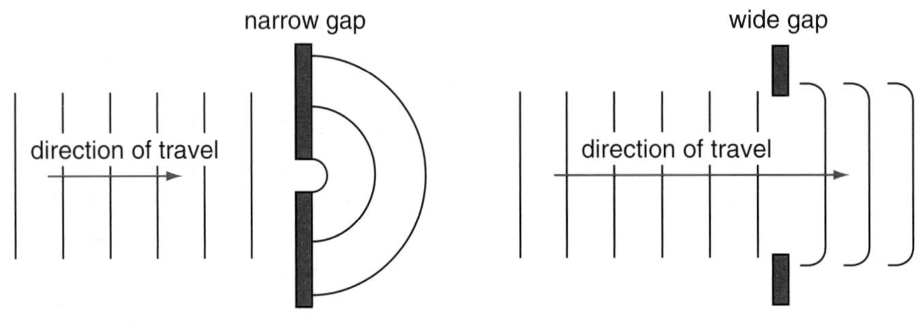

FIGURE 12.13 Diffraction of waves at a narrow and wide gap

Radio waves can also be diffracted.

The hill diffracts the waves to the house aerial.

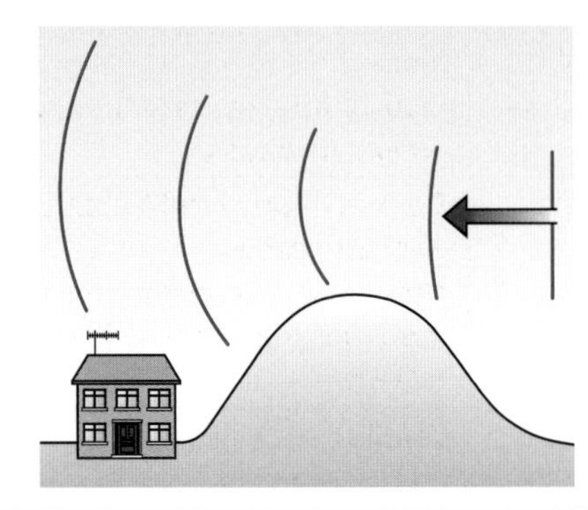

FIGURE 12.14 Diffraction of radio waves

CHECK YOUR UNDERSTANDING

1. The aerial on a house in a valley can pick up long wavelength radio waves but not short wavelength radio waves. Explain why.
2. How does the intensity of the reflected light in a glass block change as the angle between the incident ray and normal increases?

Electromagnetic waves

- Electromagnetic waves are transverse waves with a range of wavelengths and frequency.
- They all travel through space (a vacuum) at the same speed, 300 000 000 m/s.
- Different wavelengths are transmitted, reflected or absorbed differently by different materials and surfaces.
- When absorbed, electromagnetic waves make the absorbing material hotter.
- When absorbed by a conductor they may produce an alternating current (a.c.) with the same frequency as the waves.

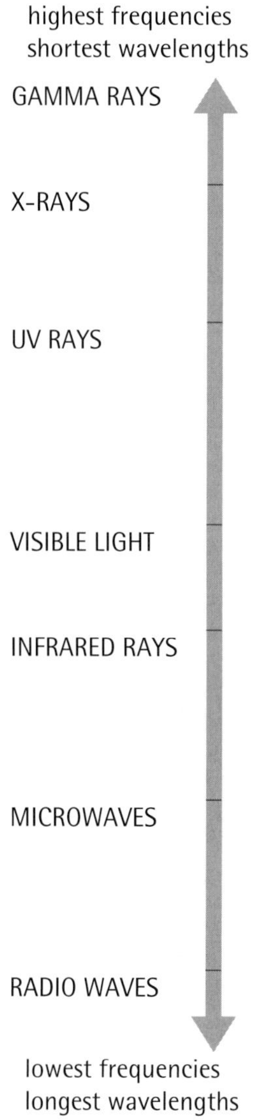

highest frequencies
shortest wavelengths

GAMMA RAYS
X-RAYS
UV RAYS
VISIBLE LIGHT
INFRARED RAYS
MICROWAVES
RADIO WAVES

lowest frequencies
longest wavelengths

Type of wave	Uses	Effect on living cells
Gamma rays	Kill harmful bacteria in food. Sterilise medical instruments. Kill cancer cells.	High doses kill normal cells. Low doses easily cause cell change leading to cancer.
X-rays	Make shadow pictures of bones (absorbed by bone and metals).	Pass through soft tissue but some will be absorbed. High doses will kill cells but low doses may cause cancer.
Ultraviolet rays	Sunbeds. Labels for security coding. Fluorescent lamps.	Can pass through skin to reach deeper tissue; this may lead to skin cancer. (Pale skin absorbs less UV than darker skin so more UV reaches the deeper tissue.)
Visible light	Seeing. Optical fibre instruments and communications.	
Infrared rays	Cooking – grills and toasters. Radiant heaters. Optical fibre communications. Remote controls for VCR and TV sets.	Absorbed by the skin and felt as heat; may cause pale skin to go red.
Microwaves	Satellite and mobile phone communications. Cooking – strongly absorbed by water molecules causing a heating effect.	All living cells contain water, so are killed or damaged if exposed to microwaves.
Radio waves	Transmit TV and radio programmes.	

FIGURE 12.15 The electromagnetic spectrum

Communications and electromagnetic waves

Radio waves send signals to different places on the Earth.

- Long wavelength radio waves reflect from the ionised layers in the upper atmosphere.
- Short wavelength radio waves can carry TV signals across small distances on the Earth.
- Microwaves are very short wavelength radio waves which penetrate the atmosphere to satellites.

  These waves are then sent back to Earth.

  This system is used by mobile phone networks and satellite TV stations.

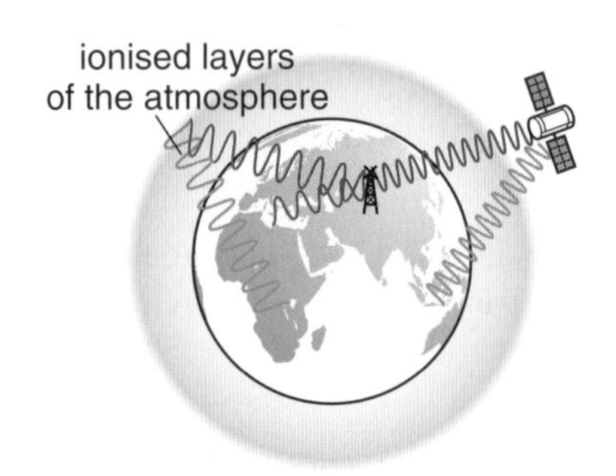

Figure 12.16 Using radio waves for communications

Signals

Sound waves can be changed to electrical signals.

These signals can follow exactly the pattern of the sound wave, given by music or speech. This is an analogue signal.

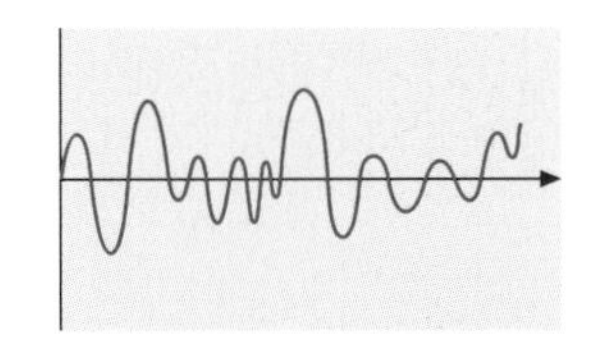

Figure 12.17 An analogue signal

Signals coded as a series of 'on or off' pulses are digital signals.

Digital signals are less likely to change the information they carry and they transfer more information in a given time than analogue signals.

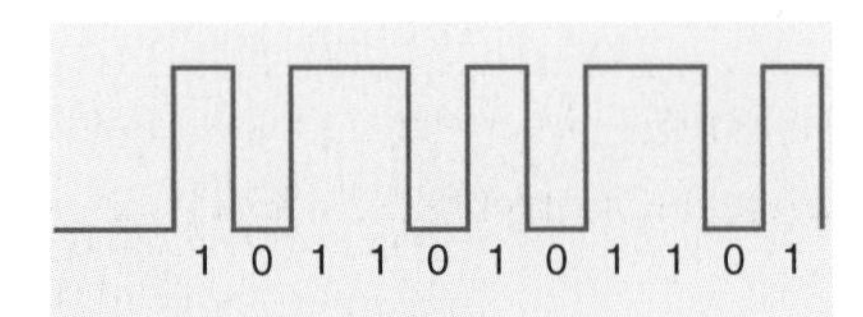

Figure 12.18 A digital signal

- Signals can be carried directly as a varying electric current in copper cables. Or the electrical signal can be transferred to a radio wave and carried in a radio transmission.
- A digital signal can be changed to light or infrared pulses and carried in an optical fibre.
- An optical fibre cable can carry more telephone messages at the same time, than a copper cable of the same diameter.
- The strength of light signals does not weaken as quickly as that of electrical signals.

Noise

Noise is the name given to the distortions picked up by the original signal.This is very likely to occur with analogue signals. The original signal becomes weaker and the relative strengths of the different frequencies change. As the signal is amplified, unwanted frequencies are also amplified, resulting in poor signal quality.

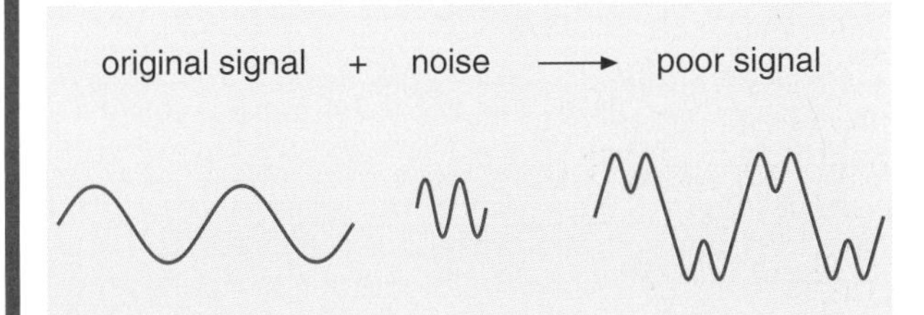

FIGURE 12.19

In digital signals, unwanted frequencies are low amplitude and interpreted as 'off' by the receiver circuit. This gives a better quality signal.

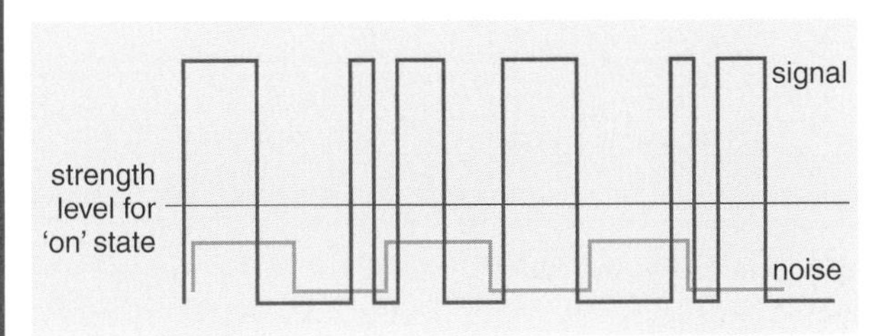

FIGURE 12.20

CHECK YOUR UNDERSTANDING

❶ List these e.m. waves in order of decreasing wavelength.

gamma rays, infrared, light, microwaves, radio waves, ultraviolet, X-rays

❷ a) When do some substances fluoresce?

b) Where is fluorescence used?

❸ Match the correct labels to each stage in this telephone system. Use each label once.

digital light signal, satellite, electrical signal,

microwaves, optical fibre cable, copper cable

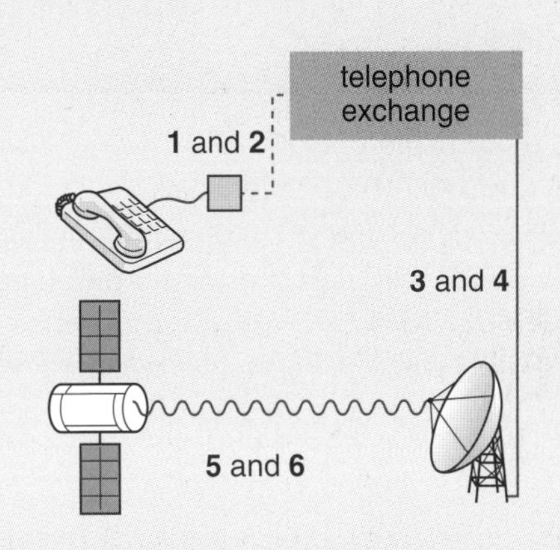

❹ Why are digital signals less likely to deteriorate during transmission?

Waves travelling through matter

Sound and ultrasound

Sound waves, produced when objects vibrate, can be shown as an oscilloscope trace.

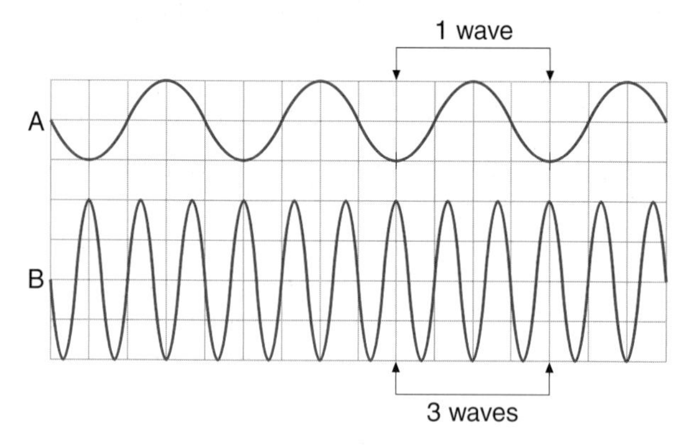

The amplitude of wave B is two times the amplitude of wave A.

Wave B has three complete waves in the time it takes wave A to complete one wave. Wave B has three times the frequency of wave A.

FIGURE 12.21 Traces of sound waves on an oscilloscope screen

The human ear can detect sound waves with frequencies from 20 Hz – 20 000 Hz (20 kHz).

Sound waves with frequencies above the upper limit of human hearing are called ultrasound or ultrasonic waves.

Ultrasonic waves are generated by electronic systems oscillating at frequencies above 20 kHz.

At low frequencies, ultrasound waves do not harm living cells. In medicine, reflected ultrasonic waves are used to produce an image of an unborn baby (pre-natal scanning).

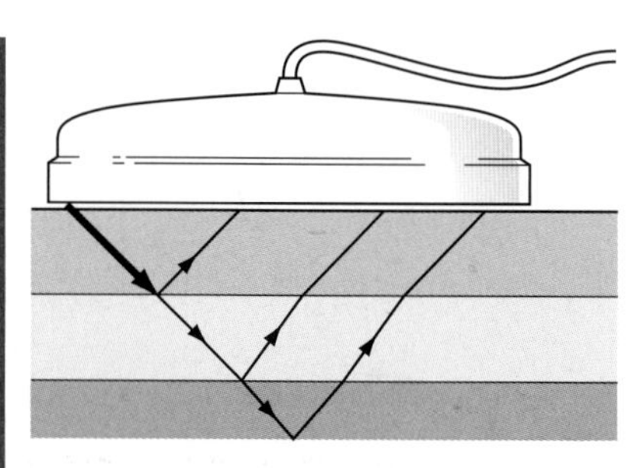

The ultrasound signal is partly reflected when it hits the boundary between two different media. The refracted part of the wave travels through the next medium, to be reflected at the second boundary, and some might travel further.

FIGURE 12.22

The different densities of the various media alter the speed of the passing ultrasound waves. Together with the changing depth of each medium, this causes the reflected parts of the signal arrive at different times at the detector. The returning signals are processed electronically, to give an image.

A similar scanning technique is used in industry to locate cracks in metal structures.

High intensity ultrasound waves are used for cleaning intricate objects, without taking them apart. The dirt particles vibrate strongly and fall off.

Seismic waves

Earthquakes cause shock waves in the Earth and the Earth's crust moves. The shock waves can travel through the interior of the Earth. These are seismic waves and they are recorded on seismographs. The arrival of the reflected and refracted wave after the initial disturbance gives the position of the earthquake.

These signals can also give information about the Earth's layered structure.

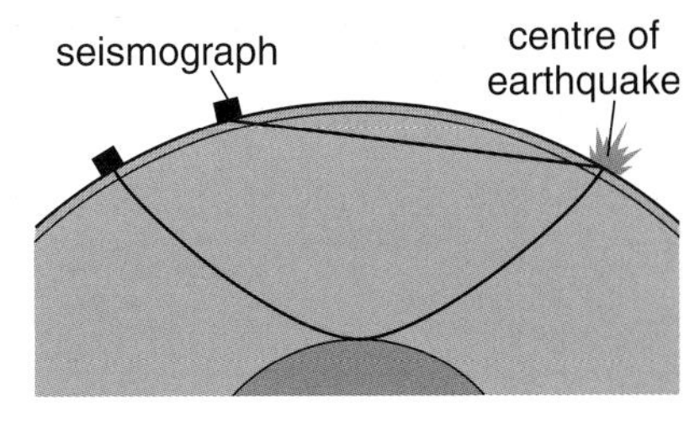

FIGURE 12.23

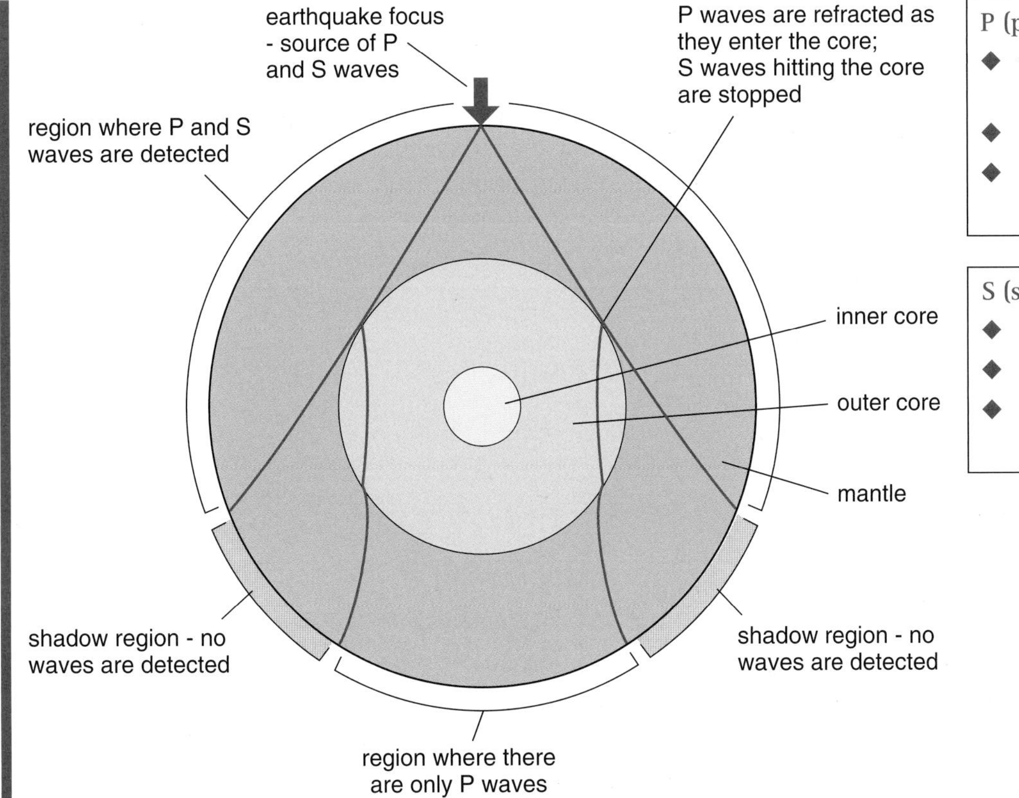

FIGURE 12.24 The paths of seismic waves through the Earth

P (primary) waves:
- travel faster, arriving first
- are longitudinal
- pass through liquids and solids

S (secondary) waves:
- travel slower
- are transverse
- pass only through solids

The waves follow curved paths as their speeds in the different layers varies.

The mantle is solid and allows both P and S waves to pass through.

The outer core is liquid so only P waves can pass through it.

CHECK YOUR UNDERSTANDING

1 a) Wave Y has an amplitude of 3 cm. What is the amplitude of wave X?

b) Wave X has a frequency of 40 Hz. What is the frequency of wave Y?

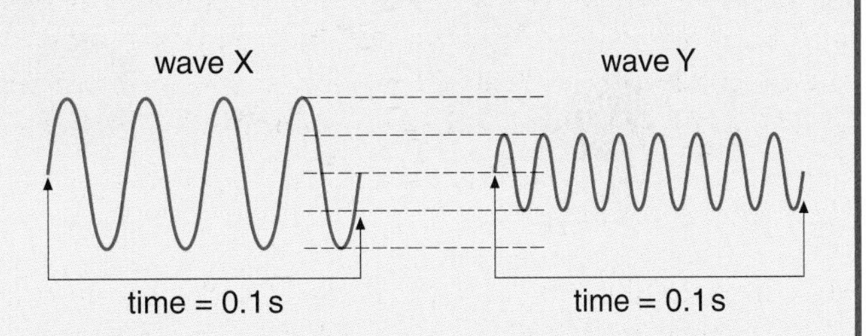

❷ Which layer

a) has the fastest speed for P waves?

b) is liquid?

Structure of the atom

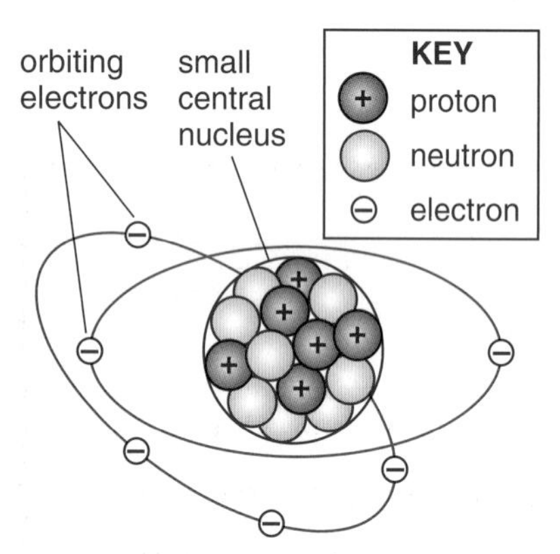

FIGURE 12.25 The basic structure of an atom

In an electrically neutral atom,
number of electrons = number of protons.

The relative masses of protons, neutrons and electrons are shown in the table.

Particle	Mass	Charge
proton	1	+1
neutron	1	0
electron	0	−1

All atoms of the same element have the same number of protons.

Protons and neutrons are both called **nucleons**.

The total number of protons and neutrons in the nucleus is the **nucleon number** or **mass number**.

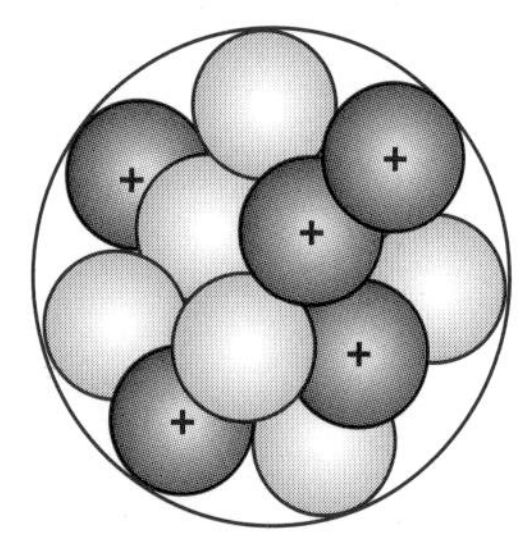

FIGURE 12.26 This nucleus has five protons and six neutrons.
Mass number = 11

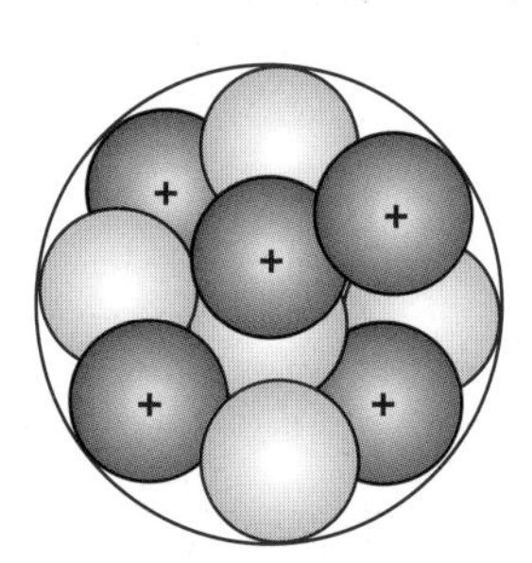

FIGURE 12.27 This nucleus has five protons and five neutrons.
Mass number = 10

An isotope of the same element has the same number of protons but a different number of neutrons. Figures 12.26 and 12.27 are isotopes of the same element.

A radioisotope is another form of the same element where the nucleus is unstable. When such a nucleus decays by emitting an α or β particle, then the structure of the nucleus changes. The new atomic nucleus has a different number of protons.

A β particle is a fast moving electron. When it is emitted, the nucleus changes – one neutron becomes a proton.

An α particle is a helium nucleus consisting of two protons and two neutrons in a strong bond.

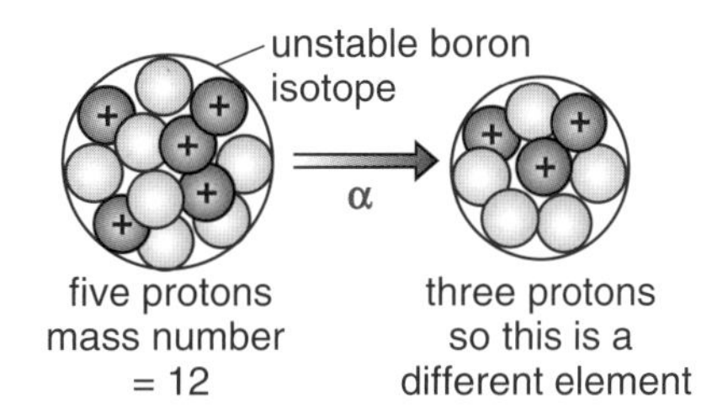

FIGURE 12.28 The radioactive decay of a boron nucleus

CHECK YOUR UNDERSTANDING

1. Which of the nuclei below:

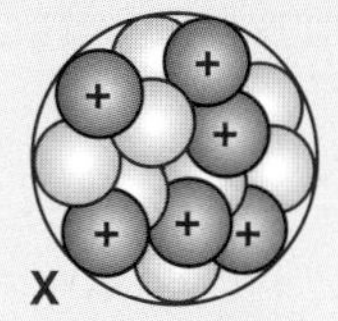

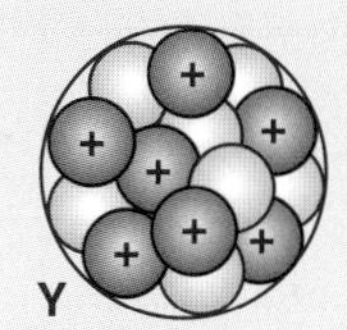

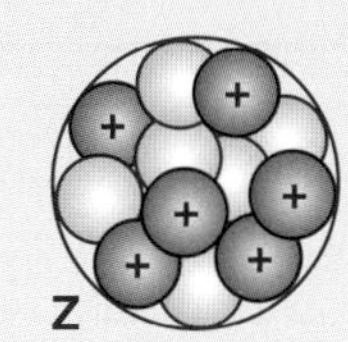

a) have the same mass number?
b) are isotopes of the same element?
c) has the highest number of protons?

Radioactivity

Radioactive substances give out radiation in the form of particles and gamma rays. They do this at random, regardless of what is done to them. Atomic nuclei of radioactive substances are unstable. When they give out radioactivity, they change their structure. These substances are called radioisotopes or radionuclides, and the process is called radioactive decay. The types of radiation are summarised below.

Type of radiation	What it is	Penetrating ability	Ionising ability
Alpha α	Large particle – a helium nucleus having 2 protons with ⊕ ⊕ charge, and 2 neutrons of no charge.	Low. Stopped by paper or 5 cm of air.	High
Beta β	Small particle – a high speed electron with ⊖ charge.	Fair. Stopped by a few mm of metal.	Fair
Gamma γ	Very short wavelength electromagnetic radiation.	High. Reduced by 10 cm of lead or several metres of concrete.	Low

Background radiation is the low level, continual radiation received mostly from natural sources, e.g. rocks, cosmic rays from space, building materials and food. A very small part of the background radiation is due to man-made sources, e.g. nuclear reactors, medical X-rays.

The dangers of radiation are reduced by thick shielding. The more dense and wider the absorbing material, the less radiation is transferred. Radioactivity can kill living things. It ionises the electrically neutral atoms or molecules in living cells. The chemical structures and functions of the cells change. The cells die or they stop working normally, causing cancers.

- Outside the body – alpha radiation is the least dangerous (unlikely to reach living cells).
  – beta and gamma radiation are the most dangerous (can reach cells of organs and be absorbed).
- Inside the body – alpha radiation is the most dangerous (strongly absorbed by cells).
  – beta and gamma radiation are less dangerous (may pass through cells without being absorbed).

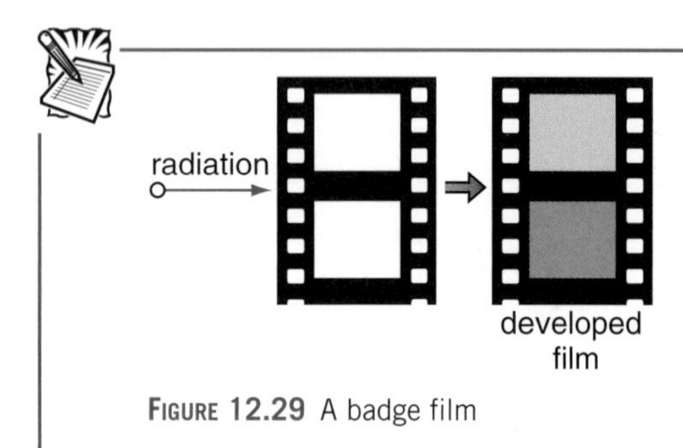

FIGURE 12.29 A badge film

A badge that detects radiation is often worn by people working with radioactive materials. The badge has a photographic film. This records the type and amount of radiation received. The darker the film after developing, the more radiation the worker has been exposed to.

Radioactive half-life is the time taken for the count rate to fall to half the starting value, or for half the number of unstable nuclei from the parent atoms to decay.

Very active samples have short half-lives as they lose their radioactivity at a fast rate.

For Figure 12.30 the time taken for the count rate to go from 1200 to 600 or from 600 to 300 is 10 hours. The half-life for this sample is 10 hours.

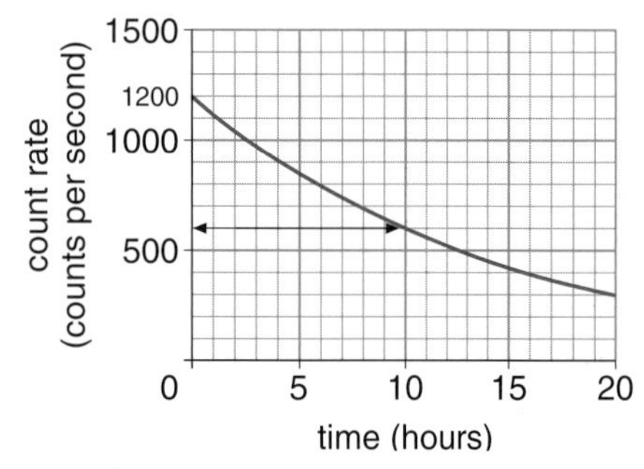

FIGURE 12.30 A graph showing radioactive decay

You need to be able to find the half-life from a graph like this.

Radioactive dating

Radioactive dating of rocks compares the proportion of original atoms to the final decay product atoms.

Example: Uranium-235 decays eventually to lead-207 with a half-life of 700 million years.

A rock sample has three atoms of lead-207 for every two atoms of uranium. How old is the sample?

60% of lead (3 × 20%) for 40% of uranium (2 × 20%)

From the graph in Figure 12.31, 40 % U line gives 950 million years.

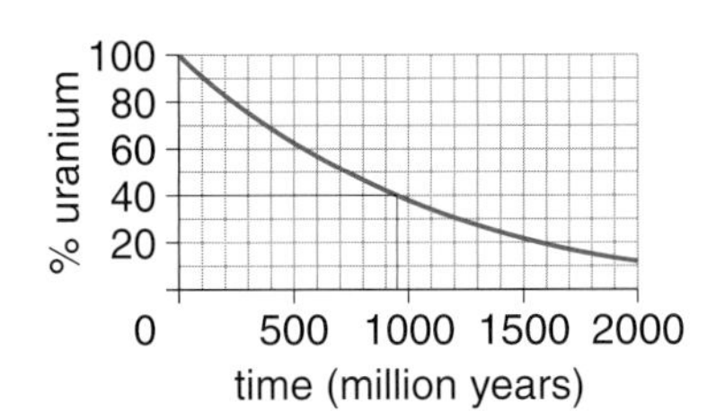

FIGURE 12.31

Using radiation

1 The ability of radiation to penetrate or be absorbed by different materials is used to control the thickness of materials. When the material passes too much radiation then it is too thin, and the rollers are adjusted.

2 The destruction of living cells by radiation is used in:

- Sterilising medical instruments, as the radiation kills the harmful organisms.
- Prolonging the shelf life of food, by reducing the number of food spoiling bacteria.
- In radiotherapy, for killing cancer cells.

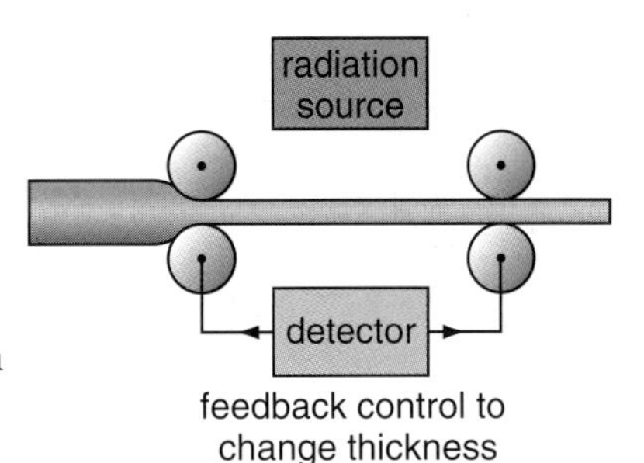

FIGURE 12.32 Controlling the thickness of materials

3 Radiation can be used to date ancient materials. The older the materials, the less radiation they emit.

4 The path of a radioactive fluid can be tracked with a detector. This is used in:

- Tracing pipe leaks, or the flow of underground streams.
- Medical tests, as a tracer to check blood flow or the action of various organs.

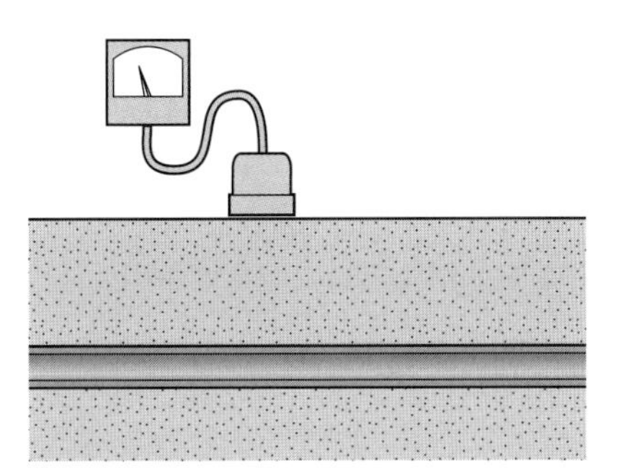

FIGURE 12.33

CHECK YOUR UNDERSTANDING

❶ Which type of radiation is most dangerous

a) when the source is inside the body?

b) when the source is some distance outside the body?

❷ The table shows the count rate from a radioactive sample decreasing with time.

Counts/minute	960	760	600	480	380	300	240	190
Time in days	0	1	2	3	4	5	6	7

a) What is the half-life of the sample?

b) How long does it take for the count rate to fall to 60 counts/min?

❸ A rock sample has 25 atoms of unstable potassium-40 for every 75 atoms of argon gas, its decay product. How old is the rock if the half-life of potassium-40 is 1300 million years?

Nuclear reactors

Nuclear reactors use **nuclear fission** reactions to produce large amounts of energy, transferred as heat.

The energy released by an atom during nuclear fission is much larger than the energy released when a chemical bond is formed between two atoms. So much more energy is released in nuclear reactors than in fossil fuel power stations.

The fuel used in nuclear reactors is uranium or plutonium – elements with large unstable nuclei.

These nuclei are bombarded by neutrons. Each nucleus splits into two smaller nuclei, with a few neutrons, and energy is released.

The neutrons from each fission reaction can themselves go on to split another uranium or plutonium nucleus. This produces a **chain reaction**.

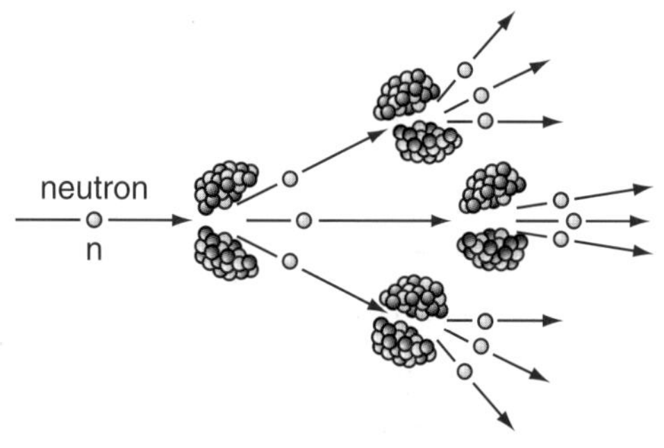

FIGURE 12.34 A chain reaction

The two smaller nuclei produced in each fission reaction are very radioactive.

Some of the waste products of nuclear fission have long half-lives and remain radioactive for hundreds of years.

Topic Test

1 Water waves of wavelength 2.5 cm pass a fixed marker at the rate of 3 waves every second.
   a) What is the frequency of the waves in hertz?
   b) Calculate the speed of these waves. Write down the equation you will use and show your working out. (4 marks)

2 Water waves cross at an angle the boundary into deep water. Describe what changes, if any, occur to the following:
   a) direction, b) speed, c) wavelength.

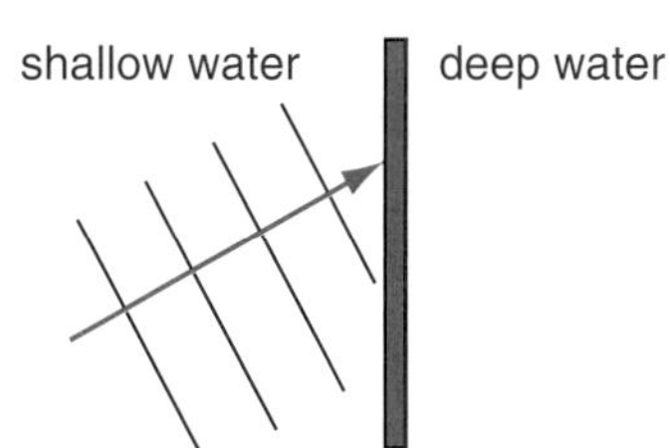

(3 marks)

3 State which waves from the electromagnetic spectrum can be used for:
   a) cooking
   b) providing shadow pictures of bones
   c) TV remote control units
   d) night-time photography
   e) obtaining a suntan. (5 marks)

4 a) What is meant by the term background radiation?

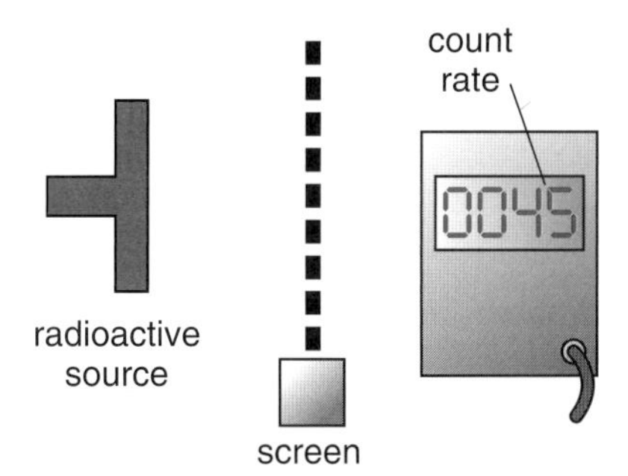

Screen	Count rate in counts/minute
No absorber	542
Thin paper	268
5 mm metal	271
10 mm lead	45

A radioactive source is placed behind different screens. The radiation detected at the other side of each screen is shown in the table. The background radiation during this investigation is 12 counts/minute.
   b) Why is the background radiation measured?
   c) What type(s) of radiation is the source emitting? Explain the reason for your choice. (5 marks)

5 A radioisotope, radon-220, decays by emitting a γ-ray and an α particle. The half-life of radon-220 is 52 seconds.
   a) What is a γ-ray?
   b) How much of the original sample is left after 156 seconds? (3 marks)

6 Which of the radioactive sources in the table could be used for:
   a) Diagnostic testing of blood flow?
   b) Controlling the thickness of metal foil?

Isotope	Emission	Half-life
sodium-24	γ	15 hours
iodine-131	β	8.1 days
strontium-90	β	28 years
cobalt-60	γ	5.3 years
americium-241	α	458 years

(2 marks)

Total: 22 marks

Physics examination questions and model answers

1 a) The table gives information about some planets.

Planet	Gravitational field strength in N/kg	Diameter of planet in thousands of km	Time for one orbit around the Sun in years
Mercury	4	4.9	0.2
Venus	9	12.0	0.6
Earth	10	12.8	1.0
Jupiter	26	143.0	12.0

i) Write down the equation that links gravitational field strength, mass and weight. *(1 mark)*

weight = mass × gravitational field strength

Always write the equation using words not symbols. Correct symbols are acceptable, but it is easy to make a mistake.

ii) An astronaut has a mass of 75 kg. Calculate the weight of the astronaut on Venus. Show clearly how you work out your answer. *(2 marks)*

weight = 75 × 9 = 675

Weight of astronaut = 675 newtons

Always show the steps in your working out. If you make a mistake with the arithmetic you can still get a mark or marks for a correct method.

iii) Why would the astronaut weigh more on the Earth than on Venus? *(1 mark)*

The gravitational field strength is higher on Earth than it is on Venus.

Use the information given in the table. The question asks for a comparison to be made. The answer must mention both Earth and Venus.

iv) Jupiter is further from the Sun than Mercury, Venus and Earth. What evidence in the table shows this? *(1 mark)*

The time taken by Jupiter to orbit once around the Sun is longer than the time taken by the other planets.

The correct information, in this case orbit time, must be used. A comparison of diameter or gravitational field strength would not gain the mark.

b) Explain briefly how stars like the Sun are thought to have been formed. *(2 marks)*

The Sun was formed from a gigantic cloud of dust and gas (mainly hydrogen). This cloud was pulled inwards and squashed into a smaller volume by the force of gravity.

The question is worth two marks, so make sure you make two clear statements. The two statements should be in the correct order.

2 The diagram shows, in a simplified form, how a telephone call can be transmitted from Britain to the USA.

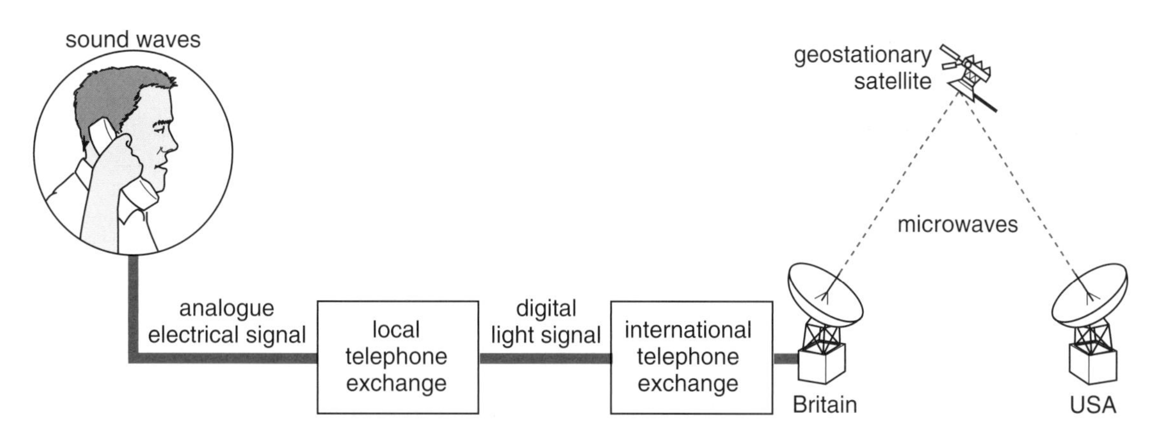

i) What is the difference between an analogue and a digital signal? You may wish to draw a diagram to help with your answer. *(2 marks)*

With an analogue signal the amplitude or the frequency or both vary continuously. With a digital signal the amplitude is either a maximum or zero as the signal is a series of on and off pulses.

> For full credit the answer must refer to both an analogue and a digital signal. The marks could also have been gained from a correct drawing of an analogue and a digital signal.

ii) Explain why the quality of an analogue signal transmitted over a long distance decreases, but the quality of a digital signal transmitted over the same distance does not change. *(3 marks)*

All signals weaken with increasing distance and need to be amplified. With an analogue signal the unwanted noise is also amplified so the quality of the signal deteriorates. With a digital signal unwanted noise may change the shape of the pulses but not the pattern. Even when amplified the pulses will be recognisable as either on or off.

> The first sentence is essential and gains one mark. To complete the answer, reference must be made to both analogue and digital signals. Make sure your answer contains no contradictions.

iii) Explain why the satellite used to receive and transmit the microwave signals is placed in a geostationary orbit. *(2 marks)*

The satellite will always be above the same point on the Earth's surface, so the transmitting and receiving dishes do not need to keep changing direction.

> Always look carefully at diagrams as they often contain details that will help you to answer the question – in this case the link between the geostationary satellite and the transmitting and receiving dishes.

Answers

Module 1 – Humans as organisms

Check your understanding

Page 4

1 We are always breathing more oxygen into the lungs and the blood is constantly carrying it away from the alveolus surface
2 a) Glucose
b) Amylase
3 a) Fatty acids and glycerol
b) Lipase
4 Hydrochloric acid and protease enzymes
5 In the villi in the small intestine

Page 6

1 Glucose + oxygen → carbon dioxide + water + energy
2 In mitochondria of all living cells
3 Movement, keeping warm, making large molecules from small ones, active transport across boundaries

Page 10

1 Platelets
2 Any three from: wash regularly, cook food well, cover food up, store food in a cool place, keep away from people with infectious diseases

Topic test

1 a) Tail to swim/head containing genes (1 mark)
b) Contain lots of haemoglobin to carry oxygen/no nucleus so more room for oxygen (1 mark)
c) Elongated so can contract and shorten (1 mark)
2 a) Nucleus to control cells activities (1 mark)
b) Cytoplasm contains mitochondria/enzymes to control chemical reactions (1 mark)
c) Membrane controls movement of substances in and out of cell (1 mark)
3 Increase the difference in concentration (1 mark)
increase the surface area of membrane (1 mark)
4 Large surface area (1 mark)
thin membranes (1 mark)
good vascular supply (1 mark)
5

Insoluble food	Enzyme	Soluble food
starch	amylase	sugars
proteins	protease	amino acids
fats	lipase	fatty acids and glycerol

(1 mark each)

6 Neutralises stomach acid (1 mark)
makes correct conditions for enzymes (1 mark)
breaks down fat droplets (1 mark)
7 Muscles between ribs contract (1 mark)
ribs move up and out (1 mark)
diaphragm muscle contracts causing it to flatten (1 mark)
volume of chest cavity increases (1 mark)
pressure decreases (1 mark)
8 Atria contract pushing blood into ventricles (1 mark)
valves close (1 mark)
ventricles contract (1 mark)
blood goes in two directions (1 mark)
ventricles relax (1 mark)
(must be in sequence)
9 Lactic acid produced in anaerobic respiration (1 mark)
must be removed/makes muscles ache (1 mark)
panting after finished exercise to get more oxygen into body (1 mark)
10 Weakened micro-organisms injected into blood (1 mark)
white cells make antibodies (1 mark)
body remembers how to make these again quickly (1 mark)
if real micro-organism gets in (1 mark)
antibodies ready quickly to destroy them (1 mark)

Module 2 – Maintenance of life

Check your understanding

Page 14

1 Hot, dry and windy
2 Because desert plants live in extremely dry conditions and so need to minimise the amount of transpiration and conserve the water in the plant

Page 19

1 Light = eye, sound = ear, taste = tongue
2 They relax
3 Stimulus = prick from pin, receptor = sense cell in finger, co-ordinator = spinal cord, effector = muscle in arm, response = moving hand away from pin

Page 20

1 Carbon dioxide, urea
2 Insulin

Page 21

1 Any three from: amino acides, ions, glucose, water
2 ADH

Page 23

1 A chemical that affects the way the body chemistry works or the way we feel
2 Any two from: alcohol, solvents, tobacco
3 Damage to brain, liver, coma, lack of self control
4 Emphysema, bronchitis, lung cancer

Topic test

1 a) Controls what enters and leaves the cell (1 mark)
b) Makes cell rigid (1 mark)
c) Absorbs light to make food (1 mark)
2 It gives it a large surface area to absorb more water (1 mark)
3 Starch, lipids, cellulose, amino acids then proteins (1 mark each)
4 Carbon dioxide + water → glucose + oxygen (1 mark)
5 a) To make proteins (1 mark)
b) For photosynthesis and respiration (1 mark)
c) To help enzymes in photosynthesis and respiration (1 mark)
6 Movement of molecules (1 mark)
from a region of high concentration to a region of low concentration (1 mark)
7 a) When they absorb ions from the soil water (1 mark)
b) It needs energy from respiration (1 mark)
8 As weedkiller (1 mark)
to root cuttings (1 mark)
to affect fruit ripening (1 mark)
9

Receptors	What it detects
skin	touch and pressure changes
tongue	chemicals so that we can taste

(2 marks)
10 a) Fine focuses light on retina (1 mark)
b) Controls amount of light entering the eye (1 mark)
11 Ciliary muscles contract to focus on near objects and relax for distant objects (1 mark)
12 Temperature, ion content, water content (1 mark each)
13 Lowers blood sugar level (1 mark)
14 Feeling ill when drug is not taken (1 mark)

Answers

Module 3 – Environment

Check your understanding

Page 25

1 Thick fur, a thick layer of fat and although they are large, they have a compact body shape with small ears
2 Food, nesting/sleeping sites, water and a mate
3 Trees keep out the light (and also take up much of the water)
4 a) Allowed the plants to grow tall
b) The foxes (predators) were deprived of an important food source so fox numbers reduced and they competed for alternative food sources
5 The tree would not be able to photosynthesise so there would be less sugar transported to the fruit so fewer apples produced
6 Long loops of Henle to increase water reabsorption – produce a small volume of concentrated urine
7 Parasites, e.g. fleas, worms, mites etc.
8 a) Fewer young raised
b) Fewer young raised
9 Organisms which cannot be easily seen are not eaten by predators so survive to breed

Page 28

1 Some of the light is reflected from the leaf surfaces and some is the wrong colour (plants can only use red and blue wavelengths for photosynthesis)
2 There is less energy lost in respiration and maintaining the biomass
3 The mass of living material at each feeding (trophic) level. This decreases up the pyramid from producer to consumers
4 Free range piglets use energy running around
5 Problems of sewage disposal, hormones and antibiotics used to prevent spread of disease. Use of herbicides and insecticides in arable (crop) production reduces biodiversity
6 Lower productivity – no artificial fertilisers used, no hormones, free range so energy used in movement

Page 30

1 Harvesting removes the mineral ions from the food chain and the ecosystem
2 The ideal conditions for composting are aerobic and moist – it will be warm from the respiration of the micro-organisms
3 Photosynthesis
4 Nitrates → plant proteins → animal proteins → ammonium compounds → nitrates
5 Micro-organisms need cellulase to break down cellulose, and protease to break down proteins

Page 32

1 Nitrates and phosphates
2 The pond water becomes green as algae reproduce, more weeds grow, and fish die
3 More rainfall in autumn so more run-off into rivers, slower plant growth so less uptake of fertiliser

Topic test

1 a) 96% (1 mark)
b) Any one from: respiration, movement, faeces, maintaining body temperature (1 mark)
c) Yes – chemical energy in the faeces passes to the decomposer pathway/food chain (1 mark)
d Any one from: by keeping the cattle confined to prevent movement, keep cattle warm (wind breaks in field or keep in barns), computerise individual food supply (1 mark)
2 A = putrifying bacteria (accept decomposing bacteria) (1 mark)
B = nitrifying bacteria (1 mark)
C = nitrates (1 mark)
3 a) The green colour is caused by an algal bloom (1 mark)
Reason – sewage contains nitrates which act as plant fertiliser, increasing growth rate (1 mark)
b) Light cannot pass through the algae (1 mark)
Rooted plants need light to photosynthesise (1 mark)
c) Increase in decomposing bacteria (1 mark)
which break down the dead weeds (1 mark)
d) The decomposer bacteria are aerobic. They use up the dissolved oxygen in the water so the fish cannot get enough oxygen for respiration (2 marks)

Answers

4

Action	Increases or decreases CO_2	Explanation
more cars on the road	Increases	are fuelled by burning fossil fuels
planting more trees	decreases	trees take CO_2 from the air as a raw material for photosynthesis
increasing the number of gas fired power stations	increases	methane is a fossil fuel
increasing the proportion of electricity produced by wind generators	decreases	wind is a renewable source so less fossil fuels will be used

5 a) Burning fossil fuels produce oxides of sulphur and nitrogen (1 mark)
they gases dissolve (1 mark)
in the moisture in clouds, the droplets fall as acid rain (1 mark)

b) Any three from:
use of low sulphur fuels will reduce sulphur dioxide
increase the proportion of people using public transport instead of cars
increase rail freight instead of road
increase the proportion of renewable energy used (3 marks)

c) Any two from:
increased use of land for building
increased quarrying for building materials
increased food requirement – more intensive farming with more use of pesticides and fertilisers
more waste to dispose of (2 marks)

Module 4 – Inheritance and selection

Check your understanding

Page 35

1 a) (i) Sperm
(ii) Ovum (plural – ova)
b) Fertilisation
c) Genes
d) Mitosis

2 Different nutrients, e.g. nitrates, different environmental conditions (light intensities, e.g. a plant grown in dim light will be tall and straggly, shortage of water, wind)

3 Environmental factors, e.g. exposure to Sun; lifestyle differences, e.g. different diet and amount of exercise

Page 37

1 Red

2 No – they will be genetically identical and so phenotypically identical if grown under the same conditions

3 Loss of allele variety in the gene pool so less variety for future selective breeding
Increasing homozygosity as the number of alternative alleles is reduced

4 Increase in uniformity in a crop
Increased occurrence of a desirable characteristic

5 The insulin has an identical structure to human insulin and will not be destroyed by the body
The insulin will not cause an allergic reaction
The insulin is cheap to produce and of consistent composition

Answers

Page 39

1 Food, water, nesting sites, mates, territory
2 At the bottom
3 A mutation in the chromosomes/DNA/genes
4 a) The resistant bacteria will not be destroyed by penicillin – they either prevent the penicillin from entering the bacterial cell or have developed an enzyme that will destroy it
b) This clone can reproduce rapidly and out-compete other strains and cause the illness
5 Change in climate increased the area covered by forests and decreased their grassland grazing area
6 Within the giraffe population there was some variation in neck length
A struggle for existence occurred when food became scarce
Those giraffes able to reach higher had more food, reared more young and these in turn would have the longer neck feature (survival of the best adapted)
This happened over many generations so that the present day, long necked giraffe evolved

Page 41

1 A heterozygous pair – one dominant and one recessive
2 50%
3 In a (straight) line
4 25%

Page 42

1 Stimulates an ovum to develop in the ovary, and stimualtes the production of oestrogen by the ovary
2 Hormone LH, released mid-cycle from the pituitary gland
3 Progesterone
4 Having seveal babies at once

Topic test

1 a) Dominant (1 mark)
b) (i)

phenotype	freckled	unfreckled
genotype	Ff	ff
gametes (circled)	F f	f
offspring	50% Ff freckled	50% ff unfreckled

(3 marks)
(ii) If this couple had 6 children we would expect 3 to have freckles (1 mark)
2 nucleus (1 mark)
DNA (1 mark)
genes (1 mark)
three bases (1 mark)
enzymes (1 mark)
hormones (1 mark)
3 a) Diploid (1 mark)
b) Diploid (1 mark)
c) Mitosis (1 mark)
d) The donor cell mother (1 mark)
as this was the source of genetic material (1 mark)
4 A dead bird might be eaten, e.g. by a fox or scavenger
or decomposed by bacteria in the aerobic conditions (2 marks)
5 a) The plants were killed (1 mark)
b) A few plants had different alleles and were able to survive/ they were resistant (i.e. an example of variation in the population) (1 mark)
c) These resistant plants were able to reproduce without competition (1 mark)
d) We would expect them to grow (1 mark)
6 23 pairs (1 mark)
FSH (1 mark)
meiosis or meiotic division (1 mark)
haploid (1 mark)
sperm (1 mark)
diploid (1 mark)
mitosis (1 mark)
progesterone (1 mark)

Answers

Module 5 – Metals

Check your understanding

Page 47

1 Relative atomic mass
2 Argon
3 70 to 75
4 Any three from:
- Lower density
- Lower melting points
- Softer
- Not so tough/strong

5 Any three from:
- Much more reactive
- Corrode more rapidly
- React with water to form soluble metal hydroxides and hydrogen
- Form white salts not coloured ones

Page 48

1 The following are the reactions:
   a) zinc + lead oxide → lead + zinc oxide
   b) does not react
   c) hydrogen + copper oxide → copper + water
2 An ore is a rock from which useful substances can be extracted economically
3 Carbon is more abundant and therefore much cheaper

Page 49

1 Goes down
2 Goes up
3 a) To increase the strength of the iron
   b) It is reacted with limestone in the blast furnace to produce slag

Page 52

1 Because the ions are fixed in position and are not able to move
2 Because the ions are separated and are free to move
3 Bauxite (Al_2O_3)
4 a) The negative electrode (cathode)
   b) Oxygen gas
   c) Because it reacts with the oxygen and burns away to form carbon dioxide
   d) (i) At the positive electrode: $2O^{2-} \rightarrow O_2 + 4e^-$
   At the negative electrode: $Al^3 + 3e^- \rightarrow Al$
   (ii) The oxide is oxidised
   (iii) The aluminium ion is reduced

5 a)

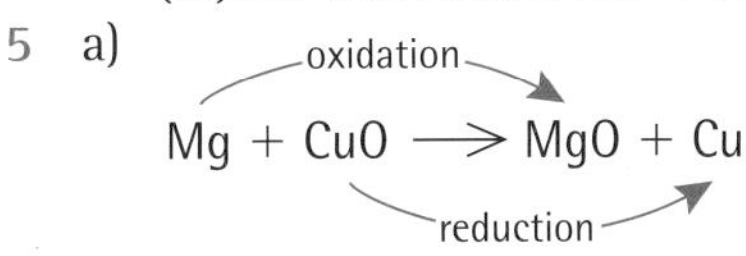

b)

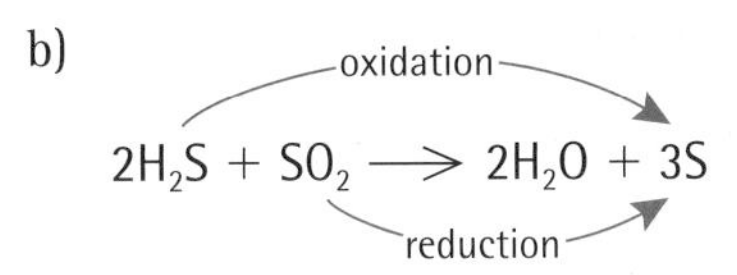

c)

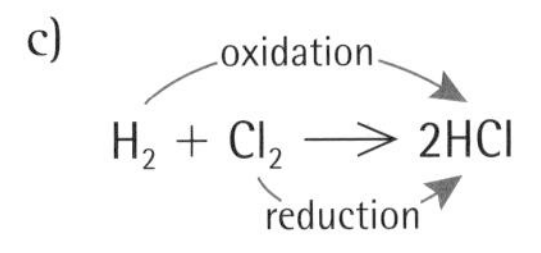

d)

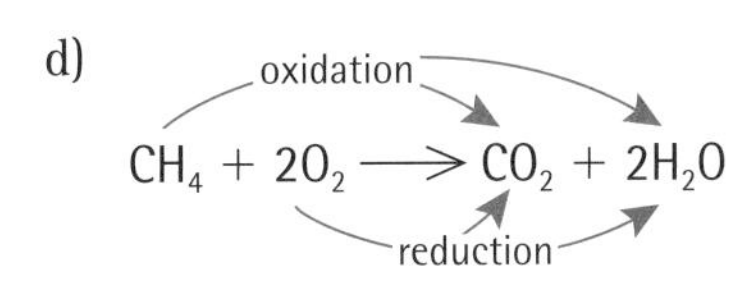

Page 54

1 Rusting
2 a) Chromium and nickel
   b) Stainless steel
3 a) Magnesium and zinc
   b) They must be higher in the reactivity series than iron
   c) Sacrificial protection
4 Because on exposure to air it gets covered with a layer of aluminium oxide. This layer seals the surface and prevents air and water from getting to the metal

Page 56

1 Water
2 a) potassium chloride
   b) lithium nitrate
   c) ammonium sulphate
3 An alkali is a base that is soluble in water
4 a) $\underline{K^+}(aq) + OH^-(aq) + H^+(aq) + \underline{NO_3}^-(aq) \rightarrow \underline{K^+}(aq) + \underline{NO_3}^-(aq) + H_2O(l)$
   b) Spectator ions underlined in the equation above
   c) $OH^-(aq) + H^+(aq) \rightarrow H_2O(l)$

Answers

Topic test

1 Mn and Ru (2 marks)
2 Magnesium and carbon (2 marks)
3 a) coke (1 mark)
b) hot air (1 mark)
c) limestone (1 mark)
d) iron ore (1 mark)
4 a) (iii) (1 mark)
b) (ii) (1 mark)
c) (iv) (1 mark)
d) (i) (1 mark)
5 a) Aluminium is extracted by electrolysis (1 mark)
b) Iron is extracted by heating it with carbon (1 mark)
c) Copper is purified by electrolysis (1 mark)
6 Adding chromium (and nickel) to make stainless-steel (1 mark)
using sacrificial protection with magnesium or zinc (1 mark)
(Accept painting, cover in plastic, coat with oil)
7 Aluminium reacts with air/water (1 mark)
to form a layer of aluminium oxide (1 mark)
this layer seals the surface and prevents any air or water getting to it (1 mark)
8 Any acid (e.g. sulphuric, citric etc.) Accept just the word 'acid' (1 mark)
9 a)

Acid	Base/alkali	Salt
sulphuric acid	sodium hydroxide (or oxide)	sodium sulphate
hydrochloric acid	potassium hydroxide	potassium chloride
nitric acid	copper oxide	copper nitrate

(3 marks)
b) Neutralisation (1 mark)
c) Water (1 mark)
10 a) In each case the reaction that takes place is
$H^+(aq) + OH^-(aq) \rightarrow H_2O(l)$ (1 mark)
All other ions are spectator ions (1 mark)
b) Some of the energy released in the neutralisation is used (1 mark)
to ionise the weak (and therefore unionised) base (1 mark)

Module 6 – Earth materials

Check your understanding

Page 59

1 a) limestone (calcium carbonate) → quicklime (calcium oxide) + carbon dioxide
b) quicklime (calcium oxide) + water → slaked lime (calcium hydroxide)
c) limestone (calcium carbonate) + sulphuric acid → calcium sulphate + carbon dioxide + water
2 Because it is too alkaline and could 'over compensate' making the water alkaline – which would be just as damaging
3 Making iron in the blast furnace

Page 61

1 A compound that contains carbon and hydrogen only
2 Fractional distillation
3 Refinery gases, gasoline (petrol), kerosene (paraffin), gas oil (diesel), fuel oil, bitumen
4 Colour, viscosity, boiling point, flammability, number of carbon atoms in the molecules
5 Those with a large number of carbon atoms (e.g. bitumen)
6 Cracking
7 Making polymers and as fuels
8 Because plastics are not biodegradable
9 Plastics can be burned (incinerated) producing useful heat but harmful gases. Some plastics can be recycled which reduces the use of natural resources
10 Carbon dioxide and water (vapour)
11 Sulphur dioxide gas is produced. This causes acid rain, which can kill wildlife
12 A saturated hydrocarbon has carbon – carbon single bonds. An unsaturated hydrocarbon has at least one pair of carbon atoms linked by a double bond
13 The structural formula of propane is:

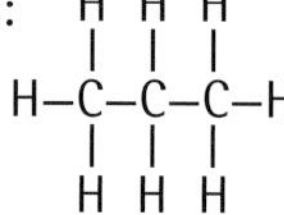

Answers

Page 63

1 By volcanic activity
2 During the first billion years of the Earth's existence
3 Carbon dioxide (converted into oxygen by plants and absorbed into oceans where it became 'locked up' in carbonate). Water vapour (formed oceans as the planet cooled). Methane (reacted with oxygen to form carbon dioxide). Ammonia (reacted with oxygen and produced nitrogen).
4 Nitrogen (80%), oxygen (20%) and other gases (including carbon dioxide, water vapour and the noble gases)
5 The reaction between ammonia and oxygen and the action of denitrifying bacteria
6

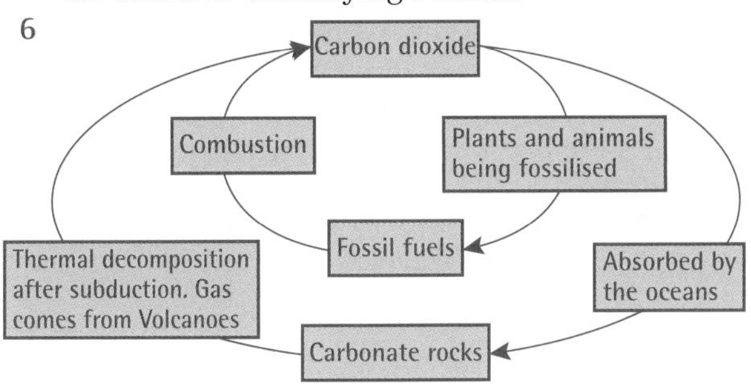

Page 64

1 The inner core of the Earth has the highest density
2 a) The main parts are (from the outside) the crust, the mantle, the outer core and the inner core
b) The mantle has the largest volume
3 The rocks are solid but they flow like a very viscous liquid

Page 65

1 They can be tilted, folded, faulted (fractured) or turned upside down
2 Tectonic activity
3 By the action of heat and pressure on existing rocks

Page 68

1 The shape of the land masses and the fossil/rock record on the two continents
2 a) Continental drift
b) Because there was no way to explain why the continents could drift apart until about 50 years later

3 a) The lithosphere is the crust and the upper part of the mantle
b) Tectonic plates
c) Convection currents in the Earth's core caused by radioactive processes
4 a) Sliding past each other, moving towards each other, moving away from each other
b) Sliding – along the San Andreas fault; moving towards each other – along the west coast of South America; moving away from each other – along the mid-Atlantic ridge
5 a) Where the plates are moving together and denser, oceanic crust slides beneath the continental crust
b) Where the plates are moving apart and the gaps formed are filled by magma

Topic test

1 a) (iv) (1 mark)
b) (iv) (1 mark)
c) (i) (1 mark)
d) (iv) (1 mark)
2 a) Faults (1 mark)
b) The movement of the Earth's crust (1 mark)
c) The crust and the upper part of the mantle (1 mark)
3 The plates move because of convection currents deep inside the Earth's core. (1 mark)
The heat that produces these currents comes from radioactive processes in the core. (1 mark)
4 C and D (2 marks)
5

$$n\left[\begin{matrix} H_2C=CH \\ \quad\quad | \\ \quad\quad CH_3 \end{matrix}\right] \longrightarrow \left[\begin{matrix} -H_2C-CH- \\ \quad\quad\quad | \\ \quad\quad\quad CH_3 \end{matrix}\right]_n$$

6 a) (iii) (1 mark)
b) (ii) (1 mark)
c) (iv) (1 mark)
d) (iv) (1 mark)
7 a) Continental plates moving apart from each other (1 mark)
b) Igneous (1 mark)
basaltic ocean crust (1 mark)

Answers

Module 7 – Patterns of chemical change

Check your understanding

Page 72

1 Gas syringe
2 One of the reactants has been completely used up

Page 73

1 Crush the marble into smaller pieces
Heat the acid
Use a concentrated solution of the acid
2 The particles move faster and are more likely to collide with each other
On collision, more particles have enough energy to get over the energy barrier (i.e. reach the activation energy)
3 Sawdust has a much larger surface area so the oxygen in the air can get to the wood more quickly

Page 79

1 A reaction that can go in either direction, depending on the conditions
2 Add white anhydrous copper sulphate powder to the liquid. If the liquid contains water, the white powder will turn blue
3 487 kJ mol^{-1} (evolved)
4 Pressure = 200 atmospheres; temperature = 450°C; catalyst of iron

Topic test

1 In concentrated acid the reacting acid particles are closer together (1 mark)
and are more likely to collide with the magnesium than in the dilute acid where they are further apart (1 mark)
2 A catalyst is a substance that speeds up a chemical reaction but remains chemically unchanged at the end (2 marks)
3 The reactants are slowly being used up (1 mark)
so their concentration decreases as the reaction proceeds (1 mark)
so there are fewer reacting molecules left to react (1 mark)
4 When one of the reactants has been completely used up (1 mark)
5 High pressures increase the concentration of the gases (1 mark)
making the reaction go faster (1 mark)
6 The vessels have to have very thick and strong walls to withstand the pressure and such vessels are very expensive to make (1 mark)
7 Low temperatures and therefore lower costs (1 mark)
8 The environment in which the enzyme is operating is constantly monitored (1 mark)
and the enzyme is immobilised by trapping it on an inert support (1 mark)
9 Enzymes are destroyed (or denatured) at high temperatures (1 mark)
10 Exothermic reactions give out heat energy (1 mark)
Endothermic reactions absorb heat energy (1 mark)
11 Activation energy (1 mark)
12 Bubble the gas through limewater (1 mark)
If it is carbon dioxide the limewater will turn cloudy (1 mark)
13 Advantage – better yields (1 mark)
Disadvantage – excess may pollute water supplies (1 mark)
14 Nitrogen from the air (1 mark)
hydrogen from natural gas (1 mark)
15 450°C (1 mark)
200 atmospheres (1 mark)
16 Iron (1 mark)
17 High temperatures make the ammonia decompose back to nitrogen and hydrogen (1 mark)
18 a) $M_r = 80$; % of N = 35% (2 marks)
b) $M_r = 132$; % of N = 21.21% (2 marks)
19 $NaHCO_3$ (4 marks)
20 0.667 g (4 marks)

Answers

Module 8 – Structures and bonding

Check your understanding

Page 85

1 a)

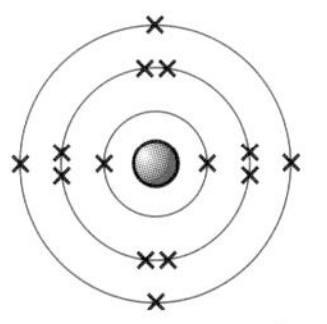

b)

2 17 protons, 17 electrons, 18 neutrons

Page 88

1 Electrons transfer from metal to non-metal elements
Oppositely charged ions are formed
Electrostatic forces of attraction hold the ions together

2

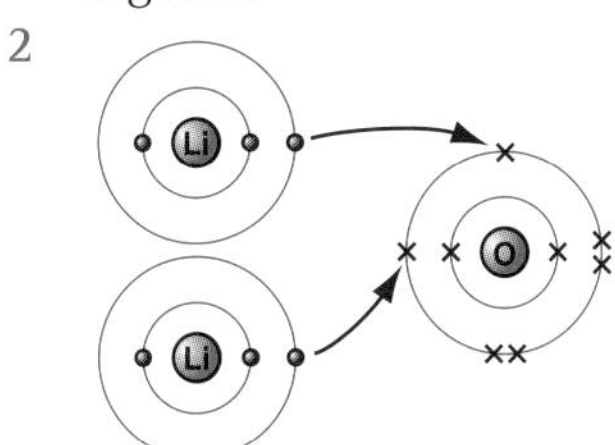

makes two Li^+ ions and one O^{2-} ion

3 In solid sodium chloride the ions are in fixed positions and cannot move. In molten sodium chloride the ions are free to move and carry the electric current

Page 91

1 a)

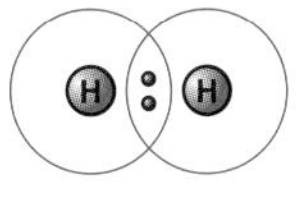

b)

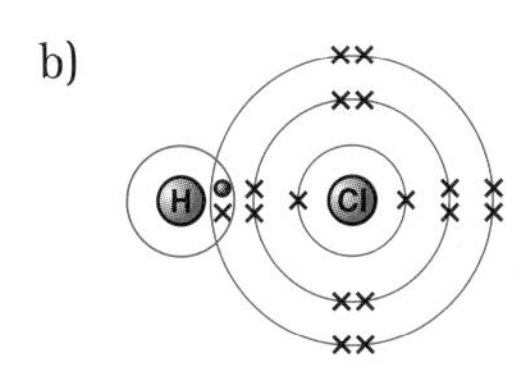

2 a) covalent
b) ionic
c) covalent

3 a) gas
b) solid
c) gas

4 They do not contain any free electrons or ions to carry the current

Topic test

1 It loses 1 electron (1 mark)

2 It gains 2 electrons (1 mark)

3 See table below

4 a) Diagram showing one magnesium atom (2,8,2) (1 mark)
transferring its two outer electrons to two separate fluorine atoms (2,7) (1 mark)
b) ionic (1 mark)
c) solid (1 mark)

5 Group 4 because it has four outer electrons (1 mark)
Period 3 because its electrons are in three energy levels (shells) (1 mark)

6 Copper sulphate consists of ions (1 mark)
In the solid state the ions are not free to move, but in solution they are (1 mark)

7 a) Na^+ and O^{2-} ions (1 mark)
b) H_2O molecules (1 mark)
c) Mg^{2+} and Cl^- ions (1 mark)
d) SO_2 molecules (1 mark)

8 They consist of giant covalent structures (1 mark)

9 a) Reactivity increases down Group 1 (1 mark)
b) Reactivity decreases down Group 7 (1 mark)

10 All their energy levels (shells) are full (1 mark)

Particle	Number of			Atomic number	Mass number
	protons	neutrons	electrons		
N atom	7	7	7	7	14
B atom	5	6	5	5	11
Al atom	13	14	13	13	27
Ca^{2+} ion	20	20	18	20	40
F^- ion	9	10	10	9	19

Table for Topic Test Q3

(1 mark each)

Answers

11 Hydrogen (1 mark)
chlorine (1 mark)
sodium hydroxide (1 mark)

12 It would slowly turn grey or darken (1 mark)

13 a) Hydrogen gas: apply a flame; gas burns with a squeaky explosion (1 mark)
b) Chlorine gas: add damp litmus paper; the litmus paper is bleached (1 mark)

14 Any one from: killing bacteria; making bleach; making hydrochloric acid; making PVC (1 mark)

15 a) NaBr (1 mark)
b) $MgBr_2$ (1 mark)
c) Na_2O (1 mark)

16 a) $1 \times H$ (1 mark)
$1 \times N$ (1 mark)
$3 \times O$ (1 mark)
b) $2 \times N$ (1 mark)
$8 \times H$ (1 mark)
$1 \times S$ (1 mark)
$4 \times O$ (1 mark)

17 a) $CH_4(g) + \underline{2}\,O_2(g) \rightarrow CO_2(g) + \underline{2}\,H_2O(l)$ (1 mark each)
b) (g) = gas (1 mark)
(l) = liquid (1 mark)

Module 9 – Energy

Check your understanding

Page 100

1 Convection. The particles in solids can only vibrate about a fixed position/are held in place by forces from neighbouring particles

2 a) Black radiates away energy/black is a good emitter of radiation
b) White is a poor absorber of radiation/good reflector of radiation

3 Double glazing, thicker window panes, thick curtains

4 14 years

Page 102

1 a) Loudspeaker (radio/electric keyboard/CD player etc.)
b) Motor
c) Lift

2 6000 J

3 joules (J), kilowatt-hours (kWh)

4 150 000 J/150 kJ

5 4776 pence/£47.76

Page 103

1 Lamp B
b) 0.02/2%
c) 93.5 J

2 a) 18 000 000 J (18 000 kJ/18 MJ)
b) 14 400 000 J (14 400 kJ/14.4 MJ)

Page 104

1 a) Carbon dioxide/CO_2
b) Sulphur dioxide /SO_2

2 Long-term radiation hazards/radioactivity lasts for thousands of years

3 Electricity produced is too expensive

4 Nuclear fuels do not produce polluting gases/carbon dioxide/sulphur dioxide/greenhouse gases/ gases that cause acid rain

Page 107

1 a) Hydroelectric b) Tidal c) Gas

2 Gas, hydroelectric

3 Satellite/any remote place/boat

4 a) £150
b) 5 years

Topic test

1 a) transferred (1 mark)
cold/cooler/cool/colder (1 mark)
radiation/conduction (1 mark)
conduction/radiation (1 mark)
slower/less (1 mark)
falls/drops (1 mark)
absorbs (1 mark)
faster (1 mark)
hotter/hot (1 mark)
b) 5 years (2 marks)

Answers

2 a) Gravitational potential energy → kinetic energy → electrical energy (1 mark)
  b) 200 000 J/200 kJ (1 mark)
  c) 500 000 J/500 kJ (1 mark)
  d) 300 000 W/300 kW (2 marks)

3 a) Less wasted energy/more useful energy (1 mark)
  b) Less fossil fuel/energy resources used to provide heating, less pollution caused in heating houses separately (1 mark)
  c) Loss of heat to surroundings/water less hot as it reaches houses (1 mark)
  d) Insulating pipes carrying hot water/using pipes of poor conducting material etc. (1 mark)

4 a) 1525 (units) (1 mark)
  b) £106.75 (1 mark)

5 a) 2p/unit (1 mark)
  b) Any two from: building more expensive, decommissioning more expensive, storing waste, waste disposal, fuel reclamation (2 marks)

6 a) 600 J (1 mark)
  b) 25 W (J/s) (1 mark)
  c) 0.125 (12.5%) (2 marks)
  d) 120 s (2 minutes) (1 mark)

Module 10 – Electricity

Check your understanding

Page 112

1 A diode only lets current flow in one direction

2 a) 12 volts
  b) The resistance goes down as the temperature goes up

3 a) b)

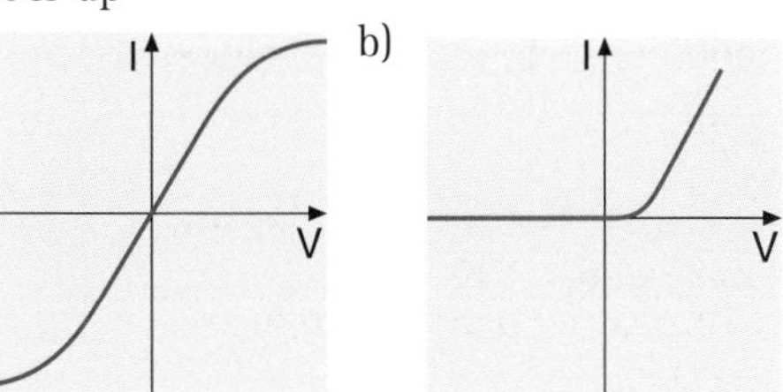

4 As light intensity increases the current increases

Page 113

1 The current creates a magnetic field around the wire. This magnetic field and that of the permanent magnets interact to produce a force on each side of the coil. The forces are in opposite directions so the coil turns.

2 It switches off the current faster than a fuse (it can also be reset)

Page 115

1 It is joined to the ground by a conductor (often a copper wire)

2 Repel – they have been given the same type of charge

3 The balloon attracts and picks up the pieces of paper

Page 118

1 Blue

2 It is a good conductor

3 Plastic or rubber (they are good insulators)

4 a)

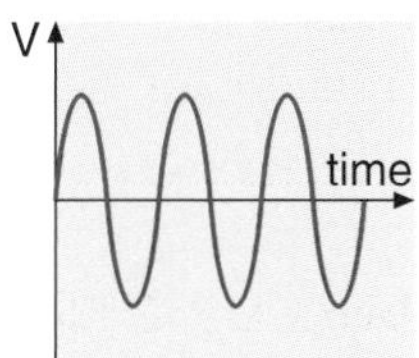

5 A current greater than the fuse rating causes the fuse to get so hot that it melts

Page 119

1 1.4 g

Page 122

1 Use a stronger magnet; rotate the coil faster; add more turns to the coil; increase the area of the coil

2 1150

3 4 A

4 6.5 A (approximately)

Answers

Topic test

1 a) conductors b) electrodes
c) electrons d) ions (1 mark each)

2 a) A (0.25 A) (1 mark)
b) B (30 C) (1 mark)
c) C (270 J) (1 mark)
d) C (2.25 W) (1 mark)

3 a) 230 volts (1 mark)
b) 50 hertz (1 mark)
c) 1380 watts (1 mark)
d) 6 amps (1 mark)

4 If the live wire touches the metal sole plate of the iron (1 mark)
a large current flows from the live wire to earth (1 mark)
causing the fuse to melt and break the circuit (1 mark)

5 a) Power = potential difference × current (1 mark)
$= 230 \times 8$ (1 mark)
$= 1840$ watts (1 mark)

b) Potential difference = current × resistance (1 mark)
$230 = 8 \times R$ (1 mark)
resistance = 29 ohms (approximately) (1 mark)

6 As the particles pass the metal grid they become charged the same as the grid (1 mark)
the particles are repelled by the grid and attracted to the collecting plates (1 mark)
the particles which stick to the plates are knocked off and removed (1 mark)

7 a) Positive (1 mark)
b) Directly proportional (1 mark)

8 Joins the coil to the rest of the circuit (1 mark)

9 $\frac{V_p}{V_s} = \frac{N_p}{N_s}$ (1 mark)
$\frac{230}{V_s} = \frac{1000}{100}$ (1 mark)
$V_s = 23$ volts (1 mark)

Module 11 – Forces

Check your understanding

Page 126

1 Velocity includes direction

2

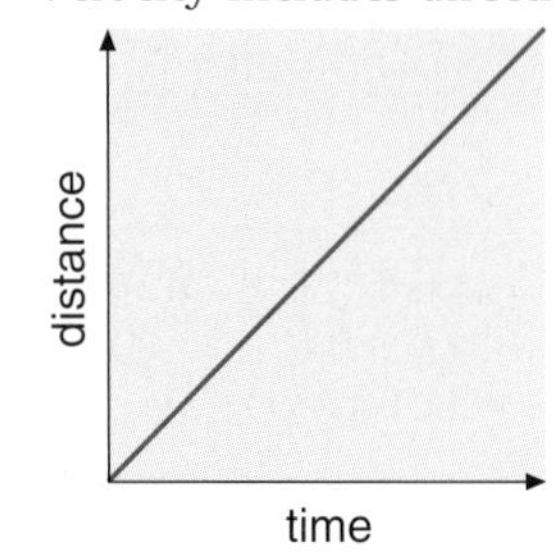

3 40 m/s^2

4 a) 1.5 m/s^2
b) 228 m

Page 128

1 3.25 N

2 The force of gravity and air resistance are in the opposite direction to the ball's motion

3 The lorry has a greater mass than a car. So a greater force is needed to produce the same deceleration ($F = m \times a$).

4 400 N

Page 131

1 The motorcyclist's reaction time (affected by alcohol, certain drugs, being tired); weather conditions (fog, ice, heavy rain etc); condition of the motorcycle (worn tyres, worn brakes)

2 1000 joules

3 Elastic potential energy

4 12 000 joules

Page 133

1 Gravity

2 So that they remain above the same point on the Earth's surface

3 They are then able to scan the whole of the Earth's surface (at regular intervals)

4 As the comet approaches the Sun, the force increases; as the comet moves away from the Sun, the force decreases

Page 136

1 Possibility that there was once water on the planet; fossil-like structures in rock

2 Will contract to become a white dwarf

Answers

3 Light reaching the Earth has a longer wavelength than expected so the source of the light (a galaxy) must be moving away from the Earth
4 Nuclei of lighter elements fuse to form heavier elements, called nuclear fusion
5 A black hole is so dense that nothing, not even light, can escape its gravitational field

Topic test

1 a) 750 metres (1 mark)
  b) 450 seconds (1 mark)
  c) (i) Part A (1 mark)
   (ii) Gradient $= \frac{500}{100}$ (1 mark)
   $= 5$ (m/s) (1 mark)
2 k.e. $= \frac{1}{2} \times$ mass $\times$ speed^2 (1 mark)
  $= \frac{1}{2} \times 400 \times 18 \times 18$ (1 mark)
  $= 64\,000$ joules (1 mark)
3 Suitable examples include: communications, monitoring weather patterns, spying on countries (1 mark each)
4 Explodes as a supernova (1 mark)
  leaving a dense neutron star (1 mark)
  that if it has enough mass becomes a black hole (1 mark)
5 Living organisms produce (chemical) changes to the atmosphere (1 mark)
  so it would be different from how it would have been with physical processes only (1 mark)
6 Using radio telescopes (1 mark)
  to search for recognisable radio signals from space (1 mark)
7 a) Acceleration = gradient of line (1 mark)
  $= \frac{12}{5}$ (1 mark)
  $= 2.4$ m/s^2 (1 mark)
  b) Distance = area under graph line (1 mark)
  $= 13 \times 12$ (1 mark)
  $= 156$ metres (1 mark)
8 The forces are unbalanced (1 mark)
  the forces opposing motion (air resistance/drag) are bigger than the forward force (1 mark)
9 The stopping distance increases (1 mark)
  less friction between the tyres and the road (1 mark)
10 Weight = mass $\times$ gravitational field strength (1 mark)
  $= 70 \times 1.6$ (1 mark)
  $= 112$ newtons (1 mark)

Module 12 – Waves and radiation

Check your understanding

Page 140

1 A transverse wave has the disturbance at right angles to the direction of travel
  Examples: water waves, light waves, radio waves, waves on a rope
  A longitudinal wave has the disturbance parallel to the direction of travel
  Examples: sound waves, waves along a stretched slinky spring
2 Light waves and radio waves
3 a) 12 cm b) 6 Hz c) 72 cm/s

Page 141

1 Faster
2 It increases
3 Travelling along a normal

Page 142

1 Less diffraction occurs at shorter wavelengths, so waves do not diffract round the hill
2 Increases

Page 145

1 Radio waves, microwaves, infrared, light, ultraviolet, X-rays, gamma rays
2 a) When ultraviolet radiation falls on the material, the radiation is re-emitted as visible light
  b) Used in washing powder brighteners, fluorescent lamps, security coding
3 Labels 1 and 2 = electrical signal, copper cable; labels 3 and 4 = light signal, optical fibre; labels 5 and 6 = microwaves to satellite
4 The amplitude of noise/unwanted frequencies is too low to register as the 'on' state at the receiver

Answers

Page 147

1 a) 6 cm b) 80 Hz
2 a) B b) C

Page 149

1 a) X and Y b) X and Z c) Y

Page 152

1 a) Alpha b) Gamma
2 a) 3 days b) 12 days
3 2600 million years

Topic test

1 a) 3 Hz (1 mark)
b) Wave speed = frequency × wavelength (1 mark)
= 3 × 2.5 (1 mark)
= 7.5 cm/s (1 mark)
2 a) Bends away from the normal (1 mark)
b) Increases (1 mark)
c) Increases (1 mark)
3 a) Infrared, microwaves (1 mark)
b) X-rays (1 mark)
c) Infrared (1 mark)
d) Infrared (1 mark)
e) Ultraviolet (1 mark)
4 a) The radiation continually in the environment (1 mark)
b) So the radiation emitted by the source can be worked out (1 mark)
c) Emits alpha particles – rate goes down with thin paper (1 mark)
Emits gamma rays – some radiation detected through lead (1 mark)
Does not emit beta particles – count does not go down with 5 mm metal (1 mark)
5 a) Very high frequency/very short wavelength electromagnetic wave (1 mark)
b) 12.5% (2 marks)
6 a) Sodium-24 (1 mark)
b) Strontium –90 (1 mark)

GLOSSARY/INDEX

Acceleration 124, 127 – The rate at which velocity changes.

Acid 54 – A substance that dissolves in water to give a solution with a pH of less than 7.

Acid rain 31 – Atmospheric pollution caused by burning fossil fuels.

Activation energy 70 – The minimum amount of energy needed by reactant particles before a reaction can occur.

Active transport 15 – The process by which cells take up substances against a concentration gradient. The process requires energy from respiration.

Adaptation 24 – A feature of an organism that helps it to survive in a particular environment.

Addition polymerisation 61 – A reaction in which unsaturated alkene molecules join to form saturated polymer molecules.

ADH (anti-diuretic hormone) 20 – A hormone released from the pituitary gland which targets the kidney tubules to ensure water is reabsorbed into the blood, so reducing the amount of water in the urine and controlling water balance.

Aerobic respiration 6 – Respiration that takes place in the presence of oxygen.

Air resistance (drag) 127 – A force of friction.

Alkali 54 – A base (metal oxide or hydroxide) that dissolves in water to form a solution with a pH greater than 7.

Alkanes 60 – A family of hydrocarbons with the general formula C_nH_{2n+2}. Methane (CH_4) is the simplest alkane. Alkanes have a single covalent bond between the atoms.

Alkenes 61 – A family of unsaturated hydrocarbons with the general formula C_nH_{2n}. Ethene (C_2H_4) is the simplest alkene. Alkenes have a double covalent bond between two carbon atoms.

Allele 35 – One of the different forms of a particular gene, e.g. the gene for coat colour can be B allele coding for black or b allele coding for brown.

Alloy 53 – A mixture of metals (or of carbon with a metal). Alloys can have properties different from the parent metal(s).

Alpha (α) particle 149 – A helium nucleus, i.e. two protons and two neutrons, emitted from an unstable nucleus.

Alternating current (a.c.) 117 – An electric current that reverses direction regularly.

Alveoli (alveolus) 5 – Microscopic air sacs in the lungs which act as the surface for gaseous exchange.

Amino acids 3 – The breakdown products of the digestion of proteins, and the building blocks for making new proteins.

Amplitude 139 – The maximum disturbance of a wave from the equilibrium position.

Anaerobic respiration 6 – Respiration that takes place in the absence of oxygen.

Analogue signals 144 – Signals that vary continuously in amplitude and/or frequency.

Anhydrous 77 – Crystals from which water has been removed.

Anode 50 – The positively charged electrode.

Antibodies 9 – Proteins made by some white blood cells which destroy some micro-organisms.

Aorta 7 – The main artery of the body which carries oxygenated blood away from the heart.

Arid 24 – An arid area is very dry and has a shortage of water.

Artery 7 – A blood vessel that carries blood away from the heart.

Asexual reproduction 34 – Offspring formed from one parent by mitotic cell division. The offspring and parent have identical genetic information and no variation.

Atmosphere 62 – The layer of gases around the Earth.

Atom 83 – The smallest part of an element that can exist. Atoms have a nucleus consisting of protons and neutrons around which are shells of electrons.

Atomic number 83 – The number of protons present in an atomic nucleus (and the number of electrons present in the neutral atom).

Atria (atrium) 7 – The upper chambers of the heart which receive blood from the veins.

Background radiation 150 – The low-level radiation that is always present in the environment.

Bacteria (bacterium) 9 – Single-celled organisms made up of cytoplasm and a membrane surrounded by a cell wall, with genetic material not in a distinct nucleus.

Base 55 – An oxide or hydroxide of a metal.

Battery 109 – Two or more electrical cells joined together.

Bauxite 50 – The main ore of aluminium containing aluminium oxide.

Beta (β) particle 149 – A high speed electron emitted from an unstable nucleus.

Bile 4 – A liquid produced by the gall bladder that breaks up fats into droplets.

Biodegradable 60 – Materials which can be broken down (decomposed) by bacteria.

Biomass 26 – The mass of dry matter in an organism or at one feeding level of the food web.

Blast furnace 49 – The industrial method used for extracting metals such as iron from their ores.

Bonds 86, 88 – The forces that hold atoms together.

Braking distance 129 – How far a car travels before stopping, after the brakes have been applied.

Camouflage 24 – Colouration or pattern which enables an animal to remain hidden in its environment.

Capillaries 8 – Tiny, thin-walled blood vessels which join arteries and veins and allow substances to be exchanged through their walls.

Carnivore 26 – An animal that eats other animals.

Catalyst 73 – A substance that changes the speed of a reaction, but remains unchanged after the reaction.

Cathode 50 – The negatively charged electrode.

Cell (biological) 1, 12 – The smallest part of an animal of plant.

Cell membrane 1, 12 – The very thin membrane around the cytoplasm of a cell that controls the movement of substances in and out of the cell.

Cell wall 12 – The outer part of a plant cell that gives strength and shape to the plant cell.

Cellulose 13 – The material that makes up the cell wall of plant cells.

Charge 83, 114, 119 – A feature of atomic particles. Electrons have a negative charge and protons have a positive charge. A flow of charge is an electric current.
Charge is measured in coulombs (C).

Chlorophyll 13 – A green pigment found in the leaves and stems of plants. It traps light energy for use in photosynthesis.

Chloroplast 12 – That part of the plant cell containing chlorophyll.

Chromosome 34 – A single long molecule of DNA which looks like a thread in the nucleus. The DNA carries the genetic code information as a line of genes.

Circuit breaker 113 – A device used to break a circuit very quickly.

Clone 34 – An organism produced from one parent. The clone is genetically identical to the parent.

Comet 132 – An object in a highly elliptical orbit around the Sun.

Community 25 – All the plants and animals living in one habitat.

Competition 25 – Occurs when plants or animals are fighting for food, light or space.

Compound 80 – A substance which contains two or more elements chemically joined together.

Conduction 98 – The transfer of heat energy through a material by the transfer of energy between neighbouring vibrating particles.

Continental drift 66 – The movement of the Earth's tectonic plates which has resulted in the continental masses moving apart.

Convection 98 – The transfer of heat energy in a liquid or gas (fluid) caused by differences in density. Warmer, less dense fluids rise while cooler, more dense fluids sink.

Core (Earth) 64, 147 – The innermost part of the Earth.

Count rate 150 – The number of radioactive emissions detected in a certain time.

Covalent bond 88 – The bonding of atoms caused by the sharing of pairs of electrons in their outer electron shells.

Cracking 60 – A form of thermal decomposition in which large hydrocarbon molecules are broken down into smaller ones.

Crude oil 59 – A mixture of substances, most of which are hydrocarbons, formed by the anaerobic decomposition of marine organisms over a long period of time.

Crust 64, 147 – The surface layer of the Earth.

Deforestation 30 – The removal of a large number of trees from an area by cutting down or burning.

Denaturing 74 – The process by which enzymes are destroyed when heated above a temperature of about 40°C.

Denitrifying bacteria 63 – Bacteria that convert nitrates in the soil into nitrogen gas.

Deposition 65 – The laying down in water of a layer of rock fragments.

Diffraction 142 – The spreading out of waves as they go through a gap or pass by an object.

Diffusion 2 – The movement of particles from regions where they are in high concentration to regions where they are in lower concentration.

Digital signals 144 – Signals coded as a set of pulses, either on or off.

Diode 112 – An electrical component that only conducts electricity in one direction.

Diploid 43 – A cell which contains pairs of chromosomes i.e. as found in normal body cells. Diploid cells are formed by the joining of two haploid gametes.

Direct current (d.c.) 118 – An electric current that always flows in the same direction.

Dominant allele 35, 40	–	The allele which controls an observable characteristic in the offspring when it is present on only one chromosome.
Drug 21	–	A chemical that changes the way our body works or the way we react to things.
Dynamic equilibrium 77	–	With a reversible reacction, when the forward reaction is proceeding at the same rate as the reverse reaction.
Earthing 115, 117	–	A metal object is earthed when a low resistance conductor joins the object to the Earth's surface.
Efficiency 103	–	The ratio of useful energy transferred by a device, to total energy supplied to the device.
Elastic potential energy 131	–	The energy stored in an elastic object when work is done to change its shape.
Electric current 119	–	A flow of electrons or ions.
Electrode 50	–	A negatively or positively charged conductor.
Electrolysis 50	–	The process of splitting up a chemical compound using an electric current.
Electromagnet 112	–	A device made by passing an electric current through a coil of wire.
Electromagnetic waves (spectrum) 143	–	A range of transverse waves that travel through a vacuum (space) with a common speed, but with different frequencies and wavelengths.
Electrons 83, 148	–	Negatively charged particles orbiting in shells around the atomic nucleus.
Element 83	–	A substance made up of atoms that contain the same number of protons, i.e. a substance containing only one type of atom. An element cannot be broken down into anything simpler by chemical means.
Endothermic reaction 75	–	A reaction in which heat energy is transferred from the surroundings, because more energy is needed to break the existing bonds in the reactants than is released when new bonds are made in the products.
Energy levels (shells) 83	–	Regions outside the nucleus where electrons are found.
Environment 24	–	The surroundings and conditions that affect the growth and behaviour of plants and animals.
Enzyme 3, 74	–	Protein that acts as a catalyst for chemical reactions in cells, e.g. to change large insoluble molecules to small soluble ones in digestion.
Erosion 65	–	The wearing away of the Earth's surface and transporting of the dust and rocks.
Eutrophication 32	–	The addition of extra nutrients to rivers and streams, which increases the growth rate of plants or bacteria in the water.

Exothermic reaction 75 – A reaction in which heat energy is transferred to the surroundings because more energy is given out making the new chemical bonds in the products than is taken in to break the existing bonds in the reactants.

Extinct 38 – A description of an organism that lived in the past but is no longer living today.

Faults 65 – Fractures in the Earth's crust caused by movement of the crust.

Fermentation 74 – The changing of glucose into ethanol (alcohol) and carbon dioxide by the action of enzymes in yeast.

Fertilisation 34 – The joining of the nuclei of the male and female gametes.

Fertiliser 30, 31, 78 – A chemical used to increase the growth rate and quality of plants.

Food chain 26 – A diagram which shows the feeding relationships of some organisms in an ecosystem.

Food web 27 – A diagram which shows the many feeding relationships in an environment.

Fossil 38 – The remains or imprint of plants or animals that lived millions of years ago. The remains may have been mineralised and turned to stone.

Fossil fuels 63 – Non-renewable fuels, oil, coal and natural gas, which were formed millions of years ago and therefore contain 'locked-up' carbon.

Fractional distillation 59 – A method of separating liquids whose boiling points are close together. The process is used to separate the different substances in crude oil.

Free electrons 90 – The electrons in metals that move around inside the metal and do not remain in orbit around a nucleus. The presence of these free electrons allows the metal to conduct electricity and heat.

Frequency 139 – The number of waves passing a certain point in one second. Unit is hertz (Hz).

Friction 127 – A force that tries to stop or does stop movement.

FSH 42 – Follicle stimulating hormone, which stimulates the development of an ovum in the ovary and the production of the hormone oestrogen.

Fuse 109, 116 – A wire designed to melt if too large a current flows through it.

Gamete 34 – A sex cell, e.g. the sperm is the male gamete and the ovum is the female gamete.

Gamma rays (radiation) 143, 149 – Electromagnetic waves with very high frequency and low wavelength. Emitted by the unstable nuclei of radioactive substances.

Gene 35 – A length of DNA on a chromosome which codes for a characteristic.

Generator 105, 120 – A device that transfers kinetic energy as electrical energy.

Geostationary orbit 133 – The orbit of a satellite that takes 24 hours to complete.

Geothermal energy 105 – The heat produced by the Earth by radioactive decay within rocks.

Global warming 104 – The international problem caused by increased levels of carbon dioxide and methane in the atmosphere resulting in a small increase in the Earth's temperature. The consequences are climate changes and flooding.

Glucagon 20 – A hormone released by the pancreas that causes the liver to convert glycogen into glucose.

Glycogen 20 – The form in which excess glucose in stored in the liver and muscles.

Gravitational potential energy 100 – The energy stored by an object due to its vertical position above the Earth's surface.

101 – change in gravitational potential energy = weight × change in vertical height

Gravity 133 – A force of attraction that acts between all bodies.

Greenhouse effect 103 – The effect in the atmosphere of heat energy being absorbed by gases such as carbon dioxide and methane.

Group 85 – A vertical column of elements in the Periodic Table having similar chemical properties due to the atoms of the elements having the same number of electrons in their outer shells.

Haber process 78 – The process used for the manufacture of ammonia.

Haemoglobin 1, 8 – The red pigment in red blood cells which combines with and transports oxygen.

Halide 93 – The compound formed when a halogen reacts with another element.

Half-life 150 – The time taken for the count rate of a radioactive substance to fall to half of its original value.

Halogens 91 – The name given to the elements in Group 7 of the Periodic Table.

Haploid 34, 43 – A cell which contains one copy of each chromosome, i.e. a single set as found in a gamete.

Herbivore 26 – An organism that eats only plants.

Heterozygous 40 – The chromosome pair have different alleles at a particular gene position (e.g. Bb).

Homozygous 40 – The chromosome pair have identical alleles at a particular gene position (e.g. BB).

Hormone (animal) 20, 42 – A chemical (protein) secreted by endocrine glands directly into the blood in one part of the body and carried in the blood plasma to a target organ.

Hormone (plant) 16 – A chemical (protein) that can affect the plant's growth and acts under the effect of water, light and gravity.

Hydrocarbon 59 – A compound containing only hydrogen and carbon.

Hydroelectric power 105, 106 – Electrical power generated by the flow of water from a higher to a lower level.

Hydrogen ion 54 – An ion (H^+) present in all acids.

Hydroxide ion 54 – An ion (OH^-) present in all alkalis.

Induced current 120 – The current produced when a wire that is part of a complete circuit cuts through a magnetic field.

Insulin 20 – A hormone released by the pancreas which controls the conversion of excess glucose into glycogen which is then stored in the liver and muscles.

Ion 50, 118 – An atom or group of atoms which have lost or gained electrons to become positively or negatively charged.

Ionic bond 86 – The electrostatic attraction between opposite charges responsible for holding metal and non-metal elements together in a compound. The ions are formed when the metal atoms transfer electrons to the non-metal atoms in order to achieve full outer electron shells.

Ionic equation 92 – Equation which shows the ions taking part in a reaction. In ionic equations the charges must balance as well as the number of ions/atoms involved.

Ionise 150 – To remove or add electrons to atoms or groups of atoms so giving them positive or negative charges.

Iris 17 – A ring of muscle which controls the amount of light entering the eye.

Isotope 83, 149 – Atoms of the same element which contain different numbers of neutrons.

Joule 100 – The unit of energy and work.

Kilowatt-hour 101 – A unit of electrical energy.

Kinetic energy 131 – The energy an object has because of its motion.
kinetic energy $= \frac{1}{2} \times$ mass $\times$ speed^2

Lactic acid 6 – A product of anaerobic respiration in very active muscles which is a mild tissue poison.

Lens (eye) 17 – A transparent structure within the eye that is flexible and helps light to form a sharp image on the retina during focussing.

LH 42 – Luteinising hormone, which triggers ovulation.

Light dependent resistor (LDR) 109, 111 – An electrical component whose resistance goes down when a bright light shines on it.

Limestone 58 – A sedimentary rock (mainly calcium carbonate) formed millions of years ago from the shells of small creatures.

Limiting factor 14 – A factor, such as light intensity, light wavelength, water and carbon dioxide, that limits the rate of photosynthesis in a given time.

Lithosphere 66 – The outer shell of the Earth made from the crust and the upper part of the mantle.

Longitudinal wave 139 – A wave in which energy is transferred in the same direction as the vibrations causing the wave.

Mantle 64 – The layer of the Earth between the crust and the core.

Mass number 83 – The total number of protons and neutrons in an atomic nucleus.

Metamorphic rocks 65 – Rocks formed from rocks which became buried deep underground and had their structure changed by high temperatures and/or high pressures.

Micro-organisms 9, 29 – Organisms such as bacteria and fungi which can only be seen with a microscope. Bacteria and fungi are together known as decomposers.

Meiosis 34 – Cell division that leads to the production of gametes, each gamete has only half the number of chromosomes as the parent.

Milky Way galaxy 134 – The galaxy that contains our Solar System.

Mitochondria 1 – The parts of the cell in which aerobic respiration takes place, producing cellular energy.

Mitosis 34 – Cell division that occurs during growth and asexual reproduction, producing two cells that each have the same number of chromosomes as the parent.

Mixture 59 – Two or more substances, which are usually easy to separate.

Molecule 88 – A particle containing atoms of the same or different elements bonded together. The smallest part of an element or compound that can take part in a chemical reaction.

Monomers 61 – Small molecules which join together to form a long chain of molecules called a polymer.

Mutation 38 – A sudden change occurring in a gene on a chromosome which results in a change in a feature of the organism.

Natural selection 38 – The process by which a beneficial characteristic with a greater survival value is selected and passed on so that the proportion of the allele increases. Natural selection leads to evolution.

Negative feedback 42 – The increase in one hormone preventing the release of another hormone, e.g. a rise in the level of oestrogen inhibits the release of FSH.

Neutralisation 54 – A reaction between an acid and a base or a carbonate.

Neutron 83, 148 – A particle with no electrical charge found in the nucleus of most atoms. Its mass is similar to that of a proton.

Nitrates 13, 30 – Chemicals containing NO_3^- ions, frequently used in fertilisers to help plants synthesise proteins.

Nitrifying bacteria 30 – Bacteria that oxidise ammonium compounds into nitrates.

Noble gases 92 – The name given to the elements in Group 0 of the Periodic Table.

Noise 145 – The unwanted frequencies picked up by signals during transmission.

Non-metals 85, 88 – Elements in the Periodic Table which usually have low melting points and boiling points, are poor conductors of electricity and heat, and as solids are brittle.

Nuclear fission 152 – The splitting of a large atomic nucleus to release energy.

Nucleons 148 – The protons and neutrons in the nucleus of an atom.

Nucleon number 148 – The total number of protons and neutrons in an atomic nucleus.

Nucleus (atom) 83, 148 – The central part of an atom that contains positively charged protons and uncharged neutrons.

Ohm 111 – The unit of electrical resistance.

Optical fibre 142 – A tube of plastic or glass that allows light to travel from one end to the other by repeated total internal reflection.

Orbit 132 – The path taken by an object which goes around another object.

Ore 48 – A mineral or mixture of minerals from which a metal can be extracted in economically viable amounts.

Osmosis 15 – Diffusion of water from a dilute to a more concentrated solution, through a selectively permeable membrane.

Oxidation 49 – A chemical reaction that involves the addition of oxygen
51 – and the loss of electrons.

Oxygen debt 6 – The oxygen needed to remove the lactic acid from muscles produced as a result of muscles respiring anaerobically during vigorous exercise.

Oxyhaemoglobin 8 – The chemical formed when oxygen combines with haemoglobin.

Period 85 – A horizontal row of elements in the Periodic Table.

Periodic Table 85 – The arrangement of the elements in order of increasing atomic number.

Pesticide 31 – A chemical used to kill unwanted plants or animals regarded as pests.

pH 74 – A scale used to measure acidity and alkalinity.

Phosphates 13 – Chemicals containing PO_4^{3} ions, frequently used in fertilisers to help plants photosynthesise and respire.

Photosynthesis 13 – The production of glucose by green plants from carbon dioxide and water using sunlight energy and giving out oxygen.

Plastic 60 – The common name for some types of polymer.

Polymer 60 – A long chain molecule made up of many smaller molecules called monomers.

Population 25 – The numbers of one species of plant or animal living in one habitat.

Positive feedback 42 – The increase in one hormone triggering the release of another hormone, e.g. a rise in oestrogen in the middle of the menstrual cycle triggers the release of LH.

Potassium 13 – An element used by plants to help the action of the enzymes involved in photosynthesis and respiration.

Power 101, 120 – The rate of transferring energy (doing work). The unit is the watt (W), where 1000 watts = 1 kilowatt.

Predator 25 – An organism that kills and eats another organism (known as the prey).

Prey 25 – An organism that is caught and eaten by a predator.

Products 70 – The new materials produced as a result of a chemical reaction.

Proton 83, 148 – A positively charged particle found in the nucleus of an atom.

P waves 147 – Longitudinal seismic waves which travel through solids and liquids.

Pyramid of biomass 27 – A diagram which shows by the size of the block (quantitatively) the biomass at each feeding level.

Radiation (thermal) 98 – The transfer of heat energy by electromagnetic waves travelling through space.

Radioactivity 149 – The random emission of particles and rays from an unstable atomic nucleus during radioactive decay.

Reabsorption 20 – The way in which substances needed by the body are taken back into the blood from the tubules in the kidney.

Reactants 70 – The starting materials in a chemical reaction.

Reactivity series 47 – A list of metals arranged in order of their chemical reactivity. The most reactive metals are at the top of the list.

Recessive allele 40 – An allele that must be present on both chromosomes of the pair to show in the offspring.

Red giant 135 – A relatively cool giant star.

Red shift 136 – The observational evidence that the wavelength of light from distant galaxies is shifted towards the red end of the spectrum.

Redox reaction 51 – A process in which both reduction and oxidation take place.

Reduction 48 – A chemical reaction that involves the loss of oxygen
51 – and the gain of electrons.

Reflex action 18 – A rapid automatic response to a stimulus, during which nerve impulses are sent by receptors through the nervous system to effectors.

Refraction 140 – The change in direction of a wave as it passes from one medium into another due to the change in the speed of the wave.

Relative atomic mass 46, 80 – The average mass of an atom of an element on a scale on which the mass of a hydrogen atom = 1 or the mass of the ^{12}C isotope of carbon = 12. It takes into account the relative abundance of different isotopes with different mass numbers.

Relative formula mass 80 – This is found by adding together the relative atomic masses of all the elements in the chemical formula of the substance.

Respiration 6 – A chemical reaction that occurs in all living cells to oxidise glucose to carbon dioxide and water and to release energy.

Retina 17 – A light-sensitive layer at the back of the eye which sends impulses to the brain by the optic nerve.

Reversible reaction 76 – A reaction that can proceed in either direction depending on the reaction conditions. Reactants can be changed into products which in turn can be changed back into reactants.

Root hair cell 12, 15 – Plant cells with a large surface area and thin cell wall that absorb water and mineral salts from the soil by osmosis, diffusion and active transport.

Sacrificial protection 53 – Used to reduce the rusting of iron by attaching a more reactive metal such as magnesium or zinc.

Salt 54 – A substance formed when an acid reacts with a base.

Satellite 133 – An object in orbit around the Earth.

Saturated hydrocarbons 60 – Hydrocarbons in which the carbon atoms are all linked together with single C–C bonds.

Sclera 17 – The tough outer layer of the eye.

Sedimentary rocks 65 – Rocks formed by deposition, burial and compression of weathered rock fragments or the shells of dead animals. They can also be formed by the precipitation of calcium carbonate, usually in warm, shallow seas.

Seismic waves 147 – Waves created by the vibrations caused by earthquakes.

Selective breeding 37 – Choosing a desirable characteristic and breeding plants or animals for many generations until they show this feature.

Sexual reproduction 34 – Involves two parents who each produce gametes that join together. There is genetic variation in the offspring.

Shells (energy levels) 83 – Regions outside the nucleus where electrons are found.

Slag 49 – The substance formed in the blast furnace from impurities in the iron.

Spectator ions 55 – Ions that remain unchanged during a chemical reaction.

Star 135 – A huge mass that produces its own light and heat, by nuclear fusion.

STI 42 – Sexually transmitted infection.

Stomata 12, 14 – Small holes, usually on the underside of leaves, controlled by guard cells.

Stopping distance 129 – Thinking distance + braking distance

Subduction 67 – The process of pushing part of the Earth's crust into the mantle as tectonic plates move against each other.

S waves 147 – Transverse seismic waves which travel only through solid material.

Tectonic plates 66 – The separate slow-moving adjacent sections of the Earth's lithosphere that move because of convection currents within the Earth's mantle caused by the natural radioactive processes within the Earth.

Terminal velocity 128 – The constant speed reached by a moving object when the forces (in the direction it is moving) are balanced.

Thermal decomposition 58 – The breaking down of a compound by the action of heat.

Thermistor 109, 111 – An electrical component whose resistance goes down when it gets hot.

Thinking distance 129 – How far a car travels during the driver's reaction time, before the brakes are applied.

Total internal reflection 141 – This happens when light moving through a transparent material into air hits the surface of the material at an angle bigger than the critical angle.

Transformer 121 – A device that increases or decreases an alternating voltage.

Turgor 15 – The pressure that the cytoplasm and the vacuole exert on the cell wall.

Transition elements (metals) 46 – The name given to the elements in the Periodic Table between Groups 2 and 3.

Transpiration 14 – Loss of water from the leaves of a plant by evaporation through the stomata.

Transverse wave 138 – A wave in which the energy is transferred at right angles to the vibrations causing the waves.

Ultrasound 146 – Sound waves with frequencies above the upper limit of human hearing (above 20 000 Hz).

Unsaturated hydrocarbons 61 – Hydrocarbons in which some of the carbon atoms are linked together with C=C double bonds.

Velocity 124 – Speed in a given direction.

Ventilation 5 – Movement of air in and out of the lungs during breathing.

Villi 2 – The finger-like projections in the small intestine that provide a large, thin, moist surface and good blood supply through which the soluble products of digestion are rapidly absorbed.

Wavelength 139 – The distance from a particular point on one wave to the same point on the next wave.

Weathering 65 – The chemical, physical or biological action by which rocks are broken down into rock fragments.

White dwarf 135 – A small, very dense bright star.